Manual Specialization and
the Developing Brain

This is a volume in

PERSPECTIVES IN
NEUROLINGUISTICS, NEUROPSYCHOLOGY, AND
PSYCHOLINGUISTICS

A Series of Monographs and Treatises

A complete list of titles in this series appears at the end of this volume.

Manual Specialization and the Developing Brain

Edited by

GERALD YOUNG
Department of Psychology
Glendon College
York University
Toronto, Ontario, Canada

SIDNEY J. SEGALOWITZ
Department of Psychology
Brock University
St. Catharines, Ontario, Canada

CARL M. CORTER
Centre for Research in Human Development
University of Toronto
Mississauga, Ontario, Canada

SANDRA E. TREHUB
Centre for Research in Human Development
University of Toronto
Mississauga, Ontario, Canada

1983
ACADEMIC PRESS
A Subsidiary of Harcourt Brace Jovanovich, Publishers
New York   London
Paris   San Diego   San Francisco   São Paulo   Sydney   Tokyo   Toronto

ACADEMIC PRESS, INC.
111 Fifth Avenue, New York, New York 10003

United Kingdom Edition published by
ACADEMIC PRESS, INC. (LONDON) LTD.
24/28 Oval Road, London NW1   7DX

Library of Congress Cataloging in Publication Data
Main entry under title:

Manual specialization and the developing brain.

   (Perspectives in neurolinguistics, neuropsychology,
and psycholinguistics)
   Includes bibliographical references.
   1. Cerebral dominance--Addresses, essays, lectures.
2. Motor ability in children--Addresses, essays, lectures. 3. Left- and right-handedness--Addresses, essays,
lectures. 4. Brain--Growth--Addresses, essays, lectures. I. Young, Gerald.   II. Series.
[DNLM: 1. Laterality--Physiology. 2. Motor activity--
In infancy and childhood. 3. Brain--Growth and development. WL 335 M294]
QP385.5.M35 1983   152.3'35   83-7148
ISBN 0-12-773140-7

PRINTED IN THE UNITED STATES OF AMERICA

83 84 85 86 9 8 7 6 5 4 3 2 1

Contents

I
Reviews of Lateralization Development

1
Manual Specialization and the Developing Brain: An Overview

GERALD YOUNG, CARL M. CORTER, SIDNEY J. SEGALOWITZ, and SANDRA E. TREHUB

2
Is Early Reaching Left-Handed? Review of Manual Specialization Research

GERALD YOUNG, SIDNEY J. SEGALOWITZ, PAT MISEK, I. ERCAN ALP, and RENÉE BOULET

3
Development of Hand-Use Preference during Infancy

GEORGE F. MICHEL

4
Mechanisms Underlying Instability in the Development of Hand Preference

JACQUELINE LIEDERMAN

5
Hemispheric Specialization in Infancy

DENNIS L. MOLFESE and VICTORIA J. MOLFESE

6
How Many Lateralities Are There?

SIDNEY J. SEGALOWITZ

II
Theories of Lateralization Development

IV
Infant Research

Contributors

Numbers in parentheses indicate the pages on which the authors' contributions begin.

I. Ercan Alp (13), Department of Psychology, York University, Downsview, Ontario, M3J 1P3, Canada

Paul Boissonneault (119), Department of Psychology, Glendon College, York University, Toronto, Ontario, M4N 3M6, Canada

Renée Boulet (13), Department of Psychology, Glendon College, York University, Toronto, Ontario, M4N 3M6, Canada

James G. Bowman (119), Department of Psychology, York University, Downsview, Ontario, M3J 1P3, Canada

Carl M. Corter (3, 249, 257), Centre for Research in Human Development, Erindale College, University of Toronto, Mississauga, Ontario, L5L 1C6, Canada

John M. Dowd (307), Department of Psychiatry, Albert Einstein College of Medicine, Yeshiva University, Bronx, New York 10461

Mary Finlayson (119), Department of Psychology, York University, Toronto, Ontario, M3J 1P3, Canada

Hiram E. Fitzgerald (285), Department of Psychology, Michigan State University, East Lansing, Michigan 48824

Ita Goldshmidt (395), School for Communication Disorders, Audiologic Department, Haim Sheba Medical Center, 52621, Israel

Lauren Julius Harris (177, 285, 331), Department of Psychology and Neuroscience Program, Michigan State University, East Lansing, Michigan 48824

Patricia R. Hawn (331), Department of Psychology, Michigan State University, East Lansing, Michigan 48824

Amos D. Korczyn (395), Department of Physiology and Pharmacology, Sackler School of Medicine, Tel-Aviv University, Ramat Aviv, 69978, Israel

David J. Lewkowicz (375), Illinois Institute for Developmental Disabilities, Chicago, Illinois 60608

Jacqueline Liederman (71, 321), Department of Psychology, College of Liberal Arts, Boston University, Boston, Massachusetts 02215

Carolyn J. Mebert (349), Department of Psychology, University of New Hampshire, Durham, New Hampshire 03824

Carole Methot (119), Department of Psychology, York University, Downsview, Ontario, M3J 1P3, Canada

George F. Michel[1] (33), Department of Psychiatry, John Enders Research Laboratories, Children's Hospital Medical Center, Boston, Massachusetts 02115

Pat Misek (13), Department of Psychology, Glendon College, York University, Toronto, Ontario, M4N 3M6, Canada

Dennis L. Molfese (93), Department of Psychology and School of Medicine, Southern Illinois University, Carbondale, Illinois 62901

Victoria J. Molfese (93), Department of Psychology and School of Medicine, Southern Illinois University, Carbondale, Illinois 62901

Michael Peters (141, 367), Department of Psychology, College of Social Science, University of Guelph, Guelph, Ontario, N1G 2W1, Canada

Janet Quintal (119), Department of Psychology, York University, Toronto, Ontario, M3J 1P3, Canada

Douglas S. Ramsay (161), Department of Psychology, Rutgers—The State University of New Jersey, New Brunswick, New Jersey 08903

Michael Saling (275), School of Psychology, University of the Witwatersrand, Johannesburg, 2001, South Africa

Sidney J. Segalowitz (3, 13, 111), Department of Psychology, Brock University, St. Catharines, Ontario, L2S 3A1, Canada

Nancy Shosenberg (257), Centre for Research in Human Development, Erindale College, University of Toronto, Mississauga, Ontario, L5L 1C6, Canada

Sandra E. Trehub (3, 257), Centre for Research in Human Development, Erindale College, University of Toronto, Mississauga, Ontario, L5L 1C6, Canada

Therese Treves (395), Department of Neurology, Ichilov Hospital, Tel Aviv, Israel

[1]Present address: Psychology Department, University of Massachusetts—Boston, Boston, Massachusetts 02125.

Edward Z. Tronick (307), Department of Psychology, University of Massachusetts, Amherst, Massachusetts 01003

Gerald Turkewitz (375), Department of Psychology, Hunter College, CUNY, New York, New York 10021, and Department of Psychiatry and Pediatrics, Albert Einstein College of Medicine, Yeshiva University, Bronx, New York 10461

Gerald Young (3, 13, 119, 401), Department of Psychology, Glendon College, York University, Toronto, Ontario, M4N 3M6, Canada

Preface

This book deals with how the hands acquire different skills (the development of manual specialization) and what this may tell us about the child's developing brain. In this fast-growing field, research and theory are brought together for the first time. Perspectives on what behaviors are specialized (e.g., reaching, grasping), in which direction (e.g., is early reaching really left-handed as some suggest?), when they develop, and how and why they develop are offered. The role of possible genetic, organismic, and environmental determinants of early asymmetric manual and related (e.g., head) activity are discussed. The left hemisphere's ability to control organized sequential activity (e.g., fine motor movements, speech) is often emphasized. The suggestion that such early lateralized behavior could predict later handedness, cerebral hemispheric specialization of function, and central nervous system–neurobehavioral disorganization or dysfunction makes the field interesting not only in its own right but also because of possible general and applied applications.

The book is balanced between chapters that are mostly integrative and chapters that are based on the author's own empirical research. Part I begins with a general review of the field by the editors. Then Young et al. review the research concerned with asymmetric performance of reaching and grasping related behavior in early infancy. Michel (Chapter 3) gives a general review of early manual and related preference and discusses which determinants may be involved in its development. Liederman (Chapter 4) suggests that manual specialization becomes more right lateralized and stable with development, and suggests what factors influence this trend. Next, Molfese and Molfese in Chapter 5 review the development of cerebral hemispheric specialization. Segalowitz ends this section with a perspective on the first five chapters.

Part II offers work of a more theoretical nature and is an excellent historical review as well. First, Young *et al.* (Chapter 7) suggest that the left hemisphere is characterized by superior inhibitory control and that certain parental social inputs (e.g., verbalization) can promote left hemisphere development. Peters (Chapter 8) shows how development of lateralization in the various levels of the motor system proceeds, emphasizing the decision-making skills of the left hemisphere, while Ramsay in Chapter 9 suggests that there are successive levels of hemispheric specialization for control of sequential (e.g., articulatory, manipulatory) activity. In Chapter 10, Harris surveys the past research and theory on the development of manual specialization, and relates his review to current trends. Corter gives an overview of the chapters in this section.

Part III summarizes empirical research with neonates. Trehub, Corter, and Shosenberg (Chapter 12) describe a study with both full term and preterm neonates, where basic reflexes were observed. Saling (Chapter 13) examines birth risk as a factor influencing spontaneous head turning in neonates with and without a left-hander in the family. Harris and Fitzgerald (Chapter 14) research head-turning preferences in neonates from birth to 18 months. Finally, Dowd and Tronick (Chapter 15) discuss some methodological issues in observing spontaneous arm movements in young infants using 3-D cinematography.

Part IV describes empirical research with infants beyond the neonatal period. First, Liederman (Chapter 16) reports research aimed at whether young infants are really left-hand reachers. Next, Hawn and Harris report on 2- and 5-month-olds in grasping and reaching tasks (Chapter 17). Mebert (Chapter 18) examines 4- to 10-month-olds on toy play and cognitive-based tasks. Peters (Chapter 19) investigates 6- and 12-month-olds as they reach for and hold objects. Lewkowitz and Turkewitz (Chapter 20) discuss processing asymmetries and then describe a study with 6- and 8-month-olds reaching during silence and sound presentation. In Chapter 21, Treves, Goldsmidt, and Korczyn examine how lateral preference may be related to language development in 1- to 3-year-olds. Finally, Young relates the chapters in Parts III and IV to general developmental considerations.

Professionals and graduate students interested in infancy, motor activity, and the brain will particularly find this book very useful. Those interested in language, cognitive, perceptual, social, and emotional development will also find it of value. In short, because the topic of this book stands at the intersection of the study of development and the brain, any individual seriously interested in these areas will profit from reading it. All chapters have been written explicitly for this volume, so that past, current, and novel research and theory are offered in a rapidly developing field.

Several individuals and institutions have contributed to helping us complete this project. Ronald Cohen and Micael Lacroix offered thoughtful advice about several chapters, and Jane Pham Van and Gail Hamer provided superb secretarial help. The Natural Sciences and Engineering Research Council of Canada partially supported the editorial process. Finally, André Roch Lecours was kind enough to offer office space, some funds, and a conducive environment at the Laboratoire Théophile-Alajouanine of the Centre Hospitalier Côte-des-Neiges in Montréal during the final stages of the preparation of this volume. To others who have helped in one way or another, especially our families, we thank you.

I

Reviews of Lateralization Development

1

Manual Specialization and the Developing Brain: An Overview

GERALD YOUNG
CARL M. CORTER
SIDNEY J. SEGALOWITZ
SANDRA E. TREHUB

Introduction

How the hands have come to have different skills and preferences has intrigued us for centuries not only because of the apparent uniqueness of the right-sided trend in our species, but also because of what we may learn about the development of the brain from this trend. The study of manual preference in infancy and the related topic of the development of hemispheric specialization has seen an upsurge in the last 10 years, and the present volume is the first in the field devoted exclusively to the topic. Its aim is to provide a survey of current and past research and theory on manual preference in infancy and other lateralized behavioral functions, such as head movement, and implications for brain development. Both normal and at-risk or brain-damaged populations are considered. The questions that the book addresses are summarized in this introduction, following consideration of the definition of manual specialization and handedness.

Manual specialization can be distinguished from the traditional concept of handedness along several dimensions even though both concern lateralization of preference in manual behavior.

1. Handedness concerns consistent lateralized usage on (a) familiar; (b) highly practiced; and (c) relatively simple tasks, whereas manual specialization can concern consistent lateralized usage on (a) novel, and thus (b) unpracticed, (c) relatively complex tasks. In this sense, even some lateralized reflexive type activity of the newborn, such as prereaching and reaching behavior of the 1-month-old in certain

3

circumstances, may be seen as indices of manual specialization and not handedness.

2. On handedness tasks, performance of the preferred or dominant hand is not necessarily superior in skill to that of the nonpreferred subordinate hand. However, in manual specialization, the dominant preferred hand should be superior in skill compared to the other one.

3. Handedness is most often reflected in unilateral activity such as writing, whereas manual specialization is just as readily manifested in bimanual coordination.

4. Handedness measures generally are composed of a series of tasks almost all of which are performed by the same preferred hand. Measures of manual specialization, in contrast, can concern the nonpreferred as well as the preferred hand. For example, Ingram (1975) showed that right-handed children performed certain tasks better with the right hand (e.g., tapping) and others better with the left (e.g., hand posture imitation).

5. Finally, handedness is not linked in a one-to-one relationship with cortical dominance (Segalowitz, Chapter 6, this volume). Although most right-handed adults have left-hemisphere language control, not all do. Moreover, about one-half of all left-handed adults do not have right-hemisphere language control. In contrast, in the study of manual specialization, a hand can possess specialized skills in accordance with the specialized functions of the hemisphere that better controls it. Thus, the results of Ingram (1975) are most appropriately understood in terms of better right-hand control by the fine motor skills of the left hemisphere and better left-hand control by the spatial skills of the right hemisphere.

Questions

The various chapters manage to touch on the broad range of questions one would ask of any developing phenomenon. *What* exactly are the developing manual skills (e.g., how to best observe them)? *Which* hand is preferentially used for each of these skills? *When* in development do they manifest and change course, if at all? *Where* in the brain resides the control over this developmental unfolding? *How* do these developing manual skills emerge (e.g., genetic, organismic, environmental antecedants)? *Why* do they emerge (e.g., phylogenesis, adaptive function)?

What

BEHAVIORS

Target-related reaching and grasping behavior have been the primary behaviors studied in the field (Liederman, Chapter 4; Michel, Chapter 3;

Young, Segalowitz, Misek, Alp, & Boulet, Chapter 2, this volume). For reaching, directed arm movements, exploratory finger–hand or mouth-related activity, general activation, and nondirected arm movements have been observed. For grasping, precision and power holding, and strength, duration, and suspension measures have been investigated. Manual activity not related to an object (e.g., neonatal fisting), visual regard (e.g., Mebert, Chapter 18, this volume), reflexive (including leg) behavior (Trehub, Corter, & Shosenberg, Chapter 12), and head movements, (e.g., Harris & Fitzgerald, Chapter 14; Saling, Chapter 13) have also been examined. Liederman (Chapter 4) and Michel (Chapter 3) discuss the relevance of visual regard to the study of manual specialization; Liederman (Chapter 4) and Peters (Chapter 8) cover the relevance of reflexive behavior; and Michel (Chapter 3) and Saling (Chapter 13) deal with the relevance of head movements.

Both unimanual behavior (e.g., in reaching) and bimanual coordination (e.g., in stabilization of a toy with one hand so the other can manipulate) (Ramsay, Chapter 9) have been examined, with Peters (Chapter 8) discussing the relevance of the latter. In either case, an executive– subordinate relationship between the more active and more passive or less instrumental hand in its own right can be quite revealing. For example, perhaps one hand reaches more, whereas the other performs irrelevant or subordinate activities (e.g., nondirected activity or reaching first to assume a supporting role, as in Bresson, Maury, Pieraut-Le Bonniec, & de Schonen, 1977) in a division of labor.

Important distinctions must be made between movements ipsilateral to the side of presentation versus across the midline (Hawn & Harris, Chapter 17) and movements originating from above versus below the wrist. The proximal arm musculature is connected both contralaterally and ipsilaterally to the cerebral hemispheres, whereas the distal hand and finger musculature is connected only contralaterally to the hemispheres. Peters (Chapter 8), in particular, and Liederman (Chapter 4) discuss the pathways involved in these connections, whereas Young *et al.* (Chapter 2) speculate on how the developing hemispheres can control the arms and hands in light of the differences in how they are connected to the hemispheres.

From the preceeding, it becomes clear that manual specialization development concerns a host of skilled behaviors even early in life. Thus, the more the behaviors observed in any one study, the better the chances of seeing the complexity of the development of manual specialization. Trehub *et al.* (Chapter 12) with neonates and Mebert (Chapter 18) with older infants have especially considered a variety of behaviors, although only the former have attempted to find correlations within the set of behaviors observed.

DECODING

We must develop refined observation systems for our studies. For example, it is not only necessary to code grasping, but different styles of it. Grasping with a precision grip may be exclusively right handed at a particular age, but infrequent. In contrast, other grasps (e.g., palmar) may not be lateralized and may be quite frequent. Mebert (Chapter 18) considered such possibilities in devising her extensive coding system. Or perhaps both types of behavior occur equally often with both hands, but one hand performs them more quickly, or shows more coordination from one (fraction of a) second to the next (Dowd & Tronick, Chapter 15, in particular, and Young, Bowman, Methot, Finlayson, Quintal, & Boissonneault, Chapter 7). Next, perhaps the upper limbs have at least one of their muscles contracted in a target-directed way equally often, but in qualitatively different ways. One hand may move, after a delay, repeatedly toward the target, but not that near it, whereas the other may move right away and be held extended and static near the target. If movement, position, duration, and phase of activity were not all scored, then this subtlety would be missed. Hawn and Harris (Chapter 17) and Trehub et al. (Chapter 12) both provide examples of multiple measures related to one behavior, although not as extensive as this example. The relative proportion of one behavior to overall (directed) behavior in one hand compared to another may be different even though in terms of absolute frequency it is the same. Young et al. (Chapter 7) used hand opening both during or just before reaching–touching instead of using hand opening considered alone partly because of this possibility. Finally, developing lateralized manual behavior should be examined both in terms of continuous measurement, appropriate for investigating the degree of lateralization, for example, and discontinuous measurement, appropriate for determining the proportion of right- and left-handers, for example. Mebert (Chapter 18), Ramsay (Chapter 9), Trehub et al. (Chapter 12), and Young et al. (Chapter 7) provide appropriate examples where both types of measurement are used simultaneously in one study.

METHOD

In order to better understand what lateralized behaviors are developing, the methodological context in which they are observed must be taken into consideration. In this regard, the subjects' status has been carefully described, especially where neonates have been observed (e.g., health and state in Saling's [Chapter 13], Trehub et al.'s [Chapter 12], and Young et al.'s [Chapter 7] samples [see Harris & Fitzgerald, Chapter 14]). Controls of symmetry in terms of what the infants can see before them (e.g., Liederman, Chapter 16), the behavior of the experimenters (e.g., Ramsay, Chapter 9), and the posture of the infants (e.g., Liederman, Chapter 16; Trehub *et al.*, Chapter 12) have been instituted (also see Hawn & Harris, Chapter 17). The infants' hands are equally free or not (Hawn & Harris, Chapter 17), visible or not (Mebert, Chapter 18); the infants are presented objects unimanually or bimanually (Hawn & Harris, Chapter 17; Ramsay, Chapter 9), and the objects are within reaching distance (e.g., Young *et al.*, Chapter 7) or not (Liederman, Chapter 16). Baseline levels of activity without an object are obtained in conjunction with object activity (Liederman, Chapter 16); activity without an object is obtained by itself (Saling, Chapter 13), or object activity is examined both during sound presentation and silence (Lewkowicz & Turkewitz, Chapter 20; Young *et al.*, Chapter 7). Variations in behavior are examined across trials or time (Hawn & Harris, Chapter 17; Young *et al.*, Chapter 7), positions (Young *et al.*, Chapter 7), variations in task (Harris & Fitzgerald, Chapter 14), or complexity (Baldwin in Harris, Chapter 10). In conclusion, the study of the development of manual specialization and its relationship to the brain must continue to explore dynamically a full range of behaviors using diverse relevant methodologies.

Which

All three review chapters of early manual and related specialization emphasize that for most if not all relevant behaviors, a right-hand preference at all age periods is evident in the literature (Liederman, Chapter 4; Michel, Chapter 3; Young *et al.*, Chapter 2). The preference may not be marked or stable in any one individual, and the proportion of right-lateralized individuals in the population may not be much more than that expected by chance, but nevertheless there is a consistency in this right-side preference early in life. There may be one notable exception of import—early reaching behavior may be left-handed (Harris, Chapter 10; Michel, Chapter 3), although Young *et al.* (Chapter 2) and Liederman (Chapter 4) suggest that this is not the case. For example, Young *et al.*'s (Chapter 2) review emphasizes that the only apparent left-lateralized behaviors early in life are clearly nondirected (e.g., palmar holding, arm reflexes). This tentative conclusion does not deny that there may be a minority of consistent left-hand–preferring individuals even in early infancy. However, in the present volume this possibility has not been investigated (Liederman, Chapter 16, and Michel, Chapter 3, have examined infants who turn their heads toward the left). Also, certain subgroups of individuals may manifest a temporary loss of a right-lateralized preference but not a switch to the left (Peters, Chapter 19; Ramsay, Chapter 9; see Lewkowicz & Turkewitz, Chapter 20, and Molfese & Molfese, Chapter 5, for data concerning apparent loss of lateralization involving centrally oriented measures, and Harris & Fitzgerald, Chapter 14, for similar data involving head turning).

When

It is clear that newborns, whether full term or preterm, can manifest asymmetries in manual (and related) behavior, although the trends may not be marked (see Young *et al.*, Chapter 2, and Trehub *et al.*, Chapter 12, respectively, for manual behavior). Moreover, anatomical asymmetries in the hemispheres evident in the final months of prenatal life (Harris, Chapter 10; Molfese & Molfese, Chapter 5) provide a possible structural underpinning for such behavioral asymmetries (also see Peters, Chapter 8, on subcortical differentiation in the neonate). As mentioned, lateralization in a behavior may wane after its emergence (Harris, Chapter 10). This may be related to the temporary loss of an early reflex (Peters, Chapter 19), ceiling effects where the behavior becomes easier and automatic for the infant (Liederman, Chapter 4), or due to the emergence of higher-order lateralized mechanisms that displace or disrupt earlier developed ones (Lewkowicz & Turkewitz, Chapter 20; Ramsay, Chapter 9). There is still instability in manual preference into the first year of life (Hawn & Harris, Chapter 10; Mebert, Chapter 18; Peters, Chapter 19), but by 12–18 months it becomes quite right lateralized (Ramsay, Chapter 9; Treves, Goldshmidt, & Korczyn, Chapter 21; Young *et al.*, Chapter 7). Only longitudinal research can ascertain the actual developmental course of any one lateralized behavior, and such research has been and is being undertaken (Harris, Chapter 10; Liederman, Chapter 4; Michel, Chapter 3; Ramsay, Chapter 9; Trehub *et al.*, Chapter 12). Continuities in manual specialization will become evident in such research; there will not only be benefit in theorizing, but perhaps also in applied work such as predicting later problems from certain early patterns of lateralization.

Inevitably, such longitudinal research will also reinforce the impression that what is developing in manual specialization is neither a unitary phenomenon nor an invariant one (Harris, Chapter 10; Harris & Fitzgerald, Chapter 14; Hawn & Harris, Chapter 17; Lewkowicz & Turkewitz, Chapter 20; Liederman, Chapter 4; Michel, Chapter 3; Peters, Chapter 19; Ramsay, Chapter 9; Segalowitz, Chapter 6; Trehub *et al.*, Chapter 12). Each developmental period may be marked by somewhat different lateralized behaviors, or independent clusters of them, with each behavior or behavior cluster varying in degree, stability, and proportion of right lateralization in the population. Moreover, there may be individual differences within any one group of lateralized infants (Harris & Fitzgerald, Chapter 14; Young, Chapter 22). For example, generally right-hand preferring infants may not all be the same at any one age in patterns of lateralization because of differential conditions associated with the development of their lateralization. Nevertheless, one or several major dimensions of organization may underlie this developmental diversity, and the maximum degree of lateralization may be the same at each developmental period for at least one behavior process (Segalowitz, Chapter 6; Young, Chapter 22).

Where

The development of manual specialization appears to be a multidimensional phenomenon, and its causation is similarly complex. The hereditary component that is often emphasized concerns Annett's shift factor, which biases the left hemisphere toward specialization for language and related sequential motor activity. The environmental experiential components most frequently emphasized are intraorganismic events that generate asymmetric experiences (e.g., asymmetric position in the womb affects muscle tonus). The proposed physiology underlying the development of manual specialization is outlined in this section on "Where," whereas the following section on "How" further explores the interaction of genetic and experiential factors of this development.

The specialized role of the left hemisphere in organizing motor output even early in life is emphasized in many chapters of this volume. For example, Mebert (Chapter 18), Ramsay (Chapter 9), and Young et al. (Chapter 7) all discuss the superior ability of the left hemisphere to organize subtle, fine motor sequential activity even in the first months of life, although not in the neonatal period. At this age, the left side of the subcortex apparently plays a role in organizing movement sequences (Lewkowicz & Turkewitz, Chapter 20; Liederman, Chapter 4; Peters, Chapter 8). Regions of the left hemisphere that may be involved in early control of motor output are discussed in a number of chapters (e.g., Harris, Chapter 10; Lewkowicz & Turkewitz, Chapter 20; Liederman, Chapter 4; Michel, Chapter 3; Molfese & Molfese, Chapter 5). The interrelated levels of the hierarchically arranged motor system and how those levels increasingly lateralize with development through feedback, in part, are presented in Peters (Chapter 8). The contributions of the various peripheral, spinal, brainstem, subcortical, and higher levels (e.g., motor plans in the cortex) to the development of lateralization are rigorously analyzed. The possible role of differential maturational gradients in the development of these lateralized physiological asymmetries is discussed in Harris (Chapter 10), Liederman (Chapter 4), and Michel (Chapter 3). Since right-lateralized behavior, especially if sequentially organized, probably reflects direct left-hemisphere control even early in life, several chapters suggest that the direction of appropriate lateralized peripheral measures may directly index the direction of underlying hemispheric specialization at the individual level even in infancy. Ramsay (Chapter 9) emphasizes tapping as an appropriate index, whereas both Lewkowicz and Turkewitz (Chapter

20) and Young et al. (Chapter 7) examine interference with motor activity during stimulus (e.g., verbal) presentation.

The sequential model of left-hemisphere organization is not the only one supported in this volume. The executive model, which underscores that the left hemisphere is specialized in the control of decision making and in organizing voluntary, deliberate, or goal-oriented behavior, is also emphasized, especially in the chapters of Peters (Chapters 8 and 19) and Young et al. (Chapters 2 and 7). Chapter 7 also describes a differential inhibition skill model of the hemispheres.

Other topics dealt with concerning the physiology of the hemispheres include the concept of a critical period during development of hemispheric specialization (e.g., Ramsay, Chapter 9; Young et al., Chapter 7), the role of lateralized damage on the development of hemispheric specialization (Liederman, Chapter 4; Michel, Chapter 3; Molfese & Molfese, Chapter 5; Peters, Chapter 8; Saling, Chapter 13; Trehub et al., Chapter 12), and how the hemispheres may communicate even early in life (Liederman, Chapter 4). Finally, the specific stimulus characteristics of speech sounds differentially processed in the hemispheres from the neonatal period onward has been investigated in the Molfeses's (Chapter 5) research. The important link between the differential processing skills of the hemispheres that the Molfeses have found and the differential motor skills of the hands in development needs to be determined.

How

GENETIC FACTORS

Any model of how manual specialization develops must be based on both hereditary and environmental factors. The genetic determinants (e.g., Annett's shift factor) on the development of manual and related asymmetries are dealt with in Harris (Chapter 10), Liederman (Chapter 4), Michel (Chapter 3), Peters (Chapter 8), and Saling (Chapter 13). Saling's genetic buffering hypothesis is particularly interesting. Investigation of the effects of familial handedness on lateral behavior, a possible marker of genetic influence on such behavior, is undertaken in Hawn and Harris (Chapter 10), Liederman (Chapter 16), Saling (Chapter 13), and Young et al. (Chapter 7). How organismic and experiential factors interact in the development of manual or related specialization is discussed in Harris (Chapter 10), Harris and Fitzgerald (Chapter 14), Lewkowicz and Turkewitz (Chapter 20), Liederman (Chapter 4), Mebert (Chapter 18), Michel (Chapter 3), Saling (Chapter 13), and Young et al. (Chapter 7).

ORGANISMIC FACTORS

The specific antecedant physiological mechanisms apparently helping in the development of lateralization in manual function seem to be varied.

Although the predominant view is that early hemispheric specialization plays a major role in organizing asymmetric manual function, not all agree (e.g., Michel, Chapter 3, but see Segalowitz, Chapter 6), and a host of other factors are thought to play a role. Most of those that have been posited are factors that permit lateralized experience, even if simply in terms of kinesthetic feedback, because of their asymmetry. Michel (Chapter 3) argues that neonatal supine head position preference is an excellent predictor of later hand preference, and so is intimately linked to the development of manual specialization (also see Harris, Chapter 10; Liederman, Chapter 4). Asymmetric birth position, an index of intrauterine position, has also been explored in this regard, as well as asymmetric posture, tonic neck reflexes, sensitivity, and tonus (Harris, Chapter 10; Lewkowicz & Turkewitz, Chapter 20; Liederman, Chapter 4, Chapter 16; Michel, Chapter 3; Saling, Chapter 13; Trehub et al., Chapter 12). The role of differential hand regard and ocular dominance is examined in Harris (Chapter 10), Lewkowicz and Turkewitz (Chapter 20), Liederman (Chapter 4), Michel (Chapter 3), Peters (Chapter 8), and Treves et al. (Chapter 21). Structural factors not previously mentioned (e.g., cerebral blood supply) are especially examined in Harris (Chapter 10). At the other end of the spectrum, the role of cognition (Mebert, Chapter 18; Peters, Chapter 8; Ramsay, Chapter 9) and language (Harris, Chapter 10; Lewkowicz & Turkewitz, Chapter 20; Michel, Chapter 3; Molfese & Molfese, Chapter 5; Ramsay, Chapter 9; Treves et al., Chapter 21) in the development of manual and related specialization are also discussed.

ENVIRONMENTAL FACTORS

Experiential factors external to the organism that may influence the development of manual and related specialization have been proposed. The role of hospital practice (Harris, Chapter 10; Harris & Fitzgerald, Chapter 14; Liederman, Chapter 4; Michel, Chapter 3), parental holding and toy giving styles (Harris, Chapter 10; Mebert, Chapter 18), cultural proscriptions (Harris, Chapter 10; Liederman, Chapter 4; Michel, Chapter 3), and experience acquired in toy play (Mebert, Chapter 18) in the development of manual specialization have been described. In addition, Young et al. (Chapter 7) underlined the possible significance of left-hemisphere–oriented parental social experience.

Why

The evolution of underlying physiological mechanisms is discussed in Harris (Chapter 10) and Peters (Chapter 8), but the evolution of manual specialization development per se is not touched on in this volume. Such speculations may be premature, since primate models may apply in part by analogy and not homology to human ones. As for adaptive function of manual specialization early in life, little conclusively can be said now. Consistent lateralization of different manual skills in each hand may facilitate the coordination of these skills and/or their superior performance, even early in life. Or, perhaps early manual specialization is a byproduct of the adaptive significance for an early hemispheric specialization and has no significance in and of itself. If so, then we must be able to specify the relation between hand preference and relevant aspects of hemispheric specialization and cerebral dominance for language and explain the adaptiveness of the latter. This is, of course, no easy feat. Finally, an adaptive function may be suggested that is general enough to cover both manual and hemispheric specialization. However, any acceptable explanation must include why lateralization is consistently to one side in humans. Perhaps there is something consistently asymmetric in the environment. Jaffe's (1978) argument about how hemispheric and manual specializations evolved in the context of asymmetric face-to-face human social interaction may be pertinent in this regard.

Conclusions

This volume is concerned with many unresolved relevant issues in the growing field of manual specialization in infancy and its relation to brain development. The model that will eventually emerge about the development of manual preference, lateralization of brain function, and how these processes interrelate should be multifaceted both in the levels the model treats and the inter- and intrarelations among them (Corter, Chapter 11). The field has much to offer in and of itself and because it may both help us to understand better normal development in general (Michel, Chapter 3; Young et al., Chapter 7) and have applied implications (Saling, Chapter 13; Trehub et al., Chapter 12).

References

Bresson, F., Maury, L., Pieraut-Le Bonniec, G., & de Schonen, S. (1977). Organization of asymmetric functions in hands collaboration. Neuropsychologia 15, 311–320.
Ingram, D. (1975). Motor asymmetries in young children. Neuropsychologia 13, 95–102.
Jaffe, J. (1978). Parliamentary procedure and the brain. In A. W. Seigman & S. Feldstein (Eds.), Nonverbal behavior and communication. Hillsdale, New Jersey: Erlbaum.

2

Is Early Reaching Left-Handed? Review of Manual Specialization Research[1]

GERALD YOUNG
SIDNEY J. SEGALOWITZ
PAT MISEK
I. ERCAN ALP
RENÉE BOULET

Introduction

Is Early Reaching Left-Handed?

Is the reported left-hand preference for reaching early in life correct? The surprising possibility that young infants begin to reach with their left hand, even though most will eventually switch to the right one toward the end of the first year of life, has captivated the imagination of researchers. Discontinuities, reversals, and shifts in hand preference are suggested and inferences about corresponding shifts in hemispheric dominance and control are drawn. The first such report of early left-hand reaching (in 3–4-month-old infants) by Gesell and Ames (1947), has been widely cited. A partial replication by Seth (1973), beginning with 4-month-olds, only seemed to confirm the impression. DiFranco, Muir, and Dodwell (1978) and McDonnell (1979; McDonnell, Anderson, & Abraham, in press) have found a similar trend of left-hand reaching in 1–4-month-olds.

Let us add to this growing list. Lippman (1927) reported an increasing right-hand preference in the reaching of his subjects in the first year of life, beginning with the $4\frac{3}{4}$-month-olds. However, we noticed in the figure that presents his data (Figure 8) that indeed the left hand is the one that is preferred in the $4\frac{3}{4}$-month-olds, replicating the findings of Gesell and Ames (1947) and Seth (1973) with infants of a similar age.

[1]This review was partially supported by grant no. A7939 from the Natural Sciences and Engineering Research Council of Canada.

MANUAL SPECIALIZATION
AND THE DEVELOPING BRAIN

The results of these five studies tempt one to conclude that infants prefer to reach with the left hand perhaps from as early as the first month of life onward for a period of at least several months. If this is true, research should now be less concerned with replicating the phenomenon and instead should focus on seeking the mechanisms causing it to emerge and eventually to disappear.

Is Early Reaching Right-Handed?

The preceding conclusion about early left-hand reaching would not only be premature, but also most probably false. Table 2.1 summarizes the studies with at least two subjects concerning lateralized manual behavior in the neonate to the 4-month-old. All reaching-related behaviors show a right and not a left preference across studies, although this preference does not seem marked. The novelty of Table 2.1 is that it lists nonsignificant trends in the data, not only significant results, even if these trends were not reported by the original authors but were culled by us from their tables and figures. Also, where possible, we have applied statistical analysis to the data if the author(s) failed to do so. In this regard, we had previously shown that the testable left-hand trends in both Gesell and Ames (1947) and Seth (1973) were not significant (Young, 1977). Now, the same can be said of DiFranco *et al.*'s (1978) results, whereas Lippman's (1927) are not amenable to statistical analysis as presented.

This leaves McDonnell's (1979; McDonnell *et al.*, in press), study as the only one where a left-hand preference is reported and where statistics cannot show that such a trend is nonsignificant since McDonnell reports a *significant* left-hand preference. However, inspection of McDonnell's Figure 1 showing the situation used makes clear that forward movement to the target was not scored as claimed. Rather, the behavior that was investigated was movement away from the side baseline toward the center without regard to forward movement or the target itself.

Studies of Early Lateralized Manual Behaviors

Early Reaching-Related Behaviors

Each behavior listed in Table 2.1 is now examined in turn. Of 17 studies that have investigated directed arm movements to a target early in life, 13 reveal a right-hand preference, 4 a left. Three studies report significant results for reaching to the right at one point or another (von Hofsten, 1982;

Table 2.1
Studies of Lateralized Reaching and Grasping-Related Behaviors from Zero to Four Months

Study	Age[a] (month)	Task detail Behavior observed	Results reported[b,c] Trends evident[d] Comments	Summary
		Directed arm movements to target		
Young, Bowman, Methot, Finlayson, Quintal, and Boissonneault (Chapter 7, this volume)	1	At midline or a side. Reaching, reaching with hand open, contact.	R, especially when object at right, but also midline.[c]	R[c]
von Hofsten (1982)	1/4	Moving in horizontal circular path. Reach.	R.[c] Uncertain whether starting position counterbalanced R–L as in von Hofsten (1980) or whether only one direction used.	R[c]
Young and Wolff (1976)	3½	At midline or a side. 2 objects, 1 to a side. Swipe.	R, especially when rattle at right or midline.[c]	R[c]
Hawn and Harris (Chapter 18, this volume)	2	At a side, another object simultaneously in hand at side of presentation. Contralateral free hand reach, ipsilateral reach.	L faster Trial 1, R Trial 2 for contralateral reach.[c] R faster overall for both behaviors.[c]	R[d]
Mebert (Chapter 19, this volume)	4	(a) In a hand. Free hand approach; (b) before subject with object, hand, or both covered. Obtain object.	R free-hand approach in (a)[d]; R = L for (b)[e].	R[d]
Michel (1981, 1982)	1/4, 1½, 2¾, 3¾	At midline; 2 objects, 1 to a side. Simultaneous object contact and visual regard.	R at 3¾ months[d], since 3¾ month R reaching predicted by 0 month R head turning, which usually occurs.	R[d]
Goodwin (1981)	4½	At midline; 2 objects, 1 to a side. First approach, contact, or grasp.	R in 64% of subjects. 4½ month R reaching predicted by head turned R at 0 months, which usually occurs.	R

(continued)

Table 2.1 (Continued)

Study	Age[a] (month)	Task detail	Behavior observed	Results reported[b,c] Trends evident[d]	Comments	Summary
Korczyn, Sage, and Karplus (1978)	0	Bar horizontal across midline. First arm moved.		R overall and for longitudinal sample in days 1, 4, and 5; L = R in days 2, 3.[d]		R[d]
Bresson, Pieraut Le-Bonniec, and de Shonen (1977)	4¼	At midline on supports, experimenter's palm, or fingertips. Touching and remaining on.		R 100% on palm, 80% on board, 65% on fingertips; L 100% on cube.[d] Experimenter positioned right.		R[d]
McDonnell (1975)	4¾	At midline or at right while subject wearing leftward displacing prisms. Accurate reaching.		R in each condition, including control midline. Over conditions; of 16 subjects, 12 R (1-tail binomial).[d]		R
White (1971)	1–4½ each ½	At midline or a side. Swift, accurate swipe.		R at 2–2½ months.[d] Only preferred side of asymmetric tonic neck reflex mentioned; this usually R (White, personal communication).		R[d]
Flament (1963)	3½–4½ each ½	At midline. Reach, then grasp.		R develops earlier at 4½–4¾ months.		R
Watson (1919)	2½–4¾ each ¼	"In front". Obtain, then mouth.		R after 4 months; L when first evident at 4 months.		R
DiFranco, Muir, and Dodwell (1978)	½	At midline. Reach.		L in 59% reaches, 65% subjects (1-tail binomial, n.s.).[d]		L
Seth (1973)	4½	Bell, cube, pellet at midline. Coincidence in eye–hand direction, look and move hand, initial approach, task success (e.g., contact, grasp, manipulate).		L. True for all 4 measures for bell, but only 2 of 4 measures for cube, pellet.[d] Young (1977) found testable trends nonsignificant.		L
Gesell and Ames (1947)	2–4½, each 1	At midline. Activity and contact.		L at 3¾, 4½ months, bilateral otherwise. Young (1977) found testable trends nonsignificant.		L
Lippman (1927)	4½, 4¾	Presumably at midline. Hand extended to accept.		R at 4¾ months. However, L in data given in Figure 8 of Lippman (1927).[d]		L[d]

Study	Age	Description	Result	
de Schonen and Bresson (1982)	4¼	At midline or a side; when at midline both arms or 1 arm free. Reach and remain on.	R = L.[e]	=[e]
Ramsay (Chapter 9, this volume)	4½	At midline. Object contact.	R = L before onset of duplicated syllable babbling that developed after 4 months.[d,e]	=[d,e]
Provine and Westerman (1979)	2, 2¾, 3½, 4¼	At midline or a side; when at midline both arms or 1 arm free. Reach, then contact.	R = L.[e]	=[e]
Flament (1975)	4, 4½	At midline. Reach, then manipulate.	Mostly bilateral.[e]	=[e]
Černáček and Podivinský (1971)	3¾	At midline or a side. Reach, then grasp.	R = L.[e] Two subjects involved.	=[e]
Halverson (1931)	3¾, 4¾	At midline. Reach, then touch.	R = L.[e] Experimenter positioned left.	=[e]
Voelckel (1913)	3½–4¾	At midline. Reach.	R = L.[e] Infants not healthy.	=[e]
Finger–hand activity on target				
Mebert (Chapter 19, this volume)	4	(a) In a hand. Fine motor activity; (b) before subject, with object, hand, or both covered. Cloth removal style.	R for (a);[d] R = L for (b).[e]	R[d]
Young and Wolff (1976)	3½	1 or 2 object(s) in or near hand(s) at midline or sides. Manipulate, touch.	R for manipulate, in particular (9 of 10 lateralized trials).	R
Mouth-related activity with target				
Young and Wolff (1976)	3½	At midline or a side; 2 objects, 1 to a side. Hand to mouth region.	R for large rattle, especially at sides;[c] L for 2 object tasks and small rattle, except at midline.	R[c]
Watson (1919)	3–4 each ¼	In a hand. Bring to mouth.	R at 3, 4 months. L at 3¾ months.[d]	R
Upper limb activation before target				
Liederman (Chapter 17, this volume)	¾–2¼	Object moved to a side; head turned to a side. Forward diffuse arm movement, midline crossing.	R[c], especially if head turned—held R[c] for forward extension. Others: R = L.[e]	R[c]

(continued)

17

Table 2.1 (Continued)

Study	Age[a] (month)	Task detail	Behavior observed	Results reported[b,c] Trends evident[d] · Comments	Summary
Mebert (Chapter 19, this volume)	4	In a hand.	Gross motor activity, release (throw, drop), active in visual field, out, inactive.	R gross motor activity when object in R hand and out of visual field; R activity in visual field (trend toward significance). R gross motor activity, release, and activity out of visual field.[d]	R[c]
Young et al. (Chapter 7, this volume)	0	Bar across midline; 2 sec Consonant–vowel or tone stimuli followed by 4 sec silence.	Bar, nontarget contact.	R for bar contact; R 2–4 sec after stimuli; L during, R = L just after for nontarget contact.[c] R 2–4 sec after implies R for spontaneous contact.	R[c]
von Hofsten (1982)	1/4	Moving in horizontal circular path. Total of variety of arm movements.		R.[c] Uncertain whether starting position counterbalanced R–L.	R[c]
Coryell and Michel (1978)	1/2–2 3/4 each 1/2	Moving from side to side. Movement of hand beyond 1 small square on television grid.		R at 2 3/4 months.[c] L at 1–2 1/2 months (McDonnell, 1979).	R[c]
Michel (1981, 1982)	2 3/4	At midline. Hand movement activation during target watching.		R,[d] since 2 3/4 month hand activation correlated to later reach, predicted to be R in general.	R[d]
McDonnell et al. (in press)	1 1/4	At midline or a side. Index finger: time out of side baseline, (change in) sector position, movement toward center. Evident from figure that latter is not forward to target. Distance between hand and target, mentioned in initial brief report (McDonnell, 1979), dropped here.		L for each measure in each of 2 studies;[c] Target Position × Hand interaction for all 3 measures show that L moves more (e.g., to center) the more the target is away from left, but R does not show equivalent effect.[c] Thus, at left, hands move equally, but at midline and right, L moves more.[d]	L[c]
Seth (1973)	4 1/2	At midline. Movement.		L.	L
Young and Wolff (1976)	3 1/2	At midline or a side; 2 objects, 1 to a side. Nondirected arm movement with hand opened or closed, nondirected finger–hand activity.		R for open hand–arm movement, especially when large rattle at left; L for close hand–arm movement especially when 1 object to each side;[c] L for finger–hand	R,[c] L[c]

Source	Age (months)	Measure	Findings	Result
			activity, especially for large rattle anywhere.	
Arm activation—no target				
Valentine and Wagner (1934)	0–⅓ daily	No object. Wrist movement.	R majority of days, especially in vertical plane.[c] R for 14 subjects consistently lateralized over days (12 R, 1-tail binomial)[c,d]	R^c
Giesecke (1936)	0–¼ daily	No object. Total manual movements.	R. Across subjects over days, R = L; R on days 4–6, L on 2–3.[d]	R
Stubbs (1933)	0–⅓ daily	No object. Upper-limb movement.	R.	R
Dowd and Tronick (Chapter 15, this volume)	½, 2¼	No object. Wrist movement starts, direction changes, speed peaks.	R = L.[e]	=^e
Kessen, Hendry, and Leutzendorff (1961)	0–¼ daily	No object. Hand displacement.	R = L. R days 2, 5; L 1, 3. Apparatus asymmetrical in figure.	=
Watson and Watson (1921)	0–⅓ daily	No object. Wrist movement.	R = L.[e]	=^e
Grasp strength				
Trehub et al. (Chapter 12, this volume)	0–3½	Experimenter's finger in a hand. Intensity. See Chapter 12 for details of 3 groups of subjects and when tested.	R stronger at 7¾ months conceptional age for both premature groups,[c] R other ages;[c] R = L for terms.	R^c
Petrie and Peters (1980)	½, 1¾, 2¾, 3½	Bulb in a hand. Intensity.	R at each session.[c]	R^c
Flament (1963)	0–2½ each ½	Experimenter finger in hand. Intensity.	R at ¾–2½ months (test unspecified).[c] R trials first.	R^c

(continued)

Table 2.1 (Continued)

Study	Age[a] (month)	Task detail	Behavior observed	Results reported[b,c] Trends evident[d] / Comments	Summary
Halverson (1937a)	0–4½ each 1	Object in a hand. Tight grasp, looser close.		R grasps stronger at 0–2, 3¾ months, L at 4½, R = L at 2¾.[d]	R[d]
Pollack (1960)	0	Palms stimulated bilaterally. Vigor, latency.		R = L.[e]	=[e]
		Grasp duration			
Hawn and Harris (Chapter 18, this volume)	2	In a hand or bilaterally. Duration.		R for unimanual,[c] bimanual tasks.	R[c]
Petrie and Peters (1980)	½, 1¾, 2¾, 3½.	In a hand or bilaterally. Duration.		R for unimanual task, except for 1¾ months. For subjects consistently using same hand over 4 sessions: 18 R, 0 L (1-tail binomial)[c,d]	R[c]
Caplan and Kinsbourne (1976)	2¾	In a hand or bilaterally. Duration.		R for unimanual,[c] bimanual tasks, where parents R-handed.	R[c]
Mebert (Chapter 19, this volume)	4	In a hand. Duration.		L.[d]	L[d]
Strauss (1982)	1/10, 2¼	In a hand. Duration.		R not L increased from 1/10 to 2¼ months. However, no significant Hand × Age interaction effect reported[d]; for subjects of R-hand parents: R at 1/10, L at 2¼; for subjects of L-hand parent(s?): opposite.[d]	R, L[d]
Roberts and Smart (1981)	0	In a hand. Duration.		R = L.[e]	=[e]
		Closing hand			
Cobb, Goodwin, and Saelens (1966)	0	No object. Fisting, opening.		R both when asleep, awake.[c] For awake state, R fists when L moves, but L open when R moves (1-tail Fisher)[c,d]	R[c]

20

Study	Age	Behavior	Findings	
Goodwin and Michel (1981)	0	No object. Fisting.	R,[d] since fisting side associated with head turning side, usually R.	R[d]
Michel and Goodwin (1979)	0	No object. Fisting, opening.	R,[d] since fisting side associated with head turning side, usually R.	R[d]
Liederman and Coryell (1981, 1982)	1½	Object moved to a side or head turned to a side. Open, closed.	R = L.[e]	=[e]
Precision grasp				
Mebert (Chapter 19, this volume)	4	In a hand. Intrinsic movement possible, no palmar contact.	R.[c]	R[c]
Young and Wolff (1976)	3½	1 or 2 object(s) in or near hand(s) at midline or to sides. Thumb opposed, no palmar contact.	Mostly R; L especially for 2 objects near hands at midline.	R
Holding (precision grasp excluded)				
Young and Wolff (1976)	3½	1 or 2 object(s) in or near the hand(s) at midline or to sides. Finger and palmar contact.	L, especially for bar across midline near hands.[c]	L[c]
Mebert (Chapter 19, this volume)	4	In a hand. Power grasp, contact, have object transferred to.	L[d] for each.	L[d]
Suspension grasp				
Valentine and Wagner (1934)	0–1	Unimanual. Strength.	R.[d]	R[d]
McGraw (1940)	0–4¾ each ⅓	Unimanual. Duration.	L, especially at 1½–2½ months, also ¼, ¾, 4–4¾; R at 2¾–3¼.[d]	L[d]
Sherman, Sherman, and Flory (1936)	0–2¾ each ¼	Unimanual. Strength.	L.	L

(continued)

Table 2.1 (Continued)

Study	Age[a] (month)	Task detail Behavior observed	Results reported[b,c] Trends evident[d]	Comments	Summary
Watson (1919)	0–¾ each $\frac{1}{10}$	Unimanual. Ambiguous whether strength or duration.	L at ¼–½ months.[d]		L[d]
Halverson (1937b)	0–4½ each 1	Unimanual. Strength.	L. However, R in boys at 0–2 months, alternating with L thereafter; R in girls at 0, L thereafter;[d] R[c] at 4½ (11 of 14 subjects R, 1-tail binomial).[d]		L, R[c,d]
		Arm reflex, tremor			
Coryell and Michel (1978)	¼–2¾ each ½	No object. Arm extension in ATNR, anti-ATNR.	R,[d] since side ATNR associated with preferred-side head turn,[c] usually R; R for anti-ATNR.[c]		R[d]
Trehub et al. (Chapter 12, this volume)	0–3½	(a) Arm recoil. Frequency, duration, strength; (b) prone head turn and arm passage. Latency.	L stronger, faster at 7¾ months conceptional age for both premature groups.[c] Most other results L, except for strength, duration of arm recoil.		L[c]
Liederman and Coryell (1981, 1982)	1½	Object moved to a side; head turned to a side. Arm extension in ATNR, anti-ATNR.	L.[d] Fewer, weaker, and shorter (maximum duration) ATNRs to preferred side of spontaneous head turning in R-preferred nonbirth complication subjects. This occurred especially when following object being moved, but resistance to head turning by experimenter apparently accounted		L[d]

			for lack of similar result in other condition.	
Segalowitz and Chapman (1980)	1¼	No object; 3 groups, 2 stimulated for 1 month prior with verbal or nonverbal stimuli. Arm tremor, sign of central nervous system immaturity in prematures, examined.	L (slightly) in control group,[d] L in verbal group, R in nonverbal group.	L[d]
Liederman (Chapter 17, this volume)	1½	Object moved to a side; head turned to a side. ATNR. Spontaneous head turners: number of R = number of L.	R = L.[e]	=[e]
Cioni and Pellegrineti (1982)	0	No object; head turned to a side. Arm or leg extension spontaneously or to head turning.	R = L.[e]	=[e]

Hand watching

Coryell and Michel (1978)	¼–2¾ each ½	No object. Hand in focal vision according to body landmarks.	R at each age.[c] Most clearly at 1½ months, not clearly at 2½.[d]	R[c]
White (1971)	1–4½ each ½	(a) No object. Hand in center visual field; (b) object at a side. Target watched; (c) object in a hand, target in it, watched.	R in all cases; for (a) 1½–2½ months; for (b) 1–2; for (c) 2–3.	R
Flament (1963)	0–4¾ each ½	Object in a hand. Hand moving watched.	R develops earlier, more frequent at 2–2¾ months. Right trials first.	R

Finger movement—no target

Michel and Goodwin (1979)	0	No object. Finger movement.	R,[d] since movement side associated with head position side, usually R.	R[d]

(continued)

Table 2.1 (Continued)

Study	Age[a] (month)	Task detail	Behavior observed	Trends evident[d]	Comments	Summary
				Results reported[b,c]		
Cobb et al. (1966)	0	No object. Finger movement.		L in waking, sleeping states.[d]		L[d]
			Total movements of upper limbs			
Giesecke (1936)	¼–4¾ each ½	Total movements in home.		R. R at ½–1¾, 3½–4¾ months, L at 2–3¼.[d]		R
Lederer (1939)	4	Total movements (reaching, grasping, page turning, etc.).		L.		L
Bergeron (1947, 1948, 1949)	0–4¾	Total arm–hand movements in activities.		R = L.[e]		=[e]

[a] Ages where data reported shown. Newborns = 0. Averages, estimates obtained where necessary.
[b] Right side preferred = R, Left = L.
[c] For results column, footnote refers to specific significant result in sentence. For summary column, means that at least one significant result in indicated direction reported in results column.
[d] Reported means, tables, and/or figures show a trend in the data either not mentioned in text, opposite to one in the text, or refinement of one in the text. Sometimes statistics applied where author(s) have failed to do so (indicated by[c,d] where significant).
[e] Result is reported with no means, tables, and/or figures available to permit check of trends.

Young, Bowman, Methot, Finlayson, Quintal, & Boissonneault, Chapter 7, this volume; Young & Wolff, 1976). In the studies by Hofsten and Young et al. (Chapter 7), the subjects were about the same age as in the DiFranco et al. work. Young and Wolff's (1976) subjects were almost 4 months of age, and 7 other studies revealed a right-hand preference in reaching at about 4 months of age. These 8 studies stand in contrast to the 3 already mentioned that report a left-hand preference in this age period. There are two other reports of reaching in each of the following age periods—up to 1 month and at 2 months—and all are to the right. Overall, a right-hand preference in reaching seems evident from the neonate to the 4-month-old, the whole age period with which we are concerned.

Exploratory activity of an object, whether with finger–hand activity or with mouth-related activity, appears to be a right-handed activity in the few studies where these behaviors have been examined (all with 3–4-month-olds, e.g., bringing hand to mouth region when large rattle was held before $3\frac{1}{2}$-month-olds, Young & Wolff, 1976).

Since the right hand seems to be used for reaching and exploring early in life, the question is whether it is performing all activities more often, both directed exploratory activities and nondirected, nonfunctional ones, or whether the left hand performs nondirected subordinate behaviors more often, in a complementary division of labor with the right hand. Our understanding of McDonnell's results, mentioned earlier (i.e., early nondirected arm activity is left-handed), may lead us to conclude that the latter alternative is correct. Indeed, it may be correct, but only for the age period (average of $1\frac{1}{4}$ months) of McDonnell's study, since Coryell and Michel's (1978) data also reveal that between 1 and $2\frac{1}{2}$ months, hand activation is slightly left-handed, even though it is significantly right-handed at $2\frac{3}{4}$ months. In contrast to these two sets of data, Liederman (Chapter 16) reports a right-hand preference for forward movement (not measured with reference to the target) from $\frac{3}{4}$ to $2\frac{1}{4}$ months. These results collectively suggest a possible slight left-hand trend in overall or nondirected upper-limb activity from about 1 to $2\frac{1}{2}$ months of age.

However, infants in all other age periods studied (neonates, $2\frac{3}{4}$ months onward) reveal a significant right-hand preference for upper-limb activity before an object. Thus, the possibility of a reversal in this trend from 1 to $2\frac{1}{2}$ months of age needs to be thoroughly checked before it is considered reliable. Also, other evidence argues against such a reversal. First, arm activation by neonates when there is no target is a right-side activity in all three studies where trends are significant. Second, Young and Wolff (1976) looked at three types of nondirected target-related activity in $3\frac{1}{2}$-month-olds. Nondirected arm movement with the hand open appeared to be a right-side activity, whereas the same behavior with the hand closed showed the opposite pattern, as did nondirected finger–hand activity without arm movement (significant even when a rattle was held to the right). Thus, it may be that nondirected arm movements with signs of functional activity or behavior preparatory to functional activity (hand opening) is right sided, whereas nondirected arm or hand–finger movements without such accompanying behaviors is left sided.

Early Grasping-Related Behaviors

Grasping behavior has been examined in a variety of ways. As long as the infant is not suspended or performing some other, more passive, activity, grasping appears to be a right-hand activity. When an object is placed in one hand or another, in particular, the grasp is both stronger and longer in duration with the right hand (for all four studies revealing a preference in the former case, three at a significant level, and for three of four studies in the latter case, with all three significant). Even when the hand performs a grasping-like activity, closing, readily evident in newborns, a right preference is manifested (in all three studies with trends, one significant).

However, as was the case with nondirected target activity, when different types of grasping behavior are examined, especially in the same study, which has been the case in a few studies with 3–4-month-olds, a division of labor between the hands seems evident. In the two studies where precision grasping has been observed (Mebert, Chapter 19; this volume; Young & Wolff, 1976), a right-hand preference was found (significant for Mebert). In contrast, where holding involving palmar contact has been observed, a left-hand preference was found (significant in one task in Young & Wolff, 1976).

Note that suspension grasping has not been studied since McGraw's work in 1940, which may account for the absence of a clear trend for this behavior. The only significant result shows a right-hand preference for $4\frac{1}{2}$-month-olds (something we detected in Halverson, 1937b), but all other ages in his study and most other studies show a left-hand preference. Overall then, a left-hand preference in suspension grasping seems evident throughout the age period of the present review. Grasping while suspended is more like palmar holding than precision grasping, fitting the just-mentioned trends for these behaviors.

Other Behaviors Early in Life

When the arms are tested for reflexive activity or tremoring, a sign of central nervous system immaturity (Segalowitz & Chapman, 1980), the left hand is usually more active, especially in premature infants (in three of four studies, with significant results in Trehub, Corter, & Shosenberg, Chapter 12, this volume). The only study not to show this trend involved older infants, in part (Coryell & Michel, 1978; subjects up to $2\frac{3}{4}$ months).

For visual regard a right-hand preference is evident (all three studies were right lateralized, one significant; age period involved, 0–3 months). The only measures not to evidence a lateralized trend involved finger movements in neonates when no target was present and the broad category of total movements across activities.

Discussion

Summary

The trends in the data reach significance in a minority of studies, sometimes only for one or two results of the many reported, so that to suggest an absolute differentiation of the behavior of the hands in early infancy would be misleading. Nevertheless, it seems that throughout the age period of the present review, 0–4 months, the right hand is preferred for more directed, target-related activity, whether the proximal hand–finger–wrist (e.g., precision grasping [Mebert, Chapter 19, this volume]; manipulation [Young & Wolff, 1976]) or distal arm–shoulder musculature (e.g., reaching) is involved. This appears true whether the object is at a distance and must be watched and clearly approached before there is contact and exploration, or whether it is placed quite near or even directly in the hands, leading to grasping activity. The left hand is preferred when there is clearly nondirected activity (e.g., nondirected finger–hand activity with no arm movement, in Young & Wolff, 1976; reflexive arm behavior or more passive holding, Liederman & Coryell, 1981, 1982; and Mebert, Chapter 18, respectively). When the research performed in the 1980s is examined alone, this pattern of results favoring the right side for directed behavior early in life is especially clear and significant (e.g., von Hofsten's 1982, 3-D cinematographic analysis of reaching, with the proportion of right-side preferring individuals equivalent to what is found with adults).

Control of Early Right Upper-Limb Activity

In the following section, an attempt is made to explain how the left and right hemispheres of the brain control task-oriented lateralized manual activity early in life. The model integrates a series of current ideas about hemispheric control of movement: Brinkman and Kuypers (1973) on proximal and distal musculature control; Geschwind (1975) on exclusive left-hemisphere bilateral motor control; and a left hemisphere specialized in part to be sequential and executive, that is, to plan motor activity (Peters, Chapter 8, this volume). Thus, in one sense the model is trying to show a continuity between early and later lateralization. More important, it is trying to make explicit what we mean by the oft-repeated notion of a left-hemisphere dominance for reaching and motor behavior in childhood. However, since these ideas are extended downward to the developmental period, where the subcortex may be most relevant in asymmetric motor control, the model should be seen heuristically at this point. Also, the model does not try to explain how a minority of infants may end up being left-handed. Moreover, the model purposely excludes a discussion of the role of asymmetric head movements, hand regard, and tonus in early right-hand preference for reaching since this is done elsewhere (see Liederman, Chapter 16, and Michel, Chapter 3, in particular).

Since the distal musculature is contralaterally controlled by the cerebral hemispheres (Brinkman & Kuypers, 1973), when the right hand, finger, and wrist preference in target-directed activity manifests, one can infer left-hemisphere control. However, since the proximal musculature can be controlled both ipsilaterally and contralaterally, one can never be sure whether left- or right-hemisphere control of unilateral arm and shoulder movement in target-directed activity is taking place. At first glance, the relatively superior spatial skills of the right hemisphere (Bradshaw & Nettleton, 1981) suggests that when the right-arm preference for reaching manifests, the right hemisphere may ipsilaterally guide the right arm in reaching for a target and then the left hemisphere contralaterally guides the right hand in exploration of the target. Although this explanation may be valid, evidence with adults suggests that both left- and right-arm movements are ultimately controlled by the left hemisphere, despite the other various possibilities (Geschwind, 1975). Thus, the following explanations are not only more parsimonious because they avoid the idea of a switch in hemisphere control, they are also more consonant with the adult data (cf. Peters, 1981). When the right-reaching preference manifests in the young infant, the left hemisphere contralaterally guides the right upper limb throughout all the various phases of reaching for grasping and exploring the target, controlling the behavior either directly throughout, or directly in some phases and indirectly in others.

For continual direct control of right upper-limb activity to occur, the left hemisphere may even have to control behavior (e.g., space-related adjustments in reaching) best suited to the right hemisphere (Hypothesis A). This emphasis on continual left-hemisphere control of right upper-limb activity by the young infant fits a current conception of hemispheric specialization (see Young et al., Chapter 7, this volume). The hemispheres do not necessarily control, in daily life, the activities that they may best control in the laboratory, for what may characterize the left hemisphere is an executive control; a decision-making planning system seeking smooth sequential organization in behavior; a system that balances the costs and benefits of relinquishing control of a behavior or process to the right hemisphere. For the sake of facilitating a successful sequential flow in the young infant's target-oriented activity, the left hemisphere may often perform even those tasks (e.g., space-related reaching) best suited to the right hemisphere.

It may also be possible that the left hemisphere cedes immediate, but not ultimate, control to the right hemisphere in right-arm reaching (Hypothesis B). The left hemisphere would do this in order to take advantage of the right hemisphere's superior spatial skills. In ceding immediate control of the reach to the right hemisphere, the left hemisphere would not cede absolute, ultimate control, since it would continuously monitor and incorporate the resultant performance into its executive schemes (see Liederman, Chapter 4, this volume, for the pathways available for interhemispheric interaction early in life).

Of course, it could also be that the tentative reaching of the young infant is uncoordinated to the point that the sequencing manipulative skills of the left hemisphere are needed much more than the spatial skills of the right hemisphere (Young, 1977, p. 306). Here then, there is no cost–benefit analysis of whether motor control should be ceded to the right hemisphere, as the left hemisphere's specialized skills are appropriate for each phase of the reach, and it clearly controls the behavior throughout each phase (Hypothesis C). This is the most parsimonious of all the models presented. However, it could be that there are either age and/or individual differences so that the other models are also valid at times.

As reaching becomes more automatic or ballistic and less demanding spatially in the course of development in the first year, then the right hemisphere's special skills are probably needed less, and reaching is probably almost always directly controlled in the left hemisphere or indirectly controlled by it through subcortical mediation. Either possibility would help account for the increasing dominance of right-hand reaching toward 12 months of age (e.g., Ramsay, 1980).

Control of Early Left Upper-Limb Activity

The early left-hand preference for nondirected activity during task-oriented behavior, when it manifests, again may reflect ultimate left hemisphere control either directly or indirectly. The left hemisphere may either shunt immediate control to the right, monitoring it, and thus controlling it indirectly or, in the case of the arms and shoulders, directly control the left side ipsilaterally. However, it is more likely that such nondirected left-hand or arm activity during right-hand– or arm–directed behavior is due to an inability of the left hemisphere, either directly or indirectly, to fully inhibit nonfunctional left-side activity. Perhaps, in reflexive and some nondirected activity, the left hemisphere even cedes absolute control to the right hemisphere, freeing itself for other tasks. For example, the possible left-side preference for nondirected arm activity before a target between 1 and 2 months (see p. 25) may reflect spatial mapping behavior via direct right-hemisphere control, perhaps as a preparation for right-arm reaching or perhaps just to acquire spatial information in and of itself.

Conclusions

Simultaneous study of the manual and hemispheric activity of young infants when presented objects is needed to verify the following statements: The right upper limb seems preferred for directed activities and the left for nondirected ones from early in life onward. This occurs most probably because of a direct or indirect left-hemisphere executive control trying to ensure smooth sequential successful behavior. In such control, a fine balancing, not only of activation, but also of inhibition, is implied (a theme developed in Young et al., Chapter 7). Finally, manual and hemispheric specialization development seems not to refer to different functions and their side of lateralization in the young infant, as compared to the older child and adult, at least when examined in terms of the processes emphasized in this chapter. Rather, manual and hemispheric specialization development may simply concern changes in which behaviors come to evidence lateralization, the degree of such lateralization, and its consequent stability.

Acknowledgments

Thanks are due Sandra Trehub, Peter Wolff, and Yves Joanette for helpful comments. The writing of this chapter was completed while the first author was on sabbatical at the Laboratoire Théophile Alajouanine, Centre de Recherche, Centre Hospitalier Côte-des-Neiges, Montréal, Québec.

References

Bergeron, M. (1947). Les manifestations motrices spontanées chez l'enfant. Etude psycho-biologique. Conception d'ensemble sur la motricité de l'enfant en fonction de la maturation nerveuse de la naissance à trois mois. Paris: Herman.

Bergeron, M. (1948). Les manifestations motrices spontanées et réflexes chez l'enfant de trois à six mois: Essai sur la motricité du premier âge. Enfance 1, 392–405.

Bergeron, M. (1949). Les manifestations motrices spontanées et réflexes chez l'enfant de 3 à 6 mois (2me note sur la motricité du nourrisson). Annales Medico-psychologiques 107, 25–28.

Bradshaw, J., & Nettleton, N. (1981). The nature of hemispheric specialization in man. The Behavioral and Brain Sciences 4, 51–63.

Bresson, F., Maury, L., Pieraut-Le Bonniec, G., & de Schonen, S. (1977). Organization of asymmetric functions in hands collaboration. Neuropsychologia 15, 311–320.

Brinkman, J., & Kuypers, H. (1973). Cerebral control of contralateral and ipsilateral arm, hand, and finger movements in the split-brain rhesus monkey. Brain 96, 653–674.

Caplan, P., & Kinsbourne, M. (1976). Baby drops the rattle: Asymmetry of duration of grasp by infants. *Child Development 47*, 532–534.

Černáček, J., & Podivinský, F. (1971). Ontogenesis of handedness and somatosensory cortical response. *Neuropsychologia 9*, 219–232.

Cioni, G., & Pellegrinetti, G. (1982). Lateralization of sensory and motor functions in human neonates. *Perceptual and Motor Skills 54*, 1151–1158.

Cobb, K., Goodwin, R., & Saelens, E. (1966). Spontaneous hand position of newborn infants. *The Journal of Genetic Psychology 108*, 225–237.

Coryell, J. F., & Michel, G. F. (1978). How supine postural preferences of infants can contribute toward the development of handedness. *Infant Behavior and Development 1*, 245–257.

de Schonen, S., & Bresson, F. (1982). *When having one arm is better than two.* Unpublished manuscript.

DiFranco, D., Muir, D., & Dodwell, P. C. (1978). Reaching in very young infants. *Perception 7*, 385–392.

Flament, F. (1963). Developpement de la preference manuelle de la naissance à 6 mois. *Enfance 3*, 241–262.

Flament, F. (1975). *Coordination et prevalence manuelles chez les nourrissons.* Paris: C.N.R.S.

Geschwind, N. (1975). The apraxias: Neural mechanisms of disorders of learned movement. *American Scientist 63*, 188–195.

Gesell, A., & Ames, L. (1947). The development of handedness. *Journal of Genetic Psychology 70*, 155–175.

Giesecke, M. (1936). The genesis of hand preference. *Monograph of the Society for Research in Child Development 1*(5, Serial No. 5).

Goodwin, R. S., & Michel, G. F. (1981). Head orientation position during birth and in infant neonatal period, and hand preference at nineteen weeks. *Child Development 52*, 819–826.

Halverson, H. (1931). An experimental study of prehension in infants by means of systematic cinema records. *Genetic Psychology Monographs 10*, 107–286.

Halverson, H. (1937a). Studies of the grasping responses of early infancy, I. *Journal of Genetic Psychology 51*, 371–392.

Halverson, H. (1937b). Studies of the grasping responses of early infancy, II. *Journal of Genetic Psychology 51*, 393–424.

Kessen, W., Hendry, L., & Leutzendorff, A. (1961). Measurement of movement in the human newborn: A new technique. *Child Development 32*, 95–105.

Korczyn, A. D., Sage, J. I., & Karplus, M. (1978). Lack of limb motor asymmetry in the neonate. *Journal of Neurobiology 9*, 483–488.

Lederer, R. (1939). An exploratory investigation of handed status in the first two years of life. In R. Lederer & J. Redfield (Eds.), Studies in Infant behavior (vol. 5). *University of Iowa Studies in Child Welfare.* Iowa: Univ. of Iowa Press.

Liederman, J., & Coryell, J. (1981). Right-hand preference facilitated by rightward turning biases during infancy. *Developmental Psychobiology 14*, 439–450.

Liederman, J., & Coryell, J. (1982). The origin of left hand preference: Pathological and nonpathological influences. *Neuropsychologia 20*, 721–725.

Lippman, H. (1927). Certain behavior responses in early infancy. *Journal of Genetic Psychology 34*, 424–440.

McDonnell, P. (1975). The development of visually guided reaching. *Perception and Psychophysics 18*, 181–185.

McDonnell, P. (1979). Patterns of eye–hand coordination in the first year of life. *Canadian Journal of Psychology 33*, 253–267.

McDonnell, P., Anderson, V., & Abraham, W. (in press). Asymmetry and orientation of arm movements in three- to eight-week-old infants. *Infant Behavior and Development.*

McGraw, M. (1940). Suspension grasp behavior of the human infant. *American Journal of Diseases of Children 60*, 799–811.

Michel, G. (1981). Right-handedness: A consequence of infant supine head–orientation preference? *Science 212*, 685–687.

Michel, G. (1982). *Hand-use preference for reaching during infancy.* Unpublished manuscript.

Michel, G., & Goodwin, R. (1979). Intrauterine birth position predicts newborn supine head position preferences. *Infant Behavior and Development 2*, 29–38.

Peters, M. (1981). Handedness: Coordination of within- and between-hand alternating movements. *American Journal of Psychology 94*, 633–643.

Petrie, B. F., & Peters, M. (1980). Handedness: Left/right differences in intensity of grasp response and duration of rattle holding in infants. *Infant Behavior and Development 3*, 215–221.

Pollack, S. L. (1960). The grasp response in the neonate. *Archives of Neurology 5*, 108–115.

Provine, R. R., & Westerman, J. A. (1979). Crossing the midline: Limits of early eye–hand behavior. *Child Development 50*, 437–441.

Ramsay, D. (1980). Onset of unimanual handedness in infants. *Infant Behavior and Development 3*, 377–386.

Roberts, A., & Smart, J. (1981). An investigation of handedness and headedness in newborn babies. *Behavior and Brain Research 2*, 275–276.

Segalowitz, S. J., & Chapman, J. S. (1980). Cerebral asymmetry for speech in neonates: A behavioral measure. *Brain and Language 9*, 281–288.

Seth, G. (1973). Eye–hand co-ordination and "handedness": A developmental study of visuomotor behaviour in infancy. *British Journal of Educational Psychology 43*, 35–49.

Sherman, M., Sherman, I., & Flory, C. (1936). Infant behavior. *Comparative Psychology Monographs 12* (4, Serial No. 59).

Strauss, E. (1982). Manual persistence in infancy. *Cortex 18*, 319–321.

Stubbs, E., & Irwin, O. (1933). Laterality of limb movements of four newborn infants. *Child Development 4*, 358–359.

Valentine, W., & Wagner, I. (1934). Relative arm motility in the newborn infant. *Ohio University Studies 12*, 53–68.

Voelckel, E. 1913. Untersuchungen über die Rechtshändigkeit beim Säugling. *Zeitschrift fur Kinderheilk 8*, 351–358.

von Hofsten, C. (1980). Predictive reaching for moving objects by human infants. *Journal of Experimental Child Psychology 30*, 369–382.

von Hofsten, C. (1982). Eye–hand coordination in the newborn. *Developmental Psychology 18*, 450–461.

Watson, J. (1919). *Psychology from the standpoint of a behaviorist.* Philadelphia, Pennsylvania: Lippincott.

Watson, J., & Watson, R. (1921). Studies in infant psychology. *The Scientific Monthly 13*, 493–515.

White, B. L. (1971). *Human infants—experience and psychological development.* Englewood Cliffs, New Jersey: Prentice Hall.

Young, G. (1977). Manual specialization in infancy: Implications for lateralization of brain function. In S. Segalowitz & F. Gruber (Eds.), *Language development and neurological theory.* New York: Academic Press.

Young, G., & Wolff, P. (1976). *Lateralization of manual behavior in 15-week-olds.* Unpublished manuscript.

3

Development of Hand-Use Preference during Infancy

GEORGE F. MICHEL

Introduction

Few psychological phenomena escape the nature–nurture controversy, and human handedness is no exception (Harris, 1980; Palmer, 1964). Although several genetic models for the inheritance of handedness have been proposed (see Annett, 1978), not one has completely accounted for all the geneological data. However, failure of these genetic models does not warrant acceptance of sociocultural or training explanations of handedness (Hildreth, 1949; Provins, 1956; Provins & Cunliffe, 1972). Indeed, the success of training could depend on genotype as much as the expression of genotype could depend on training. It has been argued, however, that a genetic analysis of a behavioral character, whatever the outcome, reveals little about how that behavior develops (Hirsch, 1970; Lehrman, 1970; Michel & Moore, 1978; Tinbergen, 1963). Because behavior develops not from the interaction of genes and environment but from the interaction of the organism with its environment (Lehrman, 1953), questions about ontogeny require empirical investigations and conceptual distinctions that are different from those required by questions about heredity, whether genetic or cultural (Bateson, 1978; Schneirla, 1966).

In order to determine how handedness develops; at least four components of its ontogeny must be examined:

1. First, the phenomenon of human handedness must be characterized precisely. Similarities and differences between the limb-use preferences of other species and human handedness should be identified. Those aspects of human handedness that are species typical should be dis-

MANUAL SPECIALIZATION
AND THE DEVELOPING BRAIN

tinguished from those that are typical of individuals, and the universal aspects should be distinguished from those that are culturally restricted. Situation-specific change of hand-use preferences must be distinguished from the development or acquisition of the preference and from modification of the preference (i.e., alterations maintained in the absence of the conditions responsible for the alteration). Unless these characteristics of handedness are identified and appreciated, it is unlikely that attempts to understand its development will be successful.

2. Once handedness has been characterized, detailed descriptions of its development from initial appearance through changes (if any) in its essential characteristics should be provided for large samples of people drawn from many different cultures.

3. The environmental conditions prevalent during development must also be described for these samples. From the two descriptions generated by (1) and (2), hypotheses may be derived about environmental conditions that can produce experiential events which may influence development by inducing changes in handedness, facilitating the initial appearance or the achievement of a mature form of handedness, or maintaining a consistency of handedness across tasks, skills, and age (cf. Gottlieb, 1976).

4. Finally, handedness must be examined in relation to the individual's previous and concurrent neurobehavioral organization (i.e., cognitive as well as neurological status), if hypotheses are to be generated about how handedness develops from the interaction of the organism with its environment.

Knowledge of the characteristics of handedness, the course of its development, its environmental context, and its associated neurobehavioral organization will provide the rich descriptive framework within which appropriate developmental questions can be posed. Since much of the information about these four components of the ontogeny of handedness is incomplete, many different accounts of handedness ontogeny may be proposed.

In this chapter, I will offer a description of the ontogeny of handedness that focuses on the period of infancy and serves as contextual justification for my own research endeavors. I will argue that the emergence of a stable handedness develops, in part, on the basis of the early hand-use preferences that individuals establish during infancy. Since the results of earlier research represented infant hand-use preferences as variable, fluctuating, and unstable, I will offer evidence affirming the stability and consistency of these preferences. However, I will argue that the earliest expressions of limb-use asymmetries are distinct from, even if potential contributors to, the infant's hand-use preferences. The various types of infant hand-use preferences will then be organized into a plausible account of the developmental course of infant handedness.

The distinction between individual and population characteristics of human handedness is emphasized in this review. Since the population characteristic (the dextral bias in handedness distribution) is manifested through individual handedness, an argument is made for examining the contribution of early asymmetrical biases to the development of handedness. Therefore, the relative merits of several asymmetrically biased factors as agents responsible for the dextral bias in handedness are examined. Finally, a partial answer to the question of how the dextral bias in handedness could be induced during development is proposed.

The Development of Handedness

There is little doubt that handedness is a complex characteristic that displays interesting trends and transitions during development. The dramatic changes in manual skills that take place throughout infancy and childhood demand that handedness be evaluated in different situations (e.g., reaching for things, unimanual and bimanual object manipulation, familiar and unfamiliar tasks, tool use and tool manufacture) and by different measures (e.g., initial use, frequency of use, differential skill achievement). It is conceivable that as certain manual skills become well established and easily executed (e.g., reaching), hand-use preferences may disappear from one measure (initial use) while remaining in other measures (frequency of use) or situations (object manipulation) or may reappear in a newly emerging skill (object construction or tool manufacture). It is even possible under certain conditions for hand-use preferences to become apparent only once a certain level of mastery of a skill has been achieved. Ramsay (1980) observed primitive unimanual manipulatory skill but no hand-use preferences in 5-month-old infants. Hand-use preferences were apparent by 7 months, when unimanual manipulation skills were more complex and the primitive skills well mastered.

Whether hand-use preferences are independent of manual skill development, contribute to skill acquisition, reflect skill development, or coordinate with skill development in some complex, reciprocally interwoven way is at present unknown.

Handedness in Children and Adults

It is generally agreed that handedness does not consolidate as a stable, robust, and self-identifying condition of the individual until about 8–11 years of age (Beaumont, 1974; Belmont & Birch, 1963; Connolly & Elliot, 1972; Gesell & Ames, 1947). Hand-use preferences are apparent much earlier, but they exhibit some interesting differences from the preferences of adolescents and adults. Although children as young as 3 years show an adult-like dextral bias in the distribution of their handedness (Annett, 1970; Downey, 1928; Hildreth, 1949; Jones, 1931; Updegraff, 1932), the proportion of left-handed children (11–14%) is a good deal higher than that (4–8%) for adults (but see Peters & Durding, 1979; Peters & Pedersen, 1978). Moreover, Connolly and Elliot (1972) found that children younger than 8–9 years would readily use their nonpreferred hand if task conditions (obstacles, positional convenience) challenged the ease or efficiency of using the preferred hand. Older children and adults were found to continue using the preferred hand despite the loss of efficiency and increased difficulty created by the challenges. Thus, consolidation seems to entail at least an inflexibility of hand use and a greater proportion of right handedness (Coren, Porac, & Duncan, 1981).

It is conceivable, then, that sociocultural pressure, situational conditions, training, and the acquisition of specific manual skills are more likely to affect an individual's handedness status before handedness has consolidated at 8–11 years of age. What is unclear is whether those factors that result in the adoption of a different hand-use preference for a particular task at an early age would also result in the transfer of this new preference to other familiar and unfamiliar tasks. For some people, socially imposed hand-use preferences for writing seem also to induce shifts in hand-use preferences for other tasks. However, for the majority, hand-use preferences remain unchanged in tasks other than writing (Teng, Lee, Yang, & Chang, 1976).

Handedness during Infancy

Whatever happens to handedness during childhood, the initial establishment of hand-use preference must occur during infancy since even 2–3-year-old children exhibit preferences with a dextral bias in their distribution (Hildreth, 1949). However, it is usually assumed that the hand-use preferences of infants are neither consistent nor predictive of either child or adult handedness (Corballis & Beale, 1976; Gesell & Ames, 1947; Hildreth, 1949). Some early studies found no differences between the hands for simple manual tasks during the infant's first 6 months and a slight right-hand—use preference during the next 6-month period (Halverson, 1931; Lippman, 1927; Shirley, 1931). However, the intensive longitudinal study conducted by Gesell and Ames (1947) seems to have been the primary source of evidence indicating that the hand-use preference of infants could not be used as indicators or predictors of adult handedness.

Gesell and Ames (1947) repeatedly assessed the handedness of seven infants at monthly intervals during the first 8 to 60 weeks and at yearly intervals from ages 2 to 10. During infancy, test objects (presumably a bell, cube, and pellet) were generally presented in midline when the infant was in a supine or sitting position, and photographic and stenographic records were made of the performance. Although quantitative analyses of the photographic record were to have provided percentages of the time spent in right, left, and unimanual contact with the object, these data were not extracted for publication. Instead, descriptive analyses of the stenographic record provided information on the "actual flow of the manual behavior, taking note of all of the shifts or changes in handedness which took place within a given test situation and within the examination as a whole [p. 156]." These descriptive protocols were somehow coalesced into summary accounts of handedness for each age in which individual infants "definitely exhibited more than one type of handedness at a given age [p. 158]."

Gesell and Ames (1947) apparently used a measure and notion of hand-use preference that was peculiar enough to allow an infant's handedness to shift within a test that presumably entailed having the infant manipulate a single object. Without information about the measures of handedness used by Gesell and Ames, it is difficult to know what they assessed with this test. If their measure was percentage of contact with an object, then it should have been possible for the infant to have shown either no preference or one (right or left) preference, not both right and left handedness, as was reported.

Gesell and Ames provided too little information about their measures and mode of analysis to generate any confidence in the reliability or validity of their results. However, an earlier study of infant handedness by Lederer (1939), using validated and reliable assessment procedures, seemed to support Gesell and Ames' conclusion about the instability of infant handedness.

Lederer (1939), in a primarily cross-sectional study, found the percentages of right- and left-handed infants to be approximately equal during their first 3–11 months. Early in their second year, a majority of infants (79%) preferred to use their right hand. Lederer concluded that adultlike handedness (the dextral bias in the distribution) begins to appear only in the infant's second year. During the first year, the infant's handedness was too unstable and inconsistent to be adultlike. The latter conclusion was based on a longitudinal investigation of a small sample of infants.

The handedness of 19 infants was assessed during their first year, but there was no consistency among the assessments for either age or frequency of occurrence. Eleven infants were tested only twice, none more than four times during the year, and only one more than once during the 3–6 month period. If assessments in which no preference was revealed were excluded from analysis, then only seven (37%) of the infants showed a change in handedness.

Lederer's (1939) claim for the inconsistency of infant handedness rested heavily on the no-preference assessments. However, an infant who shows two alternative handedness assessments (right versus left) is likely to be different from one who shows a hand-use preference after an earlier no-preference assessment. Moreover, if an infant had two or three consistent handedness assessments with one interspersed no-preference assessment, it is more likely that some extraneous factor (infant state, test items, skill level required) affected the no-preference assessment than that the infant's handedness changed.

Of the 18 infants tested by Lederer during their second year, only 9 had had their handedness assessed during their first year. Of these, only 2 showed an alteration in their handedness from their first to second year. Looked at this way, first year handedness was predictive of second year handedness for 78% of the infants.

Unlike Gesell and Ames (1947), Lederer (1939) fully acknowledged the inadequacies of her longitudinal study (although she did not analyze data as just reported) and the limits these imposed on her conclusions. As the results of neither study warrant any conclusions about the stability or consistency of infant handedness, the predictive association between infant hand-use preferences and later handedness deserves further study.

Handedness and Limb-Use Asymmetries in Early Infancy

One means of assessing infant handedness is through preferred hand use when reaching for objects. However, there is some controversy about the age at which infants begin to reach for objects (Bower, 1974; DiFranco, Muir, & Dodwell, 1978; McDonnell, 1979). One compromise is to consider reaching (visually guided arm movements that bring the hand into contact with an object) as first occurring between 3 and 5 months of age (Field, 1976, 1977; Hofsten, 1979; Hofsten & Lindhagen, 1979; McDonnell, 1979), and prereaching preparatory behaviors (visually elicited arm movements) as occurring earlier (Bruner & Koslowski, 1972; McDonnell, 1979). Although it is presumed that prereaching behaviors are early forms of reaching, there is some evidence of a sinistral bias in early prereaching hand-use preferences (DiFranco et al., 1978; McDonnell, 1979; McDonnell, Anderson, & Abraham, in press) that contrasts with the dextral bias in later prereaching (Coryell & Michel, 1978) and early reaching performance (Hawn & Harris, Chapter 17, this volume). Either the early hand-use preferences of infants fluctuate between left and right predominance or prereaching behaviors are not simpler forms of reaching. The hand-use preferences exhibited in prereaching behavior may be manifestations of a neurobehavioral organization that is no longer characteristic of the infant at the age when reaching occurs.

Many aspects of the infant's limb use seem to be asymmetrical during the first 3 months. The right arm and hand are typically more active than the left (Giesecke, 1936; Stubbs & Irwin, 1933; Valentine & Wagner, 1934), and the neonate's right hand is fisted more often than the left (Cobb, Goodwin, & Saelens, 1966). Two-month-old infants typically hold a rattle longer in their right than in their left hand (Caplan & Kinsbourne, 1976). The dextral bias in these asymmetries of limb use have led most investigators to assume that these primitive actions are early forms and indicators of handedness (Petrie & Peters, 1980). However, how can the dextral bias in these primitive actions be reconciled with the sinistral bias in pre-reaching behaviors exhibited at about the same age?

It is possible that the asymmetries of limb use during the first 3 months result from a general postural asymmetry induced by the infant's supine head orientation preference (Coryell & Michel, 1978; Gesell, 1938; Gesell & Halverson, 1942). Neonates who prefer to lie with their head turned to their right will have their right hand fisted more often than their left. This asymmetrical fisting pattern is reversed for the minority of infants who prefer to lie with their heads turned to their left (Goodwin & Michel, 1981; Michel & Goodwin, 1979). A change in the infant's typical asymmetrical fisting pattern occurs when the infant turns its head, either spontaneously or as a result of experimental manipulation, in the direction opposite to that of its preference (Michel, 1982). The supine head-orientation preference also results in asymmetries of limb movement (Coryell & Cardinali, 1979; Giesecke, 1936; Liederman & Coryell, 1981).

Since the infant's head orientation is present even when seated in an infant chair (Michel, 1982), turning the head from the typically preferred rightward direction toward the midline in order to focus on a visually attractive object, for example, may stimulate left-arm movements while inhibiting right-arm movements (however, see McDonnell et al., in press). Moreover, if head orientation continues to affect asymmetrical fisting patterns, then the rightward bias in head-orientation preference could contribute to the dextral bias in rattle holding at 2 months. The head-orientation preference declines rapidly after the second month, as does its effect on the neuromotor activity of the limbs.

There are many lateral asymmetries in the behavior of young infants, and it is not my contention that all such asymmetries derive from the infant's head-orientation preference. However, the young infant is a neurobehaviorally organized system in which head orientation may have profound behavioral consequences.

Although the early limb-use asymmetries are unlikely to be simpler forms of handedness, their role in the development of handedness does require further examination. Proprioceptive and tactile–kinesthetic feedback from the asymmetrical activity of the hands could facilitate the formation of cortically lateralized sensorimotor programs involved in hand-use preferences. Head-orientation–induced asymmetries in visual regard of the right and left hand, perhaps in combination with asymmetries of neuromotor activity of the hands, may contribute to the organization of cortically lateralized sensorimotor skills, particularly those involved in visually guided reaching (Coryell & Michel, 1978).

When reaching begins to occur, it has a distinct dextral bias (Coryell & Michel, 1978; Hawn & Harris, Chapter 17, this volume; Young, 1977). Thereafter, the infant's hand-use preference for reaching remains relatively consistent throughout the first 60 weeks (Michel, 1982). Handedness was assessed at seven different ages (12, 16, 22, 32, 40, 51, and 60 weeks), and 45% of 20 infants showed no change in preference. Another 45% showed only one alteration in handedness. Therefore, 90% of the infants maintained quite consistent hand-use preference for reaching from 3 to 14 months of age. After preferences for reaching have been established, unimanual manipulation of objects begins to appear at 5 months, although hand-use preferences for manipulation do not begin to appear until 7 months (Ramsay, 1980). Simultaneous bimanual manipulation of objects occurs more than 1 month before hand-use preferences (i.e., one hand is more active and less supportive than the other) begin to appear at 10 months of age (Ramsay, Campos, & Fenson, 1979). Indeed, hand-use preferences in bimanual object manipulation only become prevalent after 12 months.

Although hand-use preferences are manifested in different situations at different times during infancy, they exhibit the same dextral bias in distribution. Moreover, an individual's hand-use preference will remain consistent from one type of manifestation to another (Ramsay, 1980). The transitions in these manifestations of hand-use preference across different situations (e.g., unimanual to bimanual manipulation) exhibit the kind of sequence and time-lag that might be expected if the later manifestations were integrated with the preferences of the earlier manifestations.

Transitions in the Development of Infant Hand-Use Preferences

It is conceivable, then, that asymmetries of visual regard and neuromotor activity of the hands that are induced by head-orientation preferences provide the basis for hand-use preferences for reaching. These reaching preferences, in turn, result in differential manual experience with objects. Since little or no bimanual manipulation or intermanual transfer of objects occurs for several months after reaching preferences have been established, the preferred hand for reaching can obtain objects and engage in more manipulation and oral and visual inspection of objects than can the nonpreferred hand. These differences in unimanual manipulatory experience, imposed by reaching preferences, can facilitate the expression of hand-use preferences for unimanual object manipulation. Hand-use preferences for reaching and object manipulation would likely facilitate the adoption of different strategies of right- and left-hand performance during bimanual manipulation. In this way, infant hand-use preferences might concatenate and spread.

Of course, the course of development proposed is undoubtedly too linear to encompass the complex reciprocal interweaving of organismic and experiential factors presumably responsible for handedness. However, the transitions described do represent the sort of probabilistic sequence frequently proposed for behavioral development (Bateson, 1976; Gottlieb, 1973). Although many factors might readily affect the transitions proposed, the relatively buffered conditions of infancy make this sequence highly probable. The present account also allows for both consistency and invariance in the development of infant hand-use preferences without assuming that the similar expressions of handedness in different situations (prereaching limb use, reaching, unimanual and bimanual object manipulation) are simply different manifestations of a unitary mode of lateralization that does not develop (Hicks & Kinsbourne, 1976).

The Character of Human Handedness

In tasks requiring the use of only one limb, most mammals prefer to use one limb more than the other (Walker, 1980). However, with any nonhuman species, the distribution of right- and left-limb—use preferences appears to be random (Annett, 1970, 1978; Walker, 1980). Only humans exhibit a nonrandom, dextrally biased distribution of their hand-use preferences. Thus, human handedness consists of two related but conceptually distinct characteristics: a hand-use preference (left or right) associated with individuals and a dextral bias in the hand-use preferences of the population.

The specific right- or left-limb—use preference for any particular individual seems to occur independently of genetics, at least for certain strains of mice (Collins, 1977). However, mice reared in conditions favoring the use of the left limb develop a left-limb preference, whereas mice reared in conditions favoring use of the right limb develop a right-limb preference (Collins, 1975). The right- or left-limb preferences of rhesus monkeys also depend on the specifics of the task and the experiential history of the animals (Warren, 1977). Therefore, it has been argued that individual differences in variability in limb-use preferences arise independently of genotype for many, if not all, mammals, including humans (Annett, 1978; Collins, 1977).

Using a systematic questionnaire and a test of unimanual performance skill, Annett (1970, 1972, 1978) found that the differences between the hands in preference and skill are continuously distributed in the population. This distribution is markedly skewed in favor of the right hand. In the absence of this "right shift," human hand-use preferences would be distributed in a manner similar to that of other mammals. Therefore, Annett concluded that some specifically nonrandom factor must superimpose a dextral bias on the individual variability of human handedness.

One possible factor for the dextral bias is the widespread cultural proscriptions of left-hand use (Dawson, 1977). Undoubtedly, cultural conditions can enhance or reduce the magnitude of the dextral bias (Teng et al., 1976). Dennis (1935) showed that even early in infancy, subtle sociocultural conditions can favor right-hand use. However, there is no evidence, even prehistoric (Coren & Porac, 1977), of any culture in which the proportions of right and left handedness were reversed or even equivalent. Therefore, Annett (1978) concluded that sociocultural pressures are unlikely sources for the initial occurrence and universal distribution of the dextral bias in human handedness.

To account for the dextral bias, Annett (1978) proposed a genetic model, involving a single allele, that distinguished individual variability in handedness from the dextral bias. Since individual variability of limb-use preference is achieved in the absence of genetic variability in other species, it is unlikely that variability in human hand-use preferences depends on genetic variability. However, since geneological studies reveal a mild heritability of human handedness (Annett, 1978), it is likely that a single allele superimposes a dextral bias on the otherwise random distribution of handedness.

Unlike other genetic models (e.g., Levy & Nagylaki, 1972) Annett's model does not directly account for left handedness. In the absence of the dextral biasing allele, left handedness and right handedness are equally likely to occur as a result of various accidental factors (e.g., position of placenta, birth position, birth trauma, neonatal medical condition, and early handling). According to Annett, many accidental factors can affect handedness throughout development; however, the occurrence of these factors would be too random among individuals to result in any systematic bias in handedness distribution.

Annett's model accounts for a good deal of the geneological data, especially the high proportion (over 55%) of right handedness among the offspring of two left-handed parents (Annett, 1974). In the absence of the dextral biasing allele, as presumably occurs in these offspring, handedness may distribute randomly. The slight dextral bias even in this population may reflect parentally and nonparentally mediated sociocultural influences. The significance of Annett's model is that it directs attention toward questions about the source of the dextral bias and away from questions about the source of the left handedness. Many factors may affect individual right and left handedness, but perhaps only one, or a few, affect the dextral bias in the population. Annett's model also implies that the dextral biasing allele may not affect handedness directly, but instead may produce asymmetries for other functions that, in turn, produce dextral bias (Annett, 1975, 1978). Therefore, any asymmetrically biased character that is developmentally antecedent to handedness should be examined as a potential precursor of the dextral bias.

Antecedents of the Dextral Bias in Handedness

Hemispheric Specialization of Function

For a large majority of people, language skills, especially speech, seem to depend on optimal functioning of the left hemisphere of the brain (Marin, Schwartz, & Saffran, 1979). The acquisition and programming of complex patterns of motor skill also seem to depend on optimal left-hemisphere functioning for a majority of people (Heilman, 1979). Since language skills involve the operation of complex motor skills (Mac-Neilage, 1980; Shankweiler & Liberman, 1976), it has been argued that the left hemisphere is specialized for the programming of serially organized, finely timed events (Bradshaw & Nettleton, 1981).

Annett (1975, 1978) has suggested that the factors responsible for the left hemisphere's specialization for language skills are also responsible for the dextral bias in handedness. Because of the decussation pattern of the pyramidal tracts, the motor cortex of the left hemisphere controls the fine motor movements of the right hand, and the motor cortex of the right hemisphere controls the left hand. Therefore, it is likely that any changes in the processing and programming characteristics of the left hemisphere will affect the skill capacities of the right hand.

Hemispheric specialization is the typical characteristic of people; only about 11–19% seem to show no evidence of hemispheric specialization for speech (Rasmussen & Milner, 1977; Ratcliff, Pila, Taylor, & Milner, 1978). Therefore, it is probable that there are some disadvantages to having the speech apparatus and language skills controlled by both hemispheres (Nottebohm, 1979). Since only 4–15% of the population have their speech controlled by their right hemisphere (Rasmussen & Milner, 1977; Ratcliff et al., 1978), it seems likely that the factors that ensure hemispheric specialization for language abilities also bias the specialization to favor the left hemisphere.

If there were some selection pressure for hemispheric specialization during the evolution of speech, then Annett's genetic model might address more the issue of the left hemispheric bias in language than that of the dextral bias in handedness (Annett, 1975, 1978). That is, the allele she postulates may enhance the capacities of the left hemisphere for processing and programming finely timed and serially organized events. Since language abilities depend on these capacities, language will depend on optimal functioning of the left hemisphere and, to the degree that handedness also depends on these capacities, right handedness will be favored. Apparently, handedness is less dependent on these capacities than are language skills since there are many left-handed individuals with left hemispheric control of language (Goodglass & Quadfasel, 1954). There is also a significant proportion of self-assessed left-handed individuals for whom the right hand is more competent and efficient for certain complex motor skills (Flowers, 1975; Heilman, 1979; Todor & Doane, 1977).

Annett's (1975) analysis of the data from several classical studies of the relations among unilateral brain damage, aphasia, and handedness provide some support for her theory. In the absence of the biasing allele (presumably, those with bilateral or right hemispheric language), the control of speech should vary randomly among right, left, and both hemispheres and independently of handedness. It might also be predicted from her model that there would be some deficiency of language abilities among those individuals who do not possess the biasing allele, even if they do exhibit the typical left hemispheric control of speech.

Thus, according to Annett's theory, the dextral bias in handedness may be a byproduct of the evolution of a genetic system to insure a left hemispheric specialization for language skills. This theory provides a new perspective on the issues of hemispheric specialization, the relation of handedness to cerebral dominance, and the origin of the dextral bias in handedness.

Annett proposed her genetic model for the dextral bias in handedness primarily because she thought none of the factors that could affect individual handedness were systematically biased, with the exception of sociocultural proscriptions. However, many of the factors that Annett acknowledged as affecting individual handedness during infancy are systematically biased in their distributions. If any of these factors can be shown to contribute to the dextral bias in handedness, then it is possible for the biasing allele to operate on the distribution of handedness through a factor other than hemispheric specialization for language.

The Asymmetric Tonic Neck Reflex

Turning the infant's head affects the position of its arms and legs (Gesell, 1938). The limbs on the side toward which the face is turned will extend, whereas the limbs on the opposite side will flex. This pattern—the asymmetric tonic neck reflex (ATNR)—is relatively rare in neonates (Paine, Brazelton, Donovan, Drorbaugh, Hubbell, & Sears, 1964) but reaches a peak around 6–8 weeks after birth (Coryell & Cardinali, 1979; Coryell & Michel, 1978). Since the ATNR frequently occurs as a result of spontaneous head turning, young infants will often exhibit an ATNR while supine. A majority of infants exhibit a rightward (face turned to their right) preference in their ATNR (Coryell & Michel, 1978; Gesell & Halverson, 1942).

Since the rightward preference predominates, Gesell and Ames (1947, 1950) suggested that the preferred direction of the infant's ATNR is predictive of its handedness. Indeed, in their study, all seven of the infants with a rightward ATNR preference were right-handed at 10 years of age. However, since both right handedness and a rightward ATNR preference are the prevailing characteristics in the population, they are very likely to cooccur in the same individual purely by chance. Of the nine infants with a leftward ATNR preference in Gesell and Ames' study, five were right-handed and four were left-handed at 10 years of age. From these data, one might merely conclude that a rightward ATNR preference is a better predictor of right-handedness than is a leftward ATNR preference.

Gesell and Ames did not offer any explanations as to how the preference in ATNR could be associated with handedness. However, others have argued that the ATNR places the extended hand into the infant's focal field of view (Coryell & Henderson, 1979; White, Castle, & Held, 1964). An ATNR preference means that one hand is in the infant's focal visual field more often than the other (Coryell & Michel, 1978). The increased visual exposure to the hand provides the infant with more experience in eye–hand coordination with that hand. This difference in visual experience of the right and left hands predicts the difference in hand movements during visually elicited reaching tasks presented at 12 weeks of age (Coryell & Michel, 1978).

Although the data of Gesell and Ames (1947) do not warrant the conclusion that the ATNR preference is a contributor to handedness, the head-orientation preference may be. Gesell and Ames began recording the infant's ATNR preferences at monthly intervals beginning at 2 months of age. Therefore, they observed ATNR preferences after their peak and at a time when an ATNR is likely to be stronger, longer lasting, and more prevalent in the direction *opposite* to the infant's supine head-orientation preference (Liederman & Coryell, 1981). Indeed, the infant's supine head-orientation preference has virtually disappeared by 12 weeks of age (Coryell & Michel, 1978), although the ATNR is still present. All of these factors might have led Gesell and Ames to identify an ATNR preference that did not correspond to the infant's earlier head-orientation preference. This would account for the rather high proportion (47%) of infants in their sample with leftward ATNR preferences. Since one hand is in the infant's visual field primarily as a result of the orientation of the infant's head, and independently of whether there is an ATNR, the infant's supine head-orientation preference might be an early contributor to the development of handedness (Michel, 1981).

Supine Head-Orientation Preference

Most newborn infants prefer to lie with their heads turned to their right (Michel, 1981; Turkewitz, Gordon, & Birch, 1965). This head-orientation preference is part of a more general postural preference involving flexion of the limbs during the first 10 days after birth (Casaer, 1979). The flexed posture of the neonate's limbs, rather than the head-orientation preference, has attracted the most interest, and several mechanisms have been proposed to account for it.

Perhaps the most intriguing was Peiper's (1963) proposal that limb flexion in neonates might occur because the globus pallidus achieved a supraspinal influence on spinal reflexes before other striatal inhibitory processes are manifested. A pallidal origin for limb flexion is suggested by the limb flexion postures that typically occur in adults with lesions of the cortex and specific portions of the corpus striatum. However, the neuro-functional organization of infants is distinct from that of adults, and the behavioral consequences of brain damage in adults only bears a superficial resemblance to the behavioral characteristics manifested by infants (Prechtl, 1981). Therefore, inferences about the functional organization of the immature nervous system drawn from information about the functional organization or disorganization of the mature nervous system may be inappropriate (Schulte, 1974; Touwen, 1974).

One mechanism that has received some empirical support (Beintema, 1968; Maekawa & Ochiai, 1975) assumes that the initial limb flexion posture of neonates results more from the properties of segmental reflexes and the properties of muscles and their afferents rather than from higher-order neural mechanisms. It seems that the alpha motoneurons controlling the flexor muscles of the neonate receive direct excitatory input from both primary and secondary spindle afferents. However, the motoneurons controlling the extensor muscles seem to receive only indirect input from the muscle spindles via secondary afferent innervation of interneurons (Schulte, 1974). Therefore, flexor muscles may receive greater excitatory input in response to postnatal gravitation-induced stretch than may the extensor muscles.

Although supraspinal control (including corticospinal influences) is possible in neonates, much of the initial postural preference may not reflect the effects of such control (Casaer, 1979). An overwhelming majority of motor cortex neurons are involved in controlling limb extension as compared to limb flexion (Georgopoulous, 1982). Thus, at the cortical level, limb extension seems to be a more likely and important event than limb flexion. Limb flexion may initially result from neuromotor tonus generated by segmented reflexes conditioned, in part, by prenatal posture.

Radiographic studies have shown that the neonate's postural preference approximates its prenatal posture (Chapple & Davidson, 1941; Dunn, 1972, 1975). Therefore, intrauterine position could be a major contributor to the organization of postnatal posture (Casaer, 1979; Schulte, 1974).

After the sixteenth week of pregnancy, the size and shape of the fetus combines with the shape of the uterus and pelvic ring to both restrict movement and make semiflexion of the limbs a more suitable posture. Whether the fetus adopts this posture or has it induced by the uterine space is unknown. There is some evidence to suggest that the fetal posture is maintained even under less restrictive conditions (Reinold, 1976). Maintenance of this posture throughout most of the latter half of pregnancy could affect the elasticity of the skin and muscles as well as calibrate some general "set-points" in the muscle spindles.

After delivery, gravity causes muscle stretch to a degree not encountered prenatally. Therefore, the muscle spindle set-points are easily violated, resulting in an increase in their activity. This increased spindle activity can combine with the greater excitation they can achieve with flexor motoneurons to produce the flexed-limb posture of the neonate. Subsequent recalibration of spindle set-points and greater supraspinal influence on both spindle and motoneural activity eventuate in a change in postural preference.

The origin of the head-orientation preference is even less well understood than the mechanisms of limb flexion but may involve asymmetries in segmental patterns rather than asymmetries in supraspinal mechanisms. It is possible that the head-orientation preference results from asymmetrically lateralized activation (semitonic) of neuromotor mechanisms at the level of the brainstem nuclei, cerebellum, thalamus, basal ganglia, and/or cortex. Such asymmetrical involvement might mark an early condition of hemispheric specialization of function. At present, there is no evidence that directly supports this notion, although it is an issue warranting further research. It is conceivable, also, that the head-orientation preference is a consequence of intrauterine position. Although it is generally assumed that the head of the fetus is maintained in a midline position, there is some evidence, based on the slight asymmetry of the jaw line that frequently appears in neonates, that the head of the fetus may be turned for prolonged periods, pressing the jaw against one shoulder (Parmelee, 1931).

Recent ultrasound recording of relatively long duration (1 hour) at various times during pregnancy show that the head of the fetus is frequently oriented from the midline position (de Vries, Visser, Huisjes, & Prechtl, 1982). At present, it is unknown:

1. How frequently and at what ages the head orientation occurs
2. What the duration of the head orientation is when it occurs
3. Whether the fetus exhibits a directional preference for the head orientation and, if so, at what phase of development does the preference occur
4. Whether there is a commonality (majority or plurality) in direction of head-orientation preferences among fetuses
5. What relation the head orientation has to fetal movements or to the structure of the intrauterine environment

If a fetal head-orientation preference is found, and if it results from some endogenous property of the fetal nervous system rather than the intrauterine environment, then the relation of this prenatal character to, and perhaps its influence on, other neural mechanisms must be explored.

Partly as a consequence of its head-orientation preference, a neonate is more responsive to auditory and tactile stimulation of one ear and cheek, respectively, than the other (Turkewitz, Moreau, & Birch, 1966). Both the lateral asymmetry in sensitivity and the asymmetry of neuromotor tonus contribute to the expression of the head-orientation preference (Hammer & Turkewitz, 1974; Liederman & Kinsbourne, 1980). However, the neuromotor asymmetry precedes the development of the sensory asymmetry (Turkewitz & Creighton, 1974).

Turkewitz (1977) has argued that the neonatal sensory and motor lateral asymmetries are early predictors of later forms of other lateralized functions, including handedness. Viviani, Turkewitz, and Karp (1978) found that the degree of lateralization (a score derived, in part, from handedness and dichotic listening measures) at 7 years of age was significantly correlated with a neonatal lateralization index (a score derived, in part, from head orientation and sensory asymmetries). However, right handedness predominates in 7-year-old children and, rightward head orientation predominates in neonates. The significance of a correlation of lateralization indexes that separately incorporate these two predominant characteristics will be confounded by nonzero expected values (Stone, 1980). If the rightward bias in neonatal head orientation does contribute to the development of the dextral bias in handedness, then infants with a leftward head-orientation preference should have the distribution of their hand-use preference significantly shifted to a sinistral bias. Neonates with a rightward head orientation should exhibit a dextral bias in the distribution of their handedness, with few, if any, becoming left-handed.

Assessment of the head-orientation preferences of 150 (81 males) neonates revealed a distribution of rightward and leftward preferences similar to that found for right and left handedness in adults (Michel, 1981). Twenty (11 males) of these neonates had their hand-use preferences for reaching assessed at 12, 16, 22, 32, 40, 51, and 60 weeks of age (Michel, 1982). Ten of the 20 were neonates who preferred to lie with their heads turned right, and 10 (6 males) preferred to lie with their heads turned left.

At 3, 6, and 8 weeks, the postneonatal supine head-orientation preference of the infants was assessed. Although the correlation between neonatal and postneonatal assessments of head orientation preference was significant, 5 of the 20 infants appeared to change their preference between the two assessments. The neonatal assessment involved a short procedure that can be affected by state changes (Michel & Goodwin, 1979). Therefore, the neonatal assessment may be a less-reliable indicator of head-orientation preference. Although the postneonatal assessment was a longer procedure, it involved (for some design reasons) more manipulation of the infant. Therefore, the assessment and character of the neonatal and postneonatal head-orientation preferences deserve further investigation.

The neonatal head-orientation preference was significantly predictive of infant hand-use preferences during infancy. However, the infant's postneonatal preference was a somewhat better predictor of consistent hand-use preference. When the 5 infants who showed a change between the two head-orientation assessments were excluded from analysis, then the infants' consistent supine head-orientation preference was a virtually perfect predictor of the distribution of hand-use preferences at every assessment age. Thus, infants with a preference for orienting their heads rightward preferred to use their right hand for reaching, whereas infants who preferred to orient their heads leftward also preferred to use their left hand.

The relation between hand-use preferences for reaching and other measures of handedness during infancy is not known. The relation of infant handedness and adult handedness is also unknown. However, if we assume that reaching preferences indicate infant handedness and that infant handedness is significantly associated with adult handedness, then the dextral bias in handedness may be dependent on the rightward bias in infant supine head-orientation preference.

The mechanisms associating head-orientation and hand-use preferences are not yet understood. The head-orientation preference results in both differential visual experience of the right and left hand and differential neuromotor activity of the hands. Visual experience of the limbs, especially in action, is important for the development of visually guided control of the limbs in kittens (Hein, 1980). Indeed, visuomotor coordination may develop for the visually experienced limb but not transfer to the limb that was not visually experienced. However, the nonpreferred hand in babies does exhibit visuomotor coordination and can be used effectively (how efficiently remains to be discovered) in reaching situations. Therefore, it is not clear how well studies of visuomotor deprivation

resulting in inability to visually control limb movements help in understanding the effects of relative differences in visual experience of the
hands on the manifestation of preference in visuomotor coordination.

Perhaps a somewhat more appropriate model might be drawn from the
work of Spinelli, Jensen, and Viana Di Prisco (1980). They trained kittens
to flex (lift) one forelimb to avoid shock. Recordings from single cells of
the somatosensory cortex showed that after training, more cells monitored
the trained limb than the untrained limb. The cells monitoring the trained
limb also showed corresponding changes in their neuroanatomy. In kittens older than 11 weeks of age, similar training does not produce such
neuroanatomical and neurophysiological changes. Recent work reveal
that these changes include motor cortex and specific areas of the hypothalamus as well (Spinelli & Jensen, 1982). Therefore, there is reason to
suggest that minor asymmetries in neuromotor action and visual experience of the left and right hand, as induced by the infant's head-orientation
preference, may produce lasting effects in the cortical mechanisms involved in hand use. Early use and experience may produce neural
changes favoring the establishment of preference.

Intrauterine Position

Because the position of the fetus is asymmetrically biased during the
last month or so of pregnancy (de Snoo, 1931; Vartan, 1945), the intrauterine position of the fetus has often been thought to contribute to the
development of handedness (Harris, 1980). Over 95% of all fetuses are
oriented in a vertex (head down) position, with the majority (60–87%)
oriented with their backs toward their mother's left side (Compte, 1828 in
Harris, 1980; Roos, 1935; de Snoo, 1931; Steele & Javert, 1942). It has been
argued that in this position the movement of the left arm of the fetus is
restricted by the mother's pelvis and backbone, thereby allowing the right
arm more activity (Moss, 1929).

Although several structural asymmetries of the intrauterine space may
ensure that the majority of fetuses will spend most of their time in the
LOT–LOA position (back to the mother's left side) during the last 6 weeks
or so before delivery (Rydberg, 1965), ultrasound techniques revealed that
the fetus is capable of extensive changes in position even just before
delivery (Reinold, 1976). Therefore, fetal activity is an important contributor to the intrauterine position, but its role in the prevalence of the
LOT–LOA position is unknown.

Birth position, the left-versus-right orientation of the fetus's head during delivery, is thought to reflect the intrauterine position of the fetus.
Churchill, Igna, and Senf (1962) found a significant association between
birth position and infant handedness (hand used to pick up and throw a
ball) at 2 years of age. Infants born in the usual left occiput transverse or

anterior (LOT–LOA) birth position tended to prefer to use their right hand, whereas there was a somewhat greater proportion of left-hand–use preference among those born in the relatively uncommon ROT–ROA birth position.

Since the infant's head-orientation preference is associated with infant handedness, Michel and Goodwin (1979) reasoned that birth position might be associated with handedness through the neonatal head-orientation preference. Examination of 109 neonates selected for almost equal numbers of ROT–ROA and LOT–LOA birth positions revealed a significant association between birth position and direction of neonatal head-orientation preference. Subsequent study (Goodwin & Michel, 1981) of an additional 104 neonates, again with equal representation of LOT–LOA and ROT–ROA birth positions, confirmed the significant association between birth position and head-orientation preference. However, whereas the head-orientation preferences of neonates with the LOT–LOA birth position were significantly right-biased, the preferences of those neonates with the ROT–ROA birth position were randomly distributed. If intrauterine position is a precursor or contributor to the development of the neonatal head-orientation preference, then those born in the ROT–ROA position should have exhibited a sinistral bias in their head-orientation preferences.

Of course, birth position may be an unreliable estimate of the predominant intrauterine position of the fetus. Overstreet (1938) reported that over one-half of the infants changed their positions 24 hours before birth. Since the LOT–LOA intrauterine position is predominant, a rather large proportion of infants with ROT–ROA birth positions will have been infants with LOT–LOA intrauterine positions (a much smaller proportion of LOT–LOA birth position infants will be similarly misclassified) if over one-half of the infants altered their intrauterine position 24 hours before birth. Therefore, the contribution of intrauterine position to neonatal head-orientation preference and handedness awaits more systematic and reliable descriptions of the fetus's position.

Three separate studies of premature infants suggest that head-orientation preferences may develop independently of either prenatal or postnatal conditions. Prechtl, Fargel, Weinmann, and Bakker (1975, 1979) report that 14 premature infants developed supine postural preferences (including head-orientation preferences) relative to their conceptual age and not time from birth. Gardner, Lewkowicz, and Turkewitz (1977) report similar results in the head-turning response for premature infants, a finding replicated by Fox and Lewis (1982).

None of these studies apparently controlled for the postural positions in which premature infants are placed while in their incubators. In some hospitals, including the hospital of the Gardner et al. (1977) study (Allan Gottfried, personal communication), premature infants are frequently placed with their heads turned to one side, often the right side. Liederman and Kinsbourne (1980) showed that about 10 hours of such placement in full term neonates is sufficient to temporarily change head-orientation preference, if the placement was opposite to the neonate's preference. Roberts and Smart (1981) found that 120 of 147 full term neonates exhibited an initial head turn to their right when tested after lying on their right side. However, only 75 (51%) of these babies turned their head initially to the right when tested after lying on their left side. Therefore, initial head turn can be affected by the neonates' previous postural position. Initial head turn is not a perfect predictor of neonatal head-orientation preference (Goodwin & Michel, 1981), but it may be more so when testing procedures are undertaken to reduce the effects of previous postural positions on asymmetrical muscle stretch activity and asymmetrical sensitivity of the sensory systems (Goodwin & Michel, 1981; Michel, 1981; Michel & Goodwin, 1979). Any consistency of postnatal placement of the premature infant's head orientation could conceivably facilitate the development of a supine head-orientation preference.

Until we know more about the intrauterine position of the fetus and the consequences of placement of the head of premature infants on the manifestation of a head-orientation preference, we must consider the contribution of the bias in intrauterine position to the dextral bias in handedness as undemonstrated but not invalidated.

Hypothetical Mechanisms of Biasing Allele Action

Genetic factors do not affect behavior directly (Wilcock, 1969); rather, they create conditions that influence the manifestation of behavior. Therefore, the biasing allele, as proposed in Annett's model, may create conditions within which several characteristics may be biased. The asymmetries of these different characteristics will be associated with one another, but not causally related.

Asymmetrical Growth of the Brain Hemispheres

LeMay (1977) reports that skull shape typically exhibits a counterclockwise torque, with a posterior protrusion of the left occipital pole and forward protrusion of the right frontal pole. This torque may not be present or may be reversed in left-handed individuals; it is supposed to be apparent by the eighth month of gestation (LeMay, 1977). If the biasing allele affects left hemispheric specialization for language in part through increased early growth, then this growth might produce a skull asymmetry that mechanically favors a rightward tilt in head-orientation preference. Of course, left hemispheric specialization for language would also favor a dextral bias in handedness, but the supine head-orientation preference and infant handedness would be only fortuitously associated (Annett, personal communication).

However, the head-orientation preference of neonates is a neuromotor pattern that is independent of skull shape. Bauermeister (1977) found no association between neonatal skull shape (measured from photographs) and neonatal head-orientation preference. Also, neonates can readily turn their heads 180° counter to the asymmetry of their occipital poles if their heads initially were positioned by an observer in a direction opposite to the preferred one (Michel & Goodwin, 1979). Turkewitz (1980) has argued that the head-turning preference begins as a neuromotor bias but quickly becomes dependent on both sensory and motor asymmetries. Thus, the head-orientation preference of infants is not a passively imposed condition of asymmetrical skull shape.

Indeed, postnatal head-orientation preference has frequently been reported to contribute to the asymmetry of skull shape (cf., Fulford & Brown, 1976; Robson, 1968). Persistent head-orientation preferences resulted in the flattening of the occipital pole and protrusion of the frontal pole on the side to which the face was turned in 77% of 35 infants 4–6 months of age (Robson, 1968). Not only was skull shape affected by head-orientation preference, but this preference also induced marked asymmetries in limb movement and posture that, in turn, were related to asymmetries of posture and gait by 2–3 years of age for all 35 children.

Sometimes the postural asymmetries induced by a persistent head-orientation preference can be quite marked in normal babies, leading to a condition called *the squint baby syndrome* (Fulford & Brown, 1976). Similar persistent head-orientation preferences in infants with cerebral palsy can result in severe plagiocephaly (asymmetrical distortion of the head) and extensive skeletal–muscular asymmetrical deformities of the trunk and limbs (the *windswept* syndrome). These deformities may be prevented by physical therapy that compensates for the obligatory head-orientation–induced postures (Fulford & Brown, 1976). Thus, head-orientation preference in infants is an actively achieved pattern that varies both in degree of persistence and direction with consequences for asymmetries of limb actions and experience.

Infant Cerebral Dominance for Language: Clinical Studies

For the past two decades, it has been commonly assumed that cerebral dominance for language is achieved during postnatal development. This notion was supported, at least in part, by Lenneberg's (1967) argument that each hemisphere initially is capable of providing the neural substrate for the effective development of speech and language functions, but that this equipotentiality decreases as puberty approaches. Lenneberg based his argument on Basser's (1962) review of the functional consequences of unilateral cerebral damage occurring at different ages. Full recovery of language functions seemed more likely the younger the individual was at the time of brain damage. However, a study by Dennis and Whitaker (1976) of three children born with hemiplegia and surgically hemidecorticate before 5 months of age (two before 28 days of age), demonstrates that language functions may not develop fully in an isolated right cerebral cortex.

When tested at 9–10 years of age, the two children without a left cerebral cortex showed more language errors than the child missing a right cerebral cortex. The deficiencies of the intact right-hemisphere children were not manifested in all language abilities. In about 44% of all the language categories tested (on which all children could be compared from the tables in the report), the right-hemisphere children performed as well as, or better than, the left-hemisphere child. The right-hemisphere children showed a specific deficiency in processing, recalling, and producing complex syntactic structures (e.g., negative passive sentences). Therefore, Dennis and Whitaker (1976) concluded that the right hemisphere, unlike the left, is not an adequate neural substrate for the organizational, syntactic, and hierarchic character of language (p. 428).

At least two qualifications should be raised concerning this conclusion. First, the surgical procedure for the right-hemisphere children spared the basal ganglia on the left side, whereas the basal ganglia on the right side of the left-hemisphere child was removed during surgery. The basal ganglia participate in a complex network of neural pathways involving the cortex and thalamus (Anderson, 1981), and they have been found to play a role in many language functions (Brunner, Kornhuber, Seemüller, Suger, & Wallesch, 1982). It is conceivable that the contralateral (left) basal ganglia, through efferent connections to thalamic nuclei, substantia nigra, etc. (Grofovà, 1978), may have interfered with the functional reorganization of the right hemisphere. Second, some of the syntactic tasks on which the right-hemisphere children showed deficiencies are rather late-appearing in normal children. Therefore, it is not yet known whether the children's poor performance represents a deficit or a delay in development. Of course, these two qualifications are more speculative than substantive. The study by Dennis and Whitaker (1976) represents the best evidence, to date, that the two hemispheres are not completely equipotential for the acquisition of language functions. Moreover, the language abilities of the left hemisphere that are not shared by the right represent the sort of hierarchically ordered programming functions that could conceivably generalize to manual skills, thereby creating a hand-use preference.

A study of an additional group of hemidecorticated subjects is less persuasive. Dennis and Kohn (1975) found that subjects with an intact left hemisphere can process passive sentences more correctly than subjects with a right hemisphere. Their sample of nine included two of the subjects (the right- and one of the left-hemidecorticate children) from Dennis and Whitaker (1976); these two were radically divergent in background from the other seven subjects. All nine had exhibited hemiplegia by 1 year of age, but the additional seven subjects, unlike the other two, had not undergone hemidecortication until some 6–14 years later and were in their 20s when tested. In this group of seven, only one of the three subjects with a left hemisphere had begun seizures before 1 year of age. The other two began seizures at 4–7 years of age. Of the four subjects with a right hemisphere, none had undergone hemidecortication before 10 years of age, although three of them had begun seizures during their first year. The fourth subject began seizures during the eighth year. Thus, the two hemisphere groups in the study are seriously confounded by differences in age at seizure onset.

Indeed, the data (Dennis & Kohn, 1975, Table 3, p. 477) show that the left-hemisphere subjects with early seizure onset performed distinctly worse than the other left-hemisphere subjects (with late seizure onset). The right-hemisphere subject with late seizure onset performed much better than the other right-hemisphere subjects (with early seizure onset). Point-biserial correlations of hemisphere group with percentage correct scores for passive affirmative and passive negative sentences yield correlations of .34 and .69, respectively. However, reorganizing the subjects into two groups according to their age at seizure onset (less than 14 months or over 4 years), irrespective of their side of hemidecortication, increases these correlations to .41 and .76. Thus, performance on these language tasks is more highly associated with age of seizure onset than with side of hemidecortication.

As interesting as the reports of Dennis and her collaborators may be, it does seem somewhat premature to draw firm conclusions about the equipotentiality of the hemispheres for language functions. The results of the Dennis and Whitaker (1976) study do lend support to Annett's claim that the biasing allele makes left-hemisphere processes more suitable for certain language functions. It would be interesting to assess the manual skills of the "unaffected" hand in these children. Presumably, the manual skills of the two right-hemisphere children would be deficient compared to those of the left-hemisphere child. Of course, equipotentiality does not require that the two hemispheres must begin with functional equivalence, only that, after damage, the undamaged hemisphere should be capable of subsuming the functions that otherwise would have been associated with the damaged hemisphere. Likewise, a lack of early functional specialization of the hemispheres would not necessitate their equipotentiality in the development of functional specialization.

Infant Cerebral Dominance for Language:
Normal Subjects

Several recent studies purport to demonstrate left-hemisphere specialization for language perception in very young infants.[1] All of these studies
exploit the categorical nature of speech-sound (phoneme) perception for
discerning hemispheric specialization. Adults easily discriminate differences between speech-sounds, or phonemes, but comparable acoustic
differences within a phoneme category are not discriminated. Much recent work demonstrates that infants also discriminate phoneme categories
(Eimas, 1975; Morse, 1979).

To account for this phonemic knowledge in infants, some have argued
that the infant's (and adult's) discriminative ability depends on the presence of the acoustic information that corresponds to phonetic features
(Eimas, 1975). It does not seem unwarranted to presume that these
speech-sound detectors will be associated more closely with the hemisphere engaged with language functions. Hence, ear differences in
speech-sound detection can be a clue to hemispheric specialization for
language.

Using the high-amplitude suckling (HAS) technique, Entus (1977)
found that infants 3–20 weeks of age exhibited a right-ear advantage for
detecting changes in speech-sounds and a left-ear advantage for detecting
changes in musical notes. The HAS technique has been used to demonstrate categorical speech-sound perception in infants (Trehub, 1979). The
technique begins with a baseline period of nonnutritive sucking, then a
speech-sound stimulus is presented contingent on the infant's high-amplitude (pressure) sucking (HAS). As a result, HAS will increase and,
subsequently, after repeated presentation of the same stimulus, decrease.
When this decrease reaches a predetermined level, a contrasting stimulus
is presented. Detection of the change in sound stimuli is inferred from an
increase in HAS. The technique does require strict adherence to certain
conventions and control procedures, some of which, unfortunately, are
missing from the Entus (1977) study. However, Entus's innovation was to
present the stimuli through stereo headphones rather than ambiently. In
this way, she could make a change in the stimulus for one ear only and
note its sensitivity to that change.

Using the same procedures (but adding several control measures to
remove experimenter bias), stimuli, and apparatus employed by Entus
(1977), Vargha-Khadem and Corballis (1979) were unable to find ear differences in speech-sound discrimination in two different attempts at rep-

[1]The various neuroanatomical studies that demonstrate early anatomical differences between the hemispheres (e.g., Witelson, 1980) have been criticized elsewhere (Marin et al.,
1979; Marshall, 1980; Rubens, 1977; Whitaker & Ojemann, 1977) for not conforming to or
revealing much about the functional difference between the hemispheres.

lication. Part of the additional control procedures involved use of a mechanical arm, in place of the experimenter's arm, to hold the nipple in the infant's mouth. Although this may have increased variability somewhat, the error terms were not significantly different between the two studies. Moreover, Vargha-Khadem and Corballis were able to demonstrate speech-sound discrimination; there just were no differences between the ears in detecting these changes in speech sounds.

One of the most frequently cited reports of hemispheric specialization in infants is that of Glanville, Best, and Levenson (1977), who use 3-month-old infants. They found no significant differences between the ears in detecting acoustic changes in a musical note (e.g., a synthesized piano or brass A versus a reed A); however, the right ear and not the left detected differences in speech-sounds (e.g., [ba] and [da] versus [ga]). They presented their stimuli in a modified dichotic listening manner. A pair of dissimilar stimuli (e.g., [ba] and [da]) were presented, one for each ear, for nine trials with about 20 sec between trials. Then, on the tenth trial, a novel stimulus of the same type as the habituation pair (e.g, [ga]) was presented to one ear. All 12 infants received the four possible test trials in counterbalanced order.

To assess discrimination, Glanville et al. (1977) measured heart rate. Heart rate was recorded for 10 sec preceding stimulus onset (prestimulus period) and for the 15 sec following stimulus offset (poststimulus period). Difference in heart rate between pre- and poststimulus periods was used to determine the cardiac-orienting response (heart-rate deceleration to novel stimuli). This particular procedure is rather different from those cardiac habituation–dishabituation procedures typically used to assess infant speech-sound discrimination (Leavitt, Brown, Morse, & Graham, 1976; Trehub, 1979).

Interpretation of the results of Glanville et al. (1977) is made particularly difficult by presentation of mean scores without measures of variability, analyses of variance performed on apparently highly skewed data, and the use of t tests for posthoc multiple comparisons. Furthermore, the data from which hemispheric specialization is inferred presents a serious confounding. They defined the cardiac-orienting response as heart-rate deceleration (beats per min) in comparisons between the pre- and poststimulus periods. The mean heart rate for the prestimulus period on those trials for which the speech-sound was changed in the left ear was the lowest of all the prestimulus periods, making it less likely that the 15-sec poststimulus period would accurately detect further deceleration. Glanville et al. discount this possibility because nine infants showed a lower rate on at least one other poststimulus period. However, although a lower heart rate may be possible, the probability distribution for poststimulus heart rate will be quite different given different prestimulus heart-rate levels.

The novelty of their procedures, the difficulty in interpreting their results, and the lack of dissociation of stimuli with hemisphere in the results warrant caution in accepting the Glanville et al. study as evidence for infant hemispheric specialization. Their study awaits both independent replication and extension to younger infants.

Electrophysiological studies of hemispheric specialization of function usually involve the identification of differences in EEG pattern or evoked potentials recorded from scalp electrodes placed on the right and left side. Rubens (1977) has warned that, because of the anatomical asymmetries of the cortex, symmetrical placement of electrodes on the scalp will not reflect symmetry or homology of underlying brain areas, especially for the T3 and T4 placements. As a result, intrahemispheric topography can be confused with interhemispheric specialization of function. If there is no dissociation between stimuli (e.g., speech versus nonspeech sounds) and hemispheric response, then a general "hemisphere effect" may simply result from differences in position of the brain areas underlying the left and right electrodes. Even dissociation might not ensure the presence of hemispheric specialization if, within each hemisphere, the processing of some stimulus characteristics of speech sounds (e.g., normal formant structure) occurs in cortical auditory areas somewhat displaced from those processing nonspeech-sound characteristics (e.g., sine wave structure). Then, the slight anatomical differences in topography between the hemispheres could place these two processing areas (present in both hemispheres) in different proximity to the left and right electrodes. The resulting phase differences could be interpreted as hemispherically distinct processing differences.

Electrophysiological recordings of cortical activity may be confounded also by small, usually uncontrolled and unnoticed movements of fingers, limb muscles, neck muscles, and tongue (Gevins et al., 1979). As there are asymmetries of fisting pattern, arm movement, head orientation, neck muscle tonus, and even tongue movements (Nottebohm, 1979; Weiffenbach, 1972) in neonates, these factors must be controlled or these response biases and the electrophysiological patterns they induce could be confused with differences in hemispheric processing (cf. Davis & Wada, 1977; Shucard, Shucard, Cummins, & Campos, 1981).

Using the technique of recording auditory evoked potentials from scalp electrodes placed over the auditory cortex of the left and right hemisphere (T3 and T4 placements), Molfese, Freeman, and Palermo (1975) found evidence for hemispheric specialization in infants. Ambiently presented speech sounds produced a larger left-hemisphere than right-hemisphere evoked potential, whereas nonspeech sounds produced a larger right-hemisphere than left-hemisphere evoked potential. Although the median age of the 10 subjects was 6 months, a week-old infant showed the same pattern of response as the older infants.

Subsequent study (Molfese, Nunez, Seibert, & Ramanaiah, 1976) of 14 neonates, using a more sophisticated analysis of the evoked potentials, found a general hemisphere effect but, apparently, no dissociation of speech and nonspeech sounds according to hemisphere. However, work with 16 neonates (Molfese & Molfese, 1979) and 11 male premature infants (Molfese & Molfese, 1980) provides evidence for differential left-hemisphere involvement in the processing of speech-sound stimuli.

Each of these two recent studies employed stimuli whose speech-sound and nonspeech-sound characteristics were more precisely manipulated. Thus, a synthesized consonant vowel pair could be presented either with speech-sound natural formant characteristics or with nonspeech-sound sine wave formant characteristics, with speech-sound phonetic transitions or with nonspeech-sound nonphonemic transitions. All stimuli were presented ambiently, and the evoked potentials were averaged into a model wave form, the components of which could be examined by factor analysis. In the study of neonates, six factors were derived that accounted for 67% of the variance, and in the study of premature infants, nine factors were derived, accounting for 83% of the variance. Each factor could be subjected to analysis of variance to assess the effects of hemisphere, stimulus type, and so forth.

Of the six factors observed in neonates, only two showed a significant effect of hemisphere. The fourth factor, representing an early component of the wave form (peaks at 32 and 192 msec after stimulus onset), seemed to reflect a left-hemisphere involvement in discriminating phonemes presented in normal formant structure. The third factor, representing a late component of the wave form (peaks at 630 msec after stimulus onset), seemed to indicate that each hemisphere could discriminate the phonemes when they were presented in normal formant form, but not in sine wave form. These results may be interpreted as demonstrating that both hemispheres are capable of speech-sound discrimination and that the left hemisphere may detect these differences slightly earlier than the right. This early detection may reflect subcortical mechanisms (Molfese & Molfese, 1980).

In the study of premature infants, five of the factors showed a general hemisphere effect. Perhaps, the skull shape of the premature infant provides a greater disparity between symmetrical scalp placements and the position of underlying homologous brain areas (Rubens, 1977). Another factor showed a left-hemisphere differentiation of phonetic from nonphonetic transitions in the stimuli when presented in normal formant structure, but the two phonemes were not discriminated. However, in the first derived factor the two phonemes were also differentiated. These results may be interpreted as suggesting that the left hemisphere is more involved in detecting differences in phonetic versus nonphonetic transitions in stimuli and also in detecting differences in phonemes. Molfese and Molfese (1980) suggest that this specialization may reflect subcortical mechanisms rather than cortical specialization.

Shucard et al. (1981) recorded auditory evoked potentials to probe stimuli (tone pairs) presented to awake 3-month-old infants while they heard either verbal or musical passages. Although the sex of the subject was related to differences in hemisphere activation, the type of passage heard had no effect. That is, in females, the left hemisphere exhibited higher-amplitude evoked potentials, whereas in males, the right hemisphere exhibited the higher amplitude. These differences occurred regardless of the type (musical or verbal) of complex auditory stimulation that the infants received. Although this technique has been used for detecting functional hemispheric specialization in adults (Shucard, Shucard, & Thomas, 1977), it may not be appropriate for infants. Therefore, it is doubtful that this study reveals much about early hemispheric specialization (see Molfese & Radtke, 1982, for additional criticism, and Shucard, Shucard, Campos, & Salamy, 1982, for reply). Electrophysiological techniques may be too primitive for use in deciding issues of brain functioning (Hillyard & Woods, 1979). At present, they are best used to confirm evidence about brain functioning acquired by other means.

The evidence for infant hemispheric specialization for processing speech-sound stimuli may be described, at best, as suggestive. The evidence does not warrant, as yet, suggestions that hemispheric specializations are equivalent to, or exact predeterminants of, later forms of specialization (Kinsbourne, 1981; Levy, 1981). In general, the evidence suggests a left-hemisphere involvement in speech-sound discrimination. This involvement may reflect subcortical mechanisms that would correspond with the evidence from Dennis and Whitaker (1976), which shows no differences in phoneme detection or production in left- and right-hemidecorticate children. Whether this subcortical, left-hemisphere, phoneme-detecting mechanism is robust enough to appear in other research remains to be seen. Whether this mechanism reflects or contributes to the development of other left-hemisphere mechanisms that are suitable to other language functions also remains to be discerned.

However, if there is a mechanism in the left hemisphere of infants to detect phonemes, then a paradox seems to be in the making. At present, the studies of infant hemispheric specialization depend on the notion of categorical perception of speech sounds requiring specialized neural detectors. Several different lines of research have come to challenge the notion of specialized property detectors for speech-sound stimuli (Kuhl, 1979; Studdert-Kennedy, 1980; Trehub, 1979). Adults have been shown to exhibit categorical perception of nonspeech-sound stimuli. Moreover, discrimination of acoustic differences within a phoneme category can be made quite easily after a brief training session. Phoneme discrimination may not occur if the stimuli are presented in different contexts. Speech-sound categorical-like perception has been observed in nonhuman species, including the chinchilla, suggesting that these perceptual abilities may reflect general properties of the mammalian auditory system. Finally, the evidence for categorical perception in infants is questionable (Butterfield & Cairns, 1974; Kuhl, 1979; Trehub, 1979). If categorical perception of speech sounds has not been adequately evaluated in infants, and if the adult evidence does not warrant postulation of specialized neural mechanisms for speech-sound perception, then one wonders exactly what the investigation of the hemispheric specialization of such perception in infants reveals.

I am not arguing that hemispheric specialization does not exist in infants, only that, if it does, it has not yet been adequately demonstrated. It is conceivable that the general properties of the auditory system that make the perception of speech sounds possible are associated more with the left than the right hemisphere in infants. Indeed, the biasing allele may ensure this form of left-hemisphere specialization for language perception, but the evaluation of this proposition requires different sorts of investigation than have been undertaken. At present, the notion that head orientation and hand-use preferences are fortuitously associated as a result of left-hemisphere dominance for language remains only a hypothesis with little evidence in its support.

Infant Head Orientation and Handedness

The direction of the infant's early head-orientation preference is virtually a perfect predictor of its hand-use preference in reaching throughout the whole of its first 14 months. If this association between head-orientation and hand-use preferences were only the fortuitous result of the impact of gene-induced, left-hemisphere dominance for language, then head-orientation preference and handedness ought to assort independently of one another in the absence of the allele. Infants suspected of lacking the biasing allele (e.g., those with leftward head-orientation preference or those with left-hand–use preference) nevertheless exhibit a significant association between the direction of their head-orientation preference and their handedness.

Although more extensive, longer-term longitudinal study of a larger sample is required, the present evidence supports the proposition that the supine head-orientation preference is both a precursor or predictor and a determinant of infant handedness. The allele, proposed by Annett to account for dextral bias in handedness, may induce the bias by promoting conditions that induce a rightward bias in infant supine head-orientation preferences. Exactly what these conditions are and how they and handedness relate to the development of hemispheric specialization remains to be determined.

Conclusions

As this chapter demonstrates, we have come some distance toward describing the early ontogeny of handedness. This description depends on a distinction between individual variability in handedness and the dextral bias in its distribution. The infant's supine head-orientation preference was found to be a probable precursor of dextral bias in handedness and an early contributor to individual variability. Moreover, an account of the process of handedness development was proposed that specified to some extent the kind of interaction between environmental conditions (especially those generated by the infant) and the infant's neuromotor capacities involved in the early organization of hand-use preferences. Although accumulation of information has been slow, we can specify the kind of information required to resolve most of the questions concerning the ontogeny of handedness. Indeed, the success of this chapter and the description of the ontogeny of handedness proposed will depend more on the quality and direction of the research it stimulates than on how fully it explains the development of handedness.

The discipline of developmental psychology is confronted with several major conceptual issues, and the study of handedness development entails the direct exploration of some of the more difficult of these. For example, one central concern of developmental psychology is how to comprehend the relationship between the developing nervous system and psychological development. It seems likely that comprehension will be easier and more successful for the sensorimotor character of handedness than, for instance, language skills. Yet many of the conceptual and empirical problems involved are the same for both phenomena, and comprehension of brain–behavior relations for the development of handedness will be relevant for other developmental phenomena. Indeed, it seems likely that many of the general issues in developmental psychology (e.g., constancy versus change in development, gene–behavior relations, experiential effects, sensitive periods) will be clarified more quickly for handedness than for other phenomena. To the extent that the clarification of such issues can generalize throughout developmental psychology, the development of handedness cannot be a trivial question.

Acknowledgments

Only a very small portion of the research reported herein was grant-supported (National Institute of Mental Health Small Grant Program, Grant No. RO3 MH 35528-01). Therefore, I greatly appreciate the generous support of the Department of Psychology of the University of Massachusetts at Boston for providing the laboratory, equipment, and facilities necessary for my research. I also thank the neonatal care unit at the Beth Israel Hospital in Massachusetts, especially William Cochran, Victoria Driscoll, and the nurses attending the Seventh South Nursery, for providing the special cooperation required for studying neonates. Celia L.

Moore and Peter H. Wolff provided helpful comments and moral support. Of course, the infants and their parents deserve the most thanks.

References

Anderson, M. E. (1981). The basal ganglia and movement. In A. L. Towe & E. A. Luschei (Eds.), *Handbook of behavioral neurobiology (Vol. 5): Motor coordination.* New York: Plenum.

Annett, M. (1970). The growth of manual preference and speed. *British Journal of Psychology 61,* 545–558.

Annett, M. (1972). The distribution of manual asymmetry. *British Journal of Psychology 63,* 343–358.

Annett, M. (1974). Handedness in the children of two left-handed parents. *British Journal of Psychology 65,* 129–131.

Annett, M. (1975). Hand preference and the laterality of cerebral speech. *Cortex 11,* 305–328.

Annett, M. (1978). Genetic and nongenetic influences on handedness. *Behavior Genetics 8,* 227–249.

Basser, L. S. (1962). Hemiplegia of early onset and the faculty of speech with special reference to the effects of hemispherectomy. *Brain 85,* 427–460.

Bateson, P. P. G. (1976). Rules and reciprocity in behavioural development. In P. P. G. Bateson & R. A. Hinde (Eds.), *Growing points in ethology.* London and New York: Cambridge Univ. Press.

Bateson, P. P. G. (1978). How does behavior develop? In P. P. G. Bateson & P. H. Klopfer (Eds.), *Perspectives in ethology.* New York: Plenum.

Bauermeister, M. (1977). *Skull shape and head turning in neonates.* Behavioral Sciences project report, Department of Psychiatric Research, Children's Hospital Medical Center, Boston, Massachusetts.

Beaumont, J. (1974). Handedness and hemisphere function. In S. Dimond & J. Beaumont (Eds.), *Hemisphere function in the human brain.* New York: Wiley.

Beintema, D. J. (1968). *A neurological study of newborn infants.* Clinics in Developmental Medicine, No. 26. Philadelphia, Pennsylvania: Lippincott.

Belmont, L., & Birch, H. G. (1963). Lateral dominance and right–left awareness in normal children. *Child Development 34,* 257–270.

Bower, T. G. R. (1974). *Development in infancy.* San Francisco, California: Freeman.

Bradshaw, J. L., & Nettleton, N. C. (1981). The nature of hemispheric specialization in man. *The Behavioral and Brain Sciences 4,* 51–91.

Bruner, J. S., & Koslowski, B. (1972). Visually preadapted constituents of manipulatory action. *Perception 1,* 3–14.

Brunner, R. J., Kornhuber, H. H., Seemüller, E., Suger, G., & Wallesch, C.-W. (1982). Basal ganglia participation in language pathology. *Brain and Language 16,* 281–299.

Butterfield, E. C., & Cairns, G. J. (1974). Discussion summary—Infant reception research. In R. L. Schiefelbusch & L. L. Lloyd (Eds.), *Language perspectives: Acquisition, retardation, and intervention.* Baltimore, Maryland: University Park Press.

Caplan, P. J., & Kinsbourne, M. (1976). Baby drops the rattle: Asymmetry of duration of grasp by infants. *Child Development 47,* 532–536.

Casaer, P. (1979). *Postural behaviour in newborn infants.* Clinics in Developmental Medicine, No. 72. Philadelphia, Pennsylvania: Lippincott.

Chapple, C., & Davidson, D. (1941). A study of the relationship between fetal position and certain congenital deformities. *Journal of Pediatrics 18,* 483–493.

Churchill, J., Igna, E., & Senf, R. (1962). The association of position at birth and handedness. *Pediatrics 29,* 307–309.

Cobb, K., Goodwin, R., & Saelens, E. (1966). Spontaneous hand positions of newborn infants. *The Journal of Genetic Psychology 108*, 225–237.

Collins, R. L. (1975). When left-handed mice live in right-handed worlds. *Science 187*, 181–184.

Collins, R. L. (1977). Toward an admissible genetic model for the inheritance of the degree and direction of asymmetry. In S. Harnad, R. W. Doty, L. Goldstein, J. Jaynes, & G. Krauthamer (Eds.), *Lateralization in the nervous system*. New York: Academic Press.

Compte, A. J. (1828). Récherches anatomico-physiologiques, relatives à la prédominance du bras droit sur le bras gauche. *Journal de Physiologie Expérimentale et Pathologie 8*, 41–80.

Connolly, K., & Elliott, J. (1972). The evolution and ontogeny of hand function. In N. Blurton Jones (Ed.), *Ethological studies of child behaviour*. London and New York: Cambridge Univ. Press.

Corballis, M. C., & Beale, I. L. (1976). *The psychology of left and right*. Hillsdale, New Jersey: Erlbaum.

Coren, S., & Porac, C. (1977). Fifty centuries of right-handedness: The historical record. *Science 198*, 631–632.

Coren, S., Porac, C., & Duncan, P. (1981). Lateral preference behavior in preschool children and young adults. *Child Development 52*, 443–450.

Coryell, J. F., & Cardinali, N. (1979). The asymmetrical tonic neck reflex in normal full-term infants. *Physical Therapy 59*, 747–753.

Coryell, J. F., & Henderson, A. (1979). Role of the asymmetrical tonic neck reflex in hand visualization in normal infants. *American Journal of Occupational Therapy 33*, 225–260.

Coryell, J. F., & Michel, G. F. (1978). How supine postural preferences of infants can contribute toward the development of handedness. *Infant Behavior and Development 1*, 245–257.

Davis, A. E., & Wada, J. A. (1977). Hemispheric asymmetries in human infants: Spectral analysis of flash and click evoked potentials. *Brain and Language 4*, 23–32.

Dawson, J. L. M. (1977). An anthropological perspective on the evolution and lateralization of the brain. In S. J. Dimond & D. A. Blizard (Eds.), *Evolution and lateralization of the brain*. New York: New York Academy of Sciences.

Dennis, M., & Kohn, B. (1975). Comprehension of syntax in infantile hemiplegics after cerebral hemidecortication: Left hemisphere superiority. *Brain and Language 2*, 472–482.

Dennis, M., & Whitaker, H. A. (1976). Language acquisition following hemidecortication: Linguistic superiority of the left over the right hemisphere. *Brain and Language 3*, 404–433.

Dennis, W. (1935). Laterality of function in early infancy under controlled conditions. *Child Development 6*, 252–258.

deVries, J. I. P., Visser, G. H. A., Huisjes, H. J., & Prechtl, H. F. R. (1982). *The emergence of fetal behaviour*. Neurobiology of Development Workshop, European Brain and Behaviour Society, March, Groningen, The Netherlands.

DiFranco, D., Muir, D., & Dodwell, P. (1978). Reaching in very young infants. *Perception 7*, 385–392.

Downey, J. E. (1928). Dextrality types and the preschool child. *National Society for the Study of Education 27*(Part II), 153–158.

Dunn, P. M. (1972). Congenital postural deformities: Perinatal associations. *Proceedings of the Royal Society of Medicine 65*, 735–738.

Dunn, P. M. (1975). Congenital postural deformities. *British Medical Bulletin 32*, 71–72.

Eimas, P. D. (1975). Developmental studies of speech perception. In L. B. Cohen & P. Salapatek (Eds.), *Infant perception: From sensation to cognition* (Vol. 2). New York: Academic Press.

Entus, A. K. (1977). Hemispheric asymmetry in processing of dichotically presented speech and non-speech stimuli by infants. In S. J. Segalowitz & F. A. Gruber (Eds.), *Language development and neurological theory*. New York: Academic Press.

Field, J. (1976). Relation of young infants' reaching behavior to stimulus distance and solidarity. *Developmental Psychology 12*, 444–448.

Field, J. (1977). Coordination of vision and prehension in young infants. *Child Development 48*, 97–103.

Flowers, K. (1975). Handedness and controlled movement. *British Journal of Psychology 66*, 39–52.

Fox, N., & Lewis, M. (1982). Motor asymmetries in preterm infants: Effects of prematurity and illness. *Developmental Psychobiology 15*, 19–23.

Fulford, G. E., & Brown, J. K. (1976). Position as a cause of deformity in children with cerebral palsy. *Developmental Medicine and Child Neurology 18*, 305–314.

Gardner, J., Lewkowicz, D., & Turkewitz, G. (1977). Development of postural asymmetry in premature human infants. *Developmental Psychobiology 10*, 471–480.

Georgopoulous, A. (1982). *Motor cortical mechanisms related to the coding of the direction of movement*. Paper presented at the Massachusetts Institute of Technology Psychology Department Colloquium, April, Cambridge, Massachusetts.

Gesell, A. (1938). The tonic neck reflex in the human infant. *Pediatrics 13*, 455–464.

Gesell, A., & Ames, L. B. (1947). The development of handedness. *Journal of Genetic Psychology 70*, 155–175.

Gesell, A., & Ames, L. B. (1950). Tonic neck reflex and symmetrotonic behavior. *Journal of Pediatrics 36*, 165–176.

Gesell, A., & Halverson, H. (1942). The daily maturation of infant behavior: A cinema study of postures, movements, and laterality. *Journal of Genetic Psychology 61*, 3–32.

Gevins, A. S., Zeitlin, G. M., Doyle, J. C., Yingling, C. D., Schaffer, R. E., Callaway, E., & Yeager, C. L. (1979). Electroencephalogram correlates of higher cortical functions. *Science 203*, 665–668.

Giesecke, M. (1936). The genesis of hand preference. *Monograph of the Society for Research in Child Development 1*(5, Serial No. 5), 1–102.

Glanville, B. B., Best, C. T., & Levenson, R. (1977). A cardiac measure of cerebral asymmetry in infant auditory perception. *Developmental Psychology 13*, 54–59.

Goodglass, H., & Quadfasel, F. A. (1954). Language laterality in left-handed aphasics. *Brain 77*, 521–548.

Goodwin, R., & Michel, G. F. (1981). Head orientation position during birth, in neonatal period, and hand preference at 19 weeks. *Child Development 52*, 819–826.

Gottlieb, G. (1973). Introduction to behavioral embryology. In G. Gottlieb (Ed.), *Behavioral embryology*. New York: Academic Press.

Gottlieb, G. (1976). The roles of experience in the development of behavior and the nervous system. In G. Gottlieb (Ed.)., *Neural and behavioral specificity*. New York: Academic Press.

Grofovà, I. (1978). Extrinsic connections of the neostriatum. In I. Divac & R. G. E. Öberg (Eds.), *The neostriatum*. New York: Pergamon.

Halverson, H. M. (1931). An experimental study of prehension in infants by means of systematic cinema records. *Genetic Psychology Monographs 10*, 107–286.

Hammer, M., & Turkewitz, G. (1974). A sensory basis for the lateral difference in the newborn infant's response to somesthetic stimulation. *Journal of Experimental Child Psychology 18*, 304–312.

Harris, L. J. (1980). Left-handedness: Early theories, facts, and fancies. In J. Herron (Ed.), *Neuropsychology of left-handedness*. New York: Academic Press.

Heilman, K. M. (1979). The neuropsychological basis of skilled movement in man. In M. S. Gazzaniga (Ed.), *Handbook of behavioral neurobiology* (Vol. 2): *Neuropsychology*. New York: Plenum.

Hein, A. (1980). The development of visually guided behavior. In C. S. Harris (Ed.), Visual coding and adaptability. Hillsdale, New Jersey: Erlbaum.

Hicks, R. E., & Kinsbourne, M. (1976). On the genesis of human handedness: A review. Journal of Motor Behavior 8, 257–266.

Hildreth, G. (1949). The development and training of hand dominance: I, II, III. Journal of Genetic Psychology 75, 197–275.

Hillyard, S. A., & Woods, D. L. (1979). Electrophysiological analysis of human brain function. In M. S. Gazzaniga (Ed.), Handbook of behavioral neurobiology (Vol. 2): Neuropsychology. New York: Plenum.

Hirsch, J. (1970). Behavior-genetic analysis and its biosocial consequences. Seminars in Psychiatry 2, 89–105.

Hofsten, C. von (1979). Development of visually directed reaching: The approach phase. Journal of Human Movement Studies 5, 160–178.

Hofsten, C. von, & Lindhagen, L. (1979). Observations on the development of reaching for moving objects. Journal of Experimental Child Psychology 28, 158–173.

Jones, H. E. (1931). Dextrality as a function of age. Journal of Experimental Psychology 14, 125–144.

Kinsbourne, M. (1981). The development of cerebral dominance. In S. B. Filskov & T. J. Boll (Eds.), Handbook of Clinical Neuropsychology. New York: Wiley.

Kuhl, P. K. (1979). Models and mechanisms in speech perception. Brain, Behavior, and Evolution 16, 374–408.

Leavitt, L. A., Brown, J. W., Morse, P. A., & Graham, F. K. (1976). Cardiac orienting and auditory discrimination in 6-week infants. Developmental Psychology 12, 514.

Lederer, R. K. (1939). An exploratory investigation of handedness status in the first two years of life. In R. Lederer & J. Redfield (Eds.), Studies in Infant Behavior (Vol. 5), Ames, Iowa: University of Iowa Studies.

Lehrman, D. S. (1953). A critique of Konrad Lorenz's theory of instinctive behavior. Quarterly Review of Biology 28, 337–363.

Lehrman, D. S. (1970). Semantic and conceptual issues in the nature-nurture problem. In L. R. Aronson, E. Tobach, D. S. Lehrman, & J. S. Rosenblatt (Eds.), Development and evolution of behavior. San Francisco, California: Freeman.

LeMay, M. (1977). Asymmetries of the skull and handedness. Journal of the Neurological Sciences 32, 243–253.

Lenneberg, E. (1967). Biological foundations of language. New York: Wiley.

Levy, J. (1981). Lateralization and its implications for variation in development. In E. S. Gollin (Ed.), Developmental plasticity. New York: Academic Press.

Levy, J., & Nagylaki, T. (1972). A model for the genetics of handedness. Genetics 72, 117–128.

Liederman, J., & Coryell, J. (1981). Right-hand preference facilitated by rightward turning biases during infancy. Developmental Psychobiology 14, 439–450.

Liederman, J., & Kinsbourne, M. (1980). The mechanism of neonatal rightward turning bias: A sensory or motor asymmetry? Infant Behavior and Development 3, 223–238.

Lippman, A. S. (1927). Certain behavior responses in early infancy. Journal of Genetic Psychology 34, 424–440.

McDonnell, P. M. (1979). Patterns of eye hand coordination in the first year of life. Canadian Journal of Psychology 33, 253–267.

McDonnell, P. M., Anderson, B. E. S., & Abraham, W. C. (in press). Asymmetry and orientation of arm movements in three- to eight-week old infants. Infant Behavior and Development.

MacNeilage, P. F. (1980). Speech production. Language and Speech 23, 2–23.

Maekawa, K., & Ochiai, Y. (1975). Electromyographic studies on flexor hypertonia of the extremeties of newborn infants. Developmental Medicine and Child Neurology 17, 440–446.

Marin, O. S. M., Schwartz, N. F., & Saffran, E. M. (1979). Origins and distribution of language. In M. S. Gazzaniga (Ed.), Handbook of behavioral neurobiology (Vol. 2): Neuropsychology. New York: Plenum.

Marshall, J. C. (1980). On the biology of language acquisition. In D. Caplan (Ed.), Biological
studies of mental processes. Cambridge, Massachusetts: MIT Press.

Michel, G. F. (1981). Right-handedness: A consequence of infant supine head-orientation
preference? Science 212, 685–687.

Michel, G. F. (1982). Ontogenetic precursors of infant handedness. Infant Behavior and
Development, 5, 156.

Michel, G. F., & Goodwin, R. (1979). Intrauterine birth position predicts newborn supine
head position preferences. Infant Behavior and Development 2, 29–38.

Michel, G. F., & Moore, C. L. (1978). Biological perspectives in developmental psychology.
Monterey, California: Brooks/Cole.

Molfese, D. L., Freeman, R. B., & Palermo, D. S. (1975). The ontogeny of brain lateralization
for speech and nonspeech stimuli. Brain and Language 2, 356–368.

Molfese, D. L., & Molfese, V. J. (1979). Hemisphere and stimulus differences as reflected in
the cortical responses of newborn infants to speech stimuli. Developmental Psychology 15, 505–511.

Molfese, D. L., & Molfese, V. J. (1980). Cortical responses of preterm infants to phonetic and
nonphonetic speech stimuli. Developmental Psychology 16, 574–581.

Molfese, D. L., Nunez, U., Seibert, S. M., & Ramanaiah, N. V. (1976). Cerebral asymmetry:
Changes in factors affecting its development. Annals of the New York Academy of
Sciences 280, 821–833.

Molfese, D. L., & Radtke, R. C. (1982). Statistical and methodological issues in "Auditory
evoked potentials and sex-related differences in brain development." Brain and Language 16, 338–341.

Morse, P. A. (1979). The infancy of infant speech perception: The first decade of research.
Brain, Behavior and Evolution 16, 351–373.

Moss, F. A. (1929). Applications of psychology. Cambridge, Massachusetts: Harvard Univ.
Press.

Nottebohm, F. (1979). Origins and mechanisms in the establishment of cerebral dominance.
In M. S. Gazzaniga (Ed.), Handbook of behavioral neurobiology (Vol. 2): Neuropsychology. New York: Plenum.

Overstreet, R. (1938). An investigation of prenatal position and handedness. Psychological
Bulletin 35, 520–521.

Paine, R. S., Brazelton, T. B., Donovan, D. E., Drorbaugh, J. E., Hubbell, J. P., Jr., & Sears, E. M.
(1964). Evolution of postural reflexes in normal infants and in the presence of chronic
brain syndromes. Neurology 14, 1036–1048.

Palmer, R. D. (1964). Development of a differentiated handedness. Psychological Bulletin 62,
257–272.

Parmelee, A. M. (1931). Molding due to intra-uterine posture. American Journal of Diseases
of Children 42, 1155–1159.

Peiper, A. (1963). Cerebral function in infancy and childhood. New York: Consultants
Bureau.

Peters, M., & Durding, B. M. (1979). Footedness in left- and right-handedness. American
Journal of Psychology 92, 133–142.

Peters, M., & Pederson, K. (1978). Incidence of left-handedness with inverted writing position in a population of 5910 elementary school children. Neuropsychologia 16,
743–746.

Petrie, B. F., & Peters, M. (1980). Handedness: Left/right differences in intensity of grasp
response and duration of holding in infants. Infant Behavior and Development 3,
215–221.

Prechtl, H. F. R. (1981). The study of neural development as a perspective of clinical problems. In K. J. Connolly & H. F. R. Prechtl (Eds.), *Maturation and development: Biological and psychological processes. Clinics in Developmental Medicine*, No. 77/78. Philadelphia, Pennsylvania: Lippincott.

Prechtl, H. F. R., Fargel, J. W., Weinmann, H. M., & Bakker, H. H. (1975). Development of motor function and body postures in preterm infants. In F. Vital-Durand & M. Jeannerod (Eds.), *Aspects of neural plasticity*. Paris: INSERM.

Prechtl, H. F. R., Fargel, J. W., Weinmann, H. M., & Bakker, H. H. (1979). Postures, motility and respiration of low-risk preterm infants. *Developmental Medicine and Child Neurology 21*, 3–27.

Provins, K. A. (1956). "Handedness" and skill. *Quarterly Journal of Experimental Psychology 8*, 79–95.

Provins, K. A., & Cunliffe, P. (1972). The reliability of some motor performance tests of handedness. *Neuropsychologia 10*, 199–206.

Ramsay, D. (1980). Onset of unimanual handedness in infants. *Infant Behavior and Development 3*, 377–386.

Ramsay, D., Campos, J. J., & Fenson, L. (1979). Onset of bimanual handedness in infants. *Infant Behavior and Development 2*, 69–76.

Rasmussen, T., & Milner, B. (1977). The role of early left-brain injury in determining lateralization of cerebral speech functions. In S. J. Dimond & D. A. Blizard (Eds.), *Evolution and lateralization of the brain*. New York: The New York Academy of Sciences.

Ratcliffe, G., Pila, C., Taylor, L. B., & Milner, B. (1978). *Arteriographic correlates of cerebral dominance for speech*. Paper presented at the International Neuropsychology Symposium, June, Oxford, England.

Reinold, E. (1976). Ultrasonics in early pregnancy. In P. J. Keller (Ed.), *Contributions to gynaecology and obstetrics* (Vol. 1). Basel: S. Karger.

Roberts, A. M., & Smart, J. L. (1981). An investigation of handedness and headedness in newborn babies. *Behavior and Brain Research 2*, 275–276.

Robson, P. (1968). Persistent head turning in the early months: Some effects in the early years. *Developmental Medicine and Child Neurology 10*, 82–92.

Roos, M. (1935). A study of some factors entering into the determination of handedness. *Child Development 6*, 91–97.

Rubens, A. B. (1977). Anatomical asymmetries of human cerebral cortex. In S. Harnad, R. W. Doty, L. Goldstein, J. Jaynes, & G. Krauthamer (Eds.), *Lateralization in the nervous system*. New York: Academic Press.

Rydberg, E. (1965). Mechanism of labor in cephalic presentation. In J. P. Greenhill (Ed.), *Obstetrics* (13th ed.). Philadelphia, Pennsylvania: Saunders.

Schneirla, T. C. (1966). Behavioral development and comparative psychology. *Quarterly Review of Biology 41*, 283–302.

Schulte, F. J. (1974). The neurological development of the neonate. In J. A. Davis & J. Dobbing (Eds.), *Scientific foundations of paediatrics*. Philadelphia, Pennsylvania: Saunders.

Shankweiler, D., & Liberman, I. Y. (1976). Exploring the relations between reading and speech. In R. M. Knights & D. J. Bakker (Eds.), *The neuropsychology of learning disorders*. Baltimore, Maryland: University Park Press.

Shirley, M. M. (1931). *The first two years: A study of twenty-five babies* (Vol. 1): *Postural and locomotor development*. Minneapolis: Univ. of Minnesota Press.

Shucard, D. W., Shucard, J. L., Campos, J. J., & Salamy, J. G. (1982). Some issues pertaining to auditory evoked potentials and sex related differences in brain development. *Brain and Language 16*, 342–347.

Shucard, D. W., Shucard, J. L., & Thomas, D. G. (1977). Auditory evoked potentials as probes of hemispheric differences in cognitive processing. *Science 197*, 1295–1298.

Shucard, J. L., Shucard, D. W., Cummins, K. R., & Campos, J. J. (1981). Auditory evoked potentials and sex related difference in brain development. *Brain and Language 13*, 91–102.

Snoo, K. de (1931). Die Lage des Kindes im Uterus, betrachtet vom Standpunkt der relativen Stabilitat. *Archiv für Gynakologie 145*, 601–648.

Spinelli, D. N., & Jensen, F. E. (1982). Plasticity, experience and resource allocation in motor cortex and hypothalamus. In C. D. Woody (Ed.), *Conditioning*. New York: Plenum.

Spinelli, D. N., Jensen, F. E., Viana Di Prisco, G. (1980). Early experience effect on dendritic branching in normally reared kittens. *Experimental Neurology 68*, 1–11.

Steele, K. B., & Javert, C. T. (1942). Mechanism of labor for transverse positions of the vertex. *Surgical Gynecology and Obstetrics 75*, 477–480.

Stone, M. A. (1980). Measures of laterality and spurious correlation. *Neuropsychologia 18*, 339–345.

Stubbs, E., & Irwin, D. C. (1933). Laterality of limb movements of four newborn infants. *Child Development 4*, 358–359.

Studdert-Kennedy, M. (1980). Speech perception. *Language and Speech 23*, 45–66.

Teng, E. L., Lee, P., Yang, K., & Chang, P. (1976). Handedness in a Chinese population: Biological, social, and pathological factors. *Science 193*, 1148–1150.

Tinbergen, N. (1963). On aims and methods of ethology. *Zeitschrift für Tierpsychologie 20*, 410–429.

Todor, J. I., & Doane, T. (1977). Handedness classification: Preference versus proficiency. *Perceptual and Motor Skills 45*, 1041–1042.

Touwen, B. C. L. (1974). Neurological development of the infant. In J. A. Davis & J. Dobbing (Eds.), *Scientific foundations of paediatrics*. Philadelphia, Pennsylvania: Saunders.

Trehub, S. E. (1979). Reflections on the development of speech perception. *Canadian Journal of Psychology 4*, 368–381.

Turkewitz, G. (1977). The development of lateral differences in the human infant. In S. Harnad, R. W. Doty, L. Goldstein, J. Jaynes, & G. Krauthamer (Eds.), *Lateralization in the nervous system*. New York: Academic Press.

Turkewitz, G. (1980). Mechanisms of neonatal rightward turning bias: A reply to Liederman and Kinsbourne. *Infant Behavior and Development 3*, 239–244.

Turkewitz, G., & Creighton, S. (1974). Changes in lateral differentiation of head posture in the human neonate. *Developmental Psychobiology 8*, 85–89.

Turkewitz, G., Gordon, E. W., & Birch, H. G. (1965). Head turning in the human neonate: Spontaneous patterns. *Journal of Genetic Psychology 107*, 143–158.

Turkewitz, G., Moreau, T., & Birch, H. G. (1966). Head position and receptor organization in the human neonate. *Journal of Experimental Psychology 4*, 169–177.

Updegraff, R. (1932). Preferential handedness in young children. *Journal of Experimental Education 1*, 134–139.

Valentine, W. L., & Wagner, I. (1934). Relative arm motility in the newborn infant. *Ohio University Studies 12*, 53–68.

Vargha-Khadem, F., & Corballis, M. D. (1979). Cerebral asymmetry in infants. *Brain and Language 8*, 1–9.

Vartan, C. K. (1945). Behavior of the fetus *in utero* with special reference to the incidence of breech presentation at term. *Journal of Obstetrics and Gynecology (British) 52*, 417–434.

Viviani, J., Turkewitz, G., & Karp, E. (1978). A relationship between laterality of functioning at 2 days and at 7 years of age. *Psychonomic Science 12*, 189–192.

Walker, S. F. (1980). Lateralization of functions in the vertebrate brain: A review. *British Journal of Psychology 71*, 329–367.

Warren, J. M. (1977). Handedness and cerebral dominance in monkeys. In S. Harnad, R. W. Doty, L. Goldstein, J. Jaynes, & G. Krauthamer (Eds.), *Lateralization in the nervous system*. New York: Academic Press.

Weiffenbach, J. M. (1972). Discrete elicited movements in the newborn's tongue. In J. F. Bosma (Ed.), *Third symposium on oral sensation and perception*. Springfield, Illinois: Thomas.

Whitaker, H. A., & Ojemann, G. A. (1977). Lateralization of higher cortical functions: A critique. In S. J. Diamond & D. A. Blizard (Eds.), *Evolution and lateralization of the brain*. New York: The New York Academy of Sciences.

White, B. L., Castle, P., & Held, R. (1964). Observations on the development of visually directed reaching. *Child Development 35*, 349–364.

Wilcock, J. (1969). Gene action and behavior: An evaluation of major gene pleiotropism. *Psychological Bulletin 72*, 1–29.

Witelson, S. F. (1980). Neuroanatomical asymmetry in left-handers: A review and implications for functional asymmetry. In J. Herron (Ed.), *Neuropsychology of left handedness*. New York: Academic Press.

Young, G. (1977). Manual specialization in infancy: Implications for lateralization of brain function. In S. J. Segalowitz & F. A. Gruber (Eds.), *Language development and neurological theory*. New York: Academic Press.

4

Mechanisms Underlying Instability in the Development of Hand Preference

JACQUELINE LIEDERMAN

Introduction

The vast literature devoted to the origins of hand preference has failed to address a central paradox: The incidence of right-hand preference is remarkably stable across cultures and centuries of civilization (Coren & Porac, 1977), yet the development of hand preference within an individual follows a variable and unstable course. As will be documented in the first section of this chapter, during early infancy, lateral preferences often fluctuate, the proportion of right-sidedness is lower than in adulthood, and there may even be periods when left-sidedness is predominant.

In the second section of this chapter, I propose a model that could account for these instabilities in the development of hand preference. A central problem for any model of "lateralization" of function is that the side of the brain that predominates during one kind of movement (e.g., writing) may not predominate during other movement (e.g., opening a jar, gesturing, or speaking). It is clear that in a substantial number of left-handed persons there are striking dissociations in hemispheric control (e.g., left-hemisphere control of language–right-hemisphere control of the preferred hand–left-hemisphere control of praxis, Heilman [1979]). Indeed, even in self-labeled right-handers there is considerable heterogeneity across measures of manual preference and performance (Hicks, 1978).

Thus, despite the fact that in the vast majority of persons the left hemisphere of the brain predominates during most forms of motor program-

71

MANUAL SPECIALIZATION
AND THE DEVELOPING BRAIN

ming, a model of the development of motor lateralization must be able to explain these not infrequent dissociations. Furthermore, there are no known deficits associated with these variant forms of lateralization. Therefore, a model cannot just dismiss these variations as instances of hemispheric reorganization in response to insult (though this may well account for some instances of the phenomenon).

Two of the prevalent models within the current literature totally fail to account for this variability. According to a single-factor maturational model of the sort advocated by Gesell, head-orientation biases are a precursor to hand preference simply because both are manifestations of the operation of a single system at different points in its development. The predictions of a strictly maturational model are not supported. As will be shown later in this chapter, neonatal lateral preference and ultimate hand preference are not strongly correlated, and neonatal lateral preference is not biased rightward to the same extent as adult hand preference.

An alternative model is an epigenetic one. Such a model would assume that an initial neural asymmetry (whose origin could either be genetic or environmental) sets up a behavioral bias that is strengthened both by the differential experience induced by that bias and the environmental pressure of a right-handed society. This model would predict that adults are more right-preferenced than infants, but it would falter on the basis of the prediction that neonatal and adult preferences should be highly correlated. Neither of these models make specific provisions for the fact that hand preferences fluctuate, nor can either of them deal with the fact that handedness is multidimensional. There are at least 10 independent dimensions of unimanual performance (Fleishman, 1972).

A third model will be presented that is a specific attempt to explain why the development of hand preference is often unstable and varies from task to task. This model, which will be referred to as the Multifactor Stochastic Model, is an expansion of Annett (1978). The first part of the model, described in the section on congruency in lateralization, identifies mechanisms that induce and sustain consistent lateralization across motor asymmetries. It will be argued that the initial head-turning bias seen in neonates reflects a central asymmetry in the motor system that is preprogrammed and inherited from the parents. The effects of this central asymmetry can be relatively clearly seen at birth because this is a time when neural factors rather than environmental factors dominate behavior. The importance of understanding this initial bias is that it is assumed to play a continuing role throughout development. This bias is perpetuated by epigenetic factors such as increased visualization of the right hand (Coryell & Michel, 1978) and differential reflex inhibition (Liederman & Coryell, 1981).

The second part of the model, described in the section on variability in lateralization, identifies mechanisms that could account for differential lateralization of motor asymmetries at various points in development. As the child develops, the subcortical system that is responsible for initial behavioral asymmetries is modified by interactions with other parts of the brain that mature somewhat later (e.g., specific regions of cortex; the corpus callosum). This model suggests that there are several systems that control movement, each developing at different times. Each system can become lateralized independently. Thus, the basic assumption is that lateralization is governed by stochastic processes: There is a high probability that behaviors will be lateralized in the same direction, but there is nothing specific wired into the brain that *guarantees* that this will occur.

According to the Multifactor Stochastic Model, the way a new system will become lateralized is affected by certain environmental factors (e.g., cultural pressure, neural insult) and organismic factors (e.g., left hemisphere vulnerability to hypoxic insult, rate of maturation, and state and variability of state). One of the assumptions of this model is that when a system is first becoming organized, that is the time when it is most vulnerable to such macro- and microenvironmental influences. Specifically, for each new level of functioning, there may be competition between the two sides of the brain for primary access to the output mechanisms. Thus, during this competition, dominance may be most labile. One of the implications of this assumption is that when a child first acquires a skill mediated by a recently developed system, lateral preference should be most labile.

In summary, the factors determining manual preference may be different at different times and one of the important components of this model is to attempt to identify points of transition between lateral preferences.

The Unstable Course of the Development of Lateral Biases in Movement

Shifts from Left Preference to Right Preference

There are several basic trends in the developmental data that must be accounted for. First, although lateral asymmetries can be observed at birth and during early infancy, there is a significant tendency for the maturing individual to become not only more right-sided, but also more consistently right-sided both in terms of preference for the use of one hand (Černáček & Podivinský, 1971; Ingram, 1975) and for congruency among other measures of lateral preference (for example, foot, eye, and ear; Coren, Porac, & Duncan, 1981).

The incidence of rightward bias during infancy is considerably lower than among adults. This fact was obscured by early reports that gave the impression that almost all neonates preferred to turn their heads right-ward (Gesell & Amatruda, 1967; Gesell & Ames, 1947). Siqueland and Lipsitt (1966) helped to perpetuate this view when they reported that the spontaneous rightward turning bias was so pervasive that it interfered with attempts to condition head turning to the left. Even the earliest systematic study of spontaneous head-turning patterns (Turkewitz, Gor-don, & Birch, 1965) indicated that 85% of all neonates restricted their movements *solely* to the right.

Turkewitz *et al.*'s (1965) very high estimate could have been an artifact of the testing procedure. Observations were initiated with the infants lying in whatever position the nursing staff had "spontaneously" placed them. These initial head positions were not reported, but, in a subsequent study conducted in the same institution, Turkewitz, Moreau, Birch, Her-bert, and Crystal (1967) mentioned that it was standard procedure for infants to be placed on their right sides. From the right, head movement to the left requires that the head be turned greater than 90°. This factor seems to explain readily why so little head movement was directed to the left of the infant's midline.

More recent studies have found that the incidence of rightward head-turning bias is approximately 75% and that substantial proportions of infants have consistent leftward biases. For example, despite slight pro-cedural variations, each of the following reports has indicated that ap-proximately 75% of the neonates sampled preferred to turn their heads rightward: Coryell and Michel, 1978—$N = 16$, 78%; Liederman, 1977—$N = 155$, 77%; Liederman, in preparation—$N = 86$, 78%; Michel and Good-win, 1979—$N = 109$, 77%; Saling, 1979—$N = 40$, 70%, 75%; Turkewitz and Creighton, 1974—$N = 70$, 76%. Some investigators have reported the incidence of leftward bias: Goodwin and Michel, 1981—16% with a sig-nificant leftward bias, 36% with some degree of leftward bias; Michel, 1981—6% with a significant leftward bias, 15% with some degree of left-ward bias; Liederman, in preparation—10% with a significant leftward bias, 17% with some degree of leftward bias; Michel and Goodwin, 1979—8% with a significant leftward bias, 23% with some degree of leftward bias.

One perplexing aspect of the development of hand preference is that most children who lack a rightward preference at birth nonetheless be-come right-handed. Analysis of this transition has been limited by the small number of longitudinal studies, most of which have contained too few left-preferenced children. For example, Viviani, Turkewitz, and Karp (1978) observed 22 children who had initially been tested at birth. The relationship between the neonatal lateral index and hand preference at age 7 was significant, but only one child became left-handed. Also, the proportion of children who lacked a rightward bias at birth and became right-handed was not reported. Thus, for our purposes, their survey is a case study in which a single child who had been more "responsive" to stimulation on the left side became left-handed.

Goodwin and Michel (1981) reported that there was a significant over-all relationship between neonatal head-position preference at birth and the hand preferred for reaching at the age of 19 weeks. Infants with a right neonatal head-position preference demonstrated a right-hand preference at 19 weeks. However, among infants with left neonatal preferences, there were no significant differences in hand preference. Only 43% (6/14) of infants with relatively weak left biases showed a 19-week left-hand pref-erence. In contrast, 75% (6/8) of those with a *consistent* neonatal left head-orientation preference continued to be left-handed. Michel (1981) picked up on this finding and, with a separate sample of infants ($N = 20$), demonstrated that children with "consistent" lateral head-turning prefer-ences at birth tend to have the same side preference for reaching at 19 weeks of age. Although the correlation was significant, 5 of the 20 infants changed their preference between assessments.

The question that remains is, what happens to the many infants with less consistent neonatal lateral preferences? For example, Coryell (person-al communication) compared the hand preference of eight 3–6-year-olds to their head-position preference at ages 1, 2, 4, 6, 8, 10, and 12 weeks. The only correlation that was significant was that involving the 6-week measure.

Even assessments as late as the fifth month can label an infant who will later prefer the right hand as a left-hander. Goodwin (personal commu-nication) tested 58 infants at ages 19 weeks and 3 years by means of a reaching task very similar to the one used in the earlier observation. Only 4 of the 18 children who were left-preferenced at 19 weeks (21%) re-mained left-preferenced at 3 years. In contrast, of the 40 infants who were right-preferenced at 19 weeks, 33 (82%) were also right-preferenced at 3 years. This was not just an artifact of her particular reaching test. She also gave the 3-year-olds a 12-item hand-preference inventory to which they responded by pantomime. Only 2 of the 18 children who were left-prefer-enced at 19 weeks (11%) indicated a preference for the left hand at age 3 years.

One could argue that the difference between the percentage of infants and adults who are right-preferenced is more apparent than real, es-pecially when a trichotomous, instead of a dichotomous, classification is employed. In a series of seven handedness surveys, an adult was consid-ered of "mixed" preference if the nonpreferred hand was preferred for even one task (Annett, 1967). With this criterion, handedness was dis-tributed according to a binomial distribution: "pure" right—65%, left—4%, mixed—31%.

One could also argue that the incidence of right preference appears lower during infancy than adulthood because of the difference in the behaviors that are sampled. Overt rightward head-turning biases are not seen during adulthood except, perhaps, under special circumstances. For example, it has been reported that people lost in a blizzard tend to circle rightward (Sorrell, 1967), but this phenomenon has not been quantified. Other lateralized behaviors observable during infancy (e.g., reaching) may be less complex than adult handedness measures. Complexity is important because differences between the hands become apparent as task complexity increases (e.g., Steingruber, 1975).

The problem with either of these arguments is that they are not sufficient to explain Goodwin's data: that most infants who reach preferentially with the left hand at 19 weeks prefer to use the right hand when tested in the same manner at age 3 years. It is on this basis that we argue that the low incidence of right-sidedness during infancy is a real phenomenon and requires explanation.

Shifts from Right Preference to Left Preference

The developmental shift toward greater dextrality, however, is not so consistently observed when profiles are examined individually. Hand preference oscillates before a clear preference is established by about 9–12 months (e.g., Černáček & Podivinský, 1971; Gesell & Ames, 1947; Seth, 1973). In Goodwin's study, 19% of 58 infants lacked a rightward bias at birth. At 19 weeks, the proportion of children lacking a rightward bias had risen to 31%, and then at 3 years, with the same measure of lateral preference, the percentage of non-right-biased children had decreased to 16%. The differences between 19% and 31% and 31% and 16% are significant (Test for the Significance of Differences in Proportion; Bruning & Kintz, 1968). Hence one must find an explanation for these not-infrequent instances when a lateral asymmetry reverses from right to left or seems to fluctuate.

Perhaps the most striking discontinuities involve stages of development when the left rather than the right hand is preferred by the majority of infants. There has been one series of studies (McDonnell, 1979; McDonnell, Anderson, & Abraham, in press) in which 14 infants were tested four times between 3 and 8 weeks. Fourteen of 15 infants moved their left hands significantly more than their right hands when presented with an object. The parents were surveyed when the children were 1 year old to estimate handedness. A switch from left- to right-hand preference occurred in 10/12 of the infants, 1/12 retained a left-hand preference, and the remaining infants switched from an equivocal hand preference to a left preference.

Higher levels of activity for the left rather than the right hand have also been reported in infants of various ages: 9–23 days (DiFranco, Muir, &

Dodwell, 1978); 4–10 weeks (Coryell & Michel, 1978); and 4–5 months (Gesell & Ames, 1947; Seth, 1973). The problem with these reports is that the degree of left-hand superiority is minimal.

The Multifactor Stochastic Model: Factors That Contribute toward Congruency in Lateralization

Genetic Factors: A Prewired Asymmetry within the Central Nervous System That Generates a Response Bias

"[R]ight-handedness appears to be the birthright of mankind [Coren & Porac, 1977, p. 632]." Based on their survey of more than 5000 years of artworks representing unimanual tool or weapon usage, Coren and Porac found that the average incidence of right-hand usage was 92%, irrespective of century or geographic location. Similarly, Hécaen and de Ajuriaguerra (1964) reviewed 48 studies of adult handedness and found that the mean incidence of dextrality was 90.6%, and that the median incidence was even higher (93.6%). Hicks and Kinsbourne (1977) reviewed published surveys of handedness conducted in such diverse locations as Japan, Western Europe, Third-World countries, and the Solomon Islands. Again, the incidence of right handedness was approximately 90%. We conclude that right handedness must be the birthright of at least 90% of mankind.

The universality of this asymmetry suggests that it is due to more than just cultural pressure. The genetic model that seems to deal best with the multidimensional nature of handedness is that of Annett (1978). According to this model, people inherit a predisposition toward a certain hand preference quite indirectly. What is inherited is a factor (the Right Shift Factor—RS+) that disposes an individual to be left-hemisphere dominant for speech and incidentally gives some advantage to the control of the right hand. In the absence of that allele on both chromosomes, either hemisphere may subserve speech and either hand may develop greater skill. Thus, inheritance of the RS+ factor does not guarantee right handedness. Instead, either right handedness, left handedness, or ambidexterity may occur according to a binomial distribution.

Liederman and Kinsbourne (1980b) have demonstrated that the tendency for newborn infants to prefer to turn their heads rightward is probably transmitted genetically in a manner consistent with Annett's (1978) model. Children whose gestation and delivery had been uncomplicated were observed a few days after birth, before their lateral preferences could have been much influenced by caretaking practices. Children with dextral parents turned preponderantly to the right in response to symmetrical stimulation, whereas those with one left-handed parent, as a group, showed no head-turning bias. These data suggest that the brain is pre-wired with reference to neural asymmetry, and that the direction of this asymmetry is inherited from the parents.

One way that this head-turning asymmetry could have implications for hand preference would be if both reflected a basic asymmetry in the central nervous system. This is in contrast, however, to the suggestion by Michel (Chapter 3, this volume) that the child's position in utero generates an asymmetry in muscle tonus that is restricted to the level of the segmental reflexes. The following pieces of evidence support the concept that there is a general asymmetrical bias within the central nervous system.

Although the head-turning preference of children is related to the position of the child's head in utero (Churchill, Igna, & Senf, 1962; Goodwin & Michel, 1981), the duration of gestation does not seem to affect the incidence of the rightward head-turning bias. Thus, Gesell and Amatruda (1967) reported that 77% of infants between the ages of 28 and 32 weeks postconception prefer to turn their heads to the right. These results have been replicated by Fox and Lewis (1982) with 34–39-week-old premature infants. From this it can be concluded that intrauterine position does not induce the child's lateral head-turning preference.

A similar argument is that the postnatal head-turning bias can be modified by manipulation of muscle tonus, but it cannot be reversed. Lieder-man and Kinsbourne (1980a) positioned newborns on their left or right sides and asked nurses to reposition them with that orientation during the course of one night. Immediately after this manipulation, they observed which way the infants preferred to turn their heads in response to stimulation. Children who had been positioned rightward manifested strong rightward head-turning biases. Children who had been positioned left-ward, as a group, manifested neither a leftward nor a rightward bias. This indicates that a reverse bias was not induced by this peripheral manipulation of muscle tonus.

During early infancy, lateral head-turning preference seems to reflect a stable trait; correlations between days of testing are high (e.g., Goodwin & Michel, 1981; Saling, 1979). In the latter study, 90% of the neonates manifested the same lateral head-turning preference on 2 successive days of testing.

The notion of an underlying central asymmetry is also supported by the presence of other turning biases, namely, that it is even evident during eye movements and occurs in response to a wide variety of stimuli. Infants' eye movements are preponderantly rightward in response to both visual (Harris & MacFarlane, 1974) and auditory stimulation (Turkewitz, Birch, Moreau, Levy, & Cornwell, 1966). Head turns are preponderantly rightward in response to tactile (Hammer & Turkewitz, 1974), olfactory (Reiser, Yonas, & Wikner, 1976), and gustatory (Liederman & Kinsbourne, 1980b) stimulation.

The asymmetry underlying the head-turning bias is more than just an asymmetry in muscle tonus. First, 6-week-old infants actively resist having their heads turned in the direction opposite to their preference (Liederman & Coryell, 1981). Second, Liederman (in preparation) observed that newborn infants who preferred to spontaneously turn their heads right turned their heads significantly further to the right than to the left, whereas those who preferred to turn left, turned their heads further to the left. Thus, children actively prefer to turn their heads in one direction more than another, and do so with greater vigor or force. Moreover, aside from asymmetries in head turning, there are other early asymmetries in movement that occur in roughly the same proportion of children (e.g., rightward-biased tongue movements (Weiffenbach, 1972), fisting of the right rather than the left hand (Cobb, Goodwin, & Saelens, 1966), and initiation of reflex stepping with the right rather than left foot (Peters & Petrie, 1979).

It should be noted that Hammer and Turkewitz (1974), Moreau, Helfgott, Weinstein, and Milner (1978), and Turkewitz (1980) have all claimed that there is an asymmetry within sensory systems (in addition to an asymmetry within the motor system) that determines the preferred direction of head turning. The specific claim has been that infants prefer to turn their heads rightward because they are more sensitive to stimulation on their right than their left side. Liederman and Kinsbourne (1980a, 1980c) reviewed the evidence for this hypothetical right-sided sensitivity and concluded that existing data could be explained solely on the basis of a neural asymmetry in motor programming. They also reported results of their own study in which children were presented with symmetric aversive stimulation. They reasoned that if rightward-turning biases were partially due to greater sensitivity on the right side, children would be more likely to withdraw and turn leftward in response to aversive stimulation. Liederman and Kinsbourne (1980a) instead found that rightward biases were strengthened (not reversed) by aversive, as opposed to nonaversive, stimulation.

Epigenetic Factors: Hand Visualization,
Reflex Inhibition, Secondary Sensory Asymmetries

The model that is being advocated suggests that the initial rightward bias present in approximately 75% of infants is perpetuated by a series of epigenetic processes. For example, as Coryell and Michel (1978) suggest, the initial head-turning asymmetry may increase visualization of the right hand and promote eye–hand coordination on that side.

Similarly, Liederman and Coryell (1981) have pointed out that the rightward turning bias involves repeated evocation of the asymmetric tonic neck reflex (ATNR) on the right side. For infants whose average age was 6 weeks, the incidence, strength, and duration of the ATNR were greatest when the head turned leftward. This was only true for children who preferred to orient rightward. The pattern of results was less clear-cut in children who preferred to orient leftward. One possible explanation for this phenomenon is that repeated evocation of the reflex on the right side hastens inhibition of the reflex and promotes volitional movement on the right side. They suggest that this is advantageous to further use of the right hand because it permits the child to turn to watch the right hand without hand position being determined by head position. Hence the right-hand movement can be used with more precision for volitional movement.

A third way that neonatal postural bias may increase the probability that lateral preferences continue to be right-sided is that there may be a change of sensory threshold consequent to the head-right position (Liederman & Kinsbourne, 1980a). Thus, children who have been lying on their right sides with their right ears occluded may subsequently be differentially sensitive to auditory or tactile stimuli on their right sides.

The Multifactor Stochastic Model: Factors That Contribute toward Variability in Lateralization

Systems That May Be Differentially Lateralized

REFLEXIVE VERSUS VOLITIONAL CONTROL

The moment of transition from reflexive to volitional movement varies with the kind of behavior, but what is noteworthy is that, some time after the first month of life, at least three reflexes become more strongly inhibited on the right rather than the left side. Thus, during the transition from reflexive to volitional behavior, Liederman (Chapter 16, this volume) suggests that there may be a surplus of movements on the left side that have been mistaken for left preference (e.g., McDonnell et al., in press).

The three reflexes that seem to be stronger on the left rather than right side during early infancy are the Babinski, Darwinian, and ATNR. For example, Tournay (1924, cited in Subirana, 1964, p. 219) observed that the Babinski reflex disappeared earlier from the right rather than the left leg in a child who became right-handed. Similarly, the Darwinian reflex (reflex grasping for the purposes of bodily support by a single hand) begins to be inhibited earlier on the right rather than left side during weeks 6–10 (McGraw, 1969, p. 28, Figure 3). Similarly, Liederman and Coryell (1981) demonstrated that head-turns to the left were more effective in eliciting the ATNR than turns to the right in 6–10-week-old infants whose head-turning preference was rightward.

Liederman (in preparation) has just completed an analysis of data from 86 full term newborn infants. Leg movements were observed when children spontaneously turned their heads to the left versus right side. In neonates, the ATNR occurs almost exclusively in the legs (Pollack, 1960). The incidence of the ATNR during right- versus left-head-turns did not differ significantly even when the degree of head turn was used as a covariate.

Since an asymmetry in the incidence of the ATNR was seen at 6 weeks but not at birth, this suggests two possible interpretations. The first is that some kind of higher-order inhibitory center is becoming functional sooner on the left than the right side of the brain. According to this interpretation, encephalization of function, at least for motor control, proceeds faster on the left side of the brain. A second interpretation is that once higher-order inhibition develops, it is imposed with greater strength on right- rather than left-sided movements. A longitudinal study conducted from birth to 12 weeks would be necessary to answer this question. Such a study is underway.

MEDIAL VERSUS LATERAL MOTOR SYSTEMS

There are two fundamental motor systems: a medial system that influences trunk and proximal extremity musculature and a lateral system that influences distal extremity musculature (Brinkman & Kuypers, 1973). Movements deriving from these respective systems could be responsible for fluctuations in lateral preference. First, it is possible that, within an individual, the medial and lateral motor systems can be controlled by different sides of the brain. The relative independence of these two systems is demonstrated by (a) the lack of correlation between proximal and distal motor ability during infancy (Loria, 1980; Touwen, 1976) and (b) the fact that there can be sparing of the more sophisticated distal system with little or no proximal system recovery (Loria, 1980). Thus, if these two systems develop relatively independently, lateralization of control may occur independently.

A second possibility is that, during early infancy, before independent use of the fingers, reaching may involve whole-arm movements that can be controlled by the ipsilaterally organized proximal system. Thus, if a child had motor control biased toward control systems on the left side of the brain, that child might readily show preference for reaching with the ipsilateral (i.e., left) arm. The result would be a period of left-sided preference reliably followed by right-handed preference for fine motor coordination tasks later in development. This precise pattern has in fact been reported by McDonnell *et al.* (in press), although this is not the way that they interpereted their results.

A SHIFT FROM EXTRACALLOSAL TO CALLOSAL
INTERHEMISPHERIC COMMUNICATION

Data will now be reviewed that suggests that, as the primary mechanism of interhemispheric interaction shifts from extracallosal to callosal
pathways, there may be a change in the degree to which the hands can
truly specialize. Specifically, two phenomena may be related to callosal
maturation. First, one hand becomes preferred during reaching for both
contralateral and ipsilateral objects. Second, it becomes possible to ex-
ecute complex bimanual movements that require differential movement
of the right and left hands.

At birth, the corpus callosum is not myelinated, and it is thought to be
nonfunctional (the infant is somewhat similar to an adult whose corpus
callosum has been severed; Gazzaniga, 1970). Although this may be an
extreme view, changes in myelinization, as well as structural development of the corpus callosum, continue well past early childhood (Hewitt,
1962). Hence the shift from interhemispheric communication that is primarily extracallosal, to interhemispheric communication that is primarily
callosal, probably does not occur at one point in time.

In the absence of the corpus callosum, there are two distinct mechanisms by which information given to one hand may be made accessible to
the other hand. An intrahemispheric mechanism involves communication of information within a hemisphere, between the crossed (contralateral) and uncrossed (ipsilateral) pathways from opposing limbs
(Dennis, 1976). Thus it is Dennis's (1976) contention that it is not until the
corpus callosum becomes functional that these ipsilateral pathways are
inhibited. A second means of extracallosal interhemispheric communication is via the corpora quadragemina and the brainstem reticular formation (Gazzaniga, 1970).

Crossing the body midline appears to depend on the corpus callosum.
Hurwitz (1971) reports that split-brain patients use their left hand to point
to locations on their left side and their right hand for the right side rather
than reaching across the body midline, which is the typical adult response. Thus, split-brain subjects show ambilateral rather than contralateral reaching.

Extending the hand across the body midline is seen in infants only after
visually directed reaching in front of the ipsilateral shoulder and to the
body midline has been achieved (Provine & Westerman, 1979). The majority of infants demonstrate contralateral reaching about 5 months of age. As
contralateral reaching emerges, the child begins to show a bilateral approach to visually guided reaching (Gesell & Ames, 1947). This further
supports the notion that there may be a milestone in development of
interhemispheric communication at that age. (It should be noted, however, that spontaneous crossing of the body midline continues to develop
through childhood, as has been demonstrated by recent research with

children aged 4–8 years, and may bear some relationship to degree of hand preference [Cermak, Quintero, & Cohen, 1980]).

This shift from ambilateral to contralateral reaching has two implications for lateral asymmetry. First, inhibition of ipsilateral reaches permits hand preferences to occur: Now the child can use the preferred hand without respect to the side of stimulation. Second, it suggests that a more general mechanism may become operative such that the side of the brain that is dominant for a particular function is able to inhibit the opposite side from participating.

The second important transition, the beginning of asymmetric bimanual movement, emerges somewhat after the onset of contralateral reaching. Such movement first surfaces during reaching (Bresson, Maury, Pieraut-Le Bonniec, & de Schonen, 1977) when the child uses the left hand to localize an object while the right hand reaches for it. Again, there is good reason to think that asymmetric bimanual movement is dependent on the functioning of the corpus callosum. Zaidel and Sperry (1972) reported that rapid movements of the arms or asymmetrical simultaneous movements are quite deficient in commissurotomy patients, even though they can perform symmetrical bimanual movements

OTHER CANDIDATES FOR SYSTEMS THAT MAY BE INDEPENDENTLY LATERALIZED

It is easy to proliferate possibilities for other neurobehavioral systems that may be independently lateralized, or lateralized to different degrees. For example, the system employed during skill acquisition may differ from that underlying automatic execution of that skill. Similarly, ballistic movements that involve little kinesthetic feedback may involve a separate mechanism from movements requiring constant feedback from the periphery. Flexion movements may be different from extension movements, and adductive movements may differ from abductive ones. One system may be preferred for strength, a different one for speed, and a third for accuracy. The number of separate dimensions for hand preference abound. The important point is that there are many conjoint forces operating to select the left side of the brain for the control of a system of movement, but, as will be documented in the next sections, there are also forces operating to permit control of a particular system to lateralize differently.

Environmental Factors That Can Cause Discontinuities in the Development of Lateral Preference

CULTURAL PRESSURE

Some of the discontinuities in the development of hand preference and inconsistencies of hand preference may be caused by left-preferenced individuals being forced to shift to right-hand use for certain activities. There is undoubtedly societal pressure in favor of right-hand preference. This is exerted by means of handling practices during infancy, parental modeling of manual behaviors, provision of tools suited to right-hand use, and social disapproval of left handedness. Thus, in China, where left handedness is strongly discouraged, activities such as eating and writing are performed with the right hand by persons who otherwise prefer the left hand for less-socialized activities (Teng, Lee, Yang, & Chang, 1976).

NEURAL INSULT

Hand preference can change in response to neural insult. For example, as compared with 10% in the general population, the incidence of left handedness averages 20% within populations of mental retardates (Gordon, 1920; Silva & Satz, 1979) and epileptics (Bolin, 1953). Indeed, the frequency of left handedness increases with degree of retardation.

The effect of neural insult on the development of hand preference may depend on the timing, the locus, and the extent of the lesion. There is a consensus that perinatal damage has the greatest effect, but the parameters of when control of the preferred hand stays in the left hemisphere or shifts to the right are not known. One kind of perinatal damage, that which is relatively restricted to the left rather than right hemisphere, may permanently switch control of the preferred hand to the right side of the brain. Thus, as Satz (1972, 1973) points out, left-hemisphere lesions occur in 75% of left-handed but only 41% of right-handed temporal lobe epileptics. Similarly, Silva and Satz (1979) examined the abnormal EEGs of a group of mental retardates. The incidence of left handedness was highest for subjects with purely unilateral lesions and lesions that were bilateral but asymmetric.

A second kind of damage, that which is limited to the motor strip within the left hemisphere, may cause a switch from right- to left-hand preference that is delayed until the second or third year of life (Bakan, Dibb, & Reed, 1973). Dominance would switch to the left hand–right hemisphere when the child discovers that the right hand is deficient for fine motor coordination. Initial head-turning biases, which are generated at a subcortical level, would not be affected.

A third kind of perinatal damage, that which is mild, may cause a temporary disruption of function within the more vulnerable left hemisphere (see pages 85–86 for a review). Minor episodes of oxygen deprivation during labor and delivery may shift function, temporarily, to the intact right hemisphere and induce a transient leftward behavioral bias.

A recent study is compatible with this interpretation. Liederman and Coryell (1982) found that the spontaneous head turns of infants with a history of birth complications were rightward-biased significantly less often than those of infants without a history of birth complications. This was particularly clear in the group of infants who would have been expected to be predominantly right-sided because of the dextrality of their parents. In the latter subgroup, rightward biases were observed in most infants without a history of perinatal trauma (64%), but in very few children with a history of trauma (16%).

Yet there is no reason to think that many of these children with perinatal complications will become left-handed. They were basically healthy infants. None had been treated in intensive care facilities. Thus, even though minimal birth complications may have no permanent effect on neurological organization, they may still serve to temporarily depress functioning of the left side of the brain and may transiently interfere with rightward-biased turning.

What requires special explanation is a switch to right hemisphere–left hand control when the right hemisphere is as damaged as the left. Seventy-eight percent of Silva and Satz's (1979) sample of mental retardates had symmetrical EEG disturbances. Despite the symmetry of the lesion, the incidence of left handedness was twice that of the general population. One possible explanation for this finding is that, when damage is extensive enough, control of the hand, to the extent that it recovers, is governed by either hemisphere with an equal probability.

Organismic Factors That Can Influence the Probability of a Shift in Lateral Preference

LEFT-HEMISPHERE VULNERABILITY TO HYPOXIC INSULT

A shift of lateral preference from right to left may be made more probable by the special vulnerability of the left side of the brain to hypoxic insult. Braun and Myers (1975) induced oxygen deficiency in monkeys and found that when only one hemisphere was affected, it was always the left hemisphere. Similarly, Hood and Perlstein (1955) and Eastman, Kohl, Marsel, and Kavaler (1962) used the incidence of right-to-left hemiplegia to make inferences about side of brain damage. Full term infants developed right hemiplegia twice as often as left hemiplegia, reflecting a higher incidence of left hemispheric lesions. Annett (1973) reports a 4:1 ratio of right-to-left hemiplegia in her sample of children.

The vulnerability of the left hemisphere may be due to its blood supply. The left arterial tree is less direct and delivers a smaller volume of blood than the right arterial tree (Braun & Walton, 1969; Carmon & Gambos, 1970). Others attribute the vulnerability of the left hemisphere to its high metabolic requirements (Bakan *et al.*, 1973) or to mechanical factors during labor and delivery. Hood and Perlstein (1955) noted that the high ratio of right-to-left hemiplegics occurred in populations of full term infants, but not in preterm infants. They suggested that the predominance of left-sided damage was due to the more common left occiput anterior (LOA) head position. In this position, the left hemisphere could be pressed by the left sacral promontory. Preterm infants would be protected from this trauma because of their small heads.

The predominance of left-hemisphere lesions cannot be solely a consequence of the high incidence of births delivered from an LOA position. Churchill (1966) reported that the left hemisphere is most vulnerable when the occiput is right rather than left. Churchill's cases consisted primarily of patients with unilateral focal motor epilepsy or hemiplegic hemiepilepsy. A left-hemisphere focus was associated with a right occiput anterior (ROA) position in 67% of the cases; a right-hemisphere focus was associated with an LOA position in 85% of the cases. Despite the lower proportion of children born from an ROA rather than LOA position, the majority of lesions were left-sided. This suggests that the left hemisphere is inherently more vulnerable to damage than the right hemisphere.

FLUCTUATIONS IN THE RATE OF GROWTH OF THE RIGHT VERSUS LEFT HEMISPHERE

If one agrees that what is lateralized at birth is the side of the brain that will control language production (Kinsbourne & Hiscock, 1976), it remains possible that other motor asymmetries may be free to be controlled by either hemisphere. Indeed, motor asymmetries may fluctuate because of differential growth spurts in the left and right hemispheres. As one side of the brain undergoes a growth spurt, that side may be able to acquire a skill more thoroughly or more quickly (Molfese & Schmidt, 1978). Thus, during periods when the right hemisphere is more developed than the left, there may be periods of left-hand preference or dominance.

There is a growing literature that has been taken to indicate that maturation of the left and right sides of the brain is asynchronous, but there is little consensus as to when each side is growing fastest. For example, Chi, Dooling, and Giles (1977) studies the rate of development of cortical gyri during gestation. Several language and motor areas developed 1 to 2 weeks earlier on the right side than on the left.

Use of EEG patterns as an index of maturity have led to conflicting conclusions. Flashing lights induce right-sided photic driving in the majority of infants, whereas in adults this response is bilateral (Crowell, Jones, Kapunai, and Nakawaga, 1973). Crowell *et al.* interpret this unilateral cortical activity as an index of early right hemispheric cerebral dominance. An alternative explanation is that the right hemisphere is more susceptible to photic driving than the left hemisphere, and that photic driving may be restricted to the right hemisphere in infants because of underdevelopment of commissural structures that would permit this activation to spread to the contralateral side.

Right-hemisphere precocity in later childhood has also been argued for on the basis of electrophysiological disturbances. Rey, Pond, and Evans (1949) found that when cases of "acquired" epilepsy were eliminated, the onset of left-sided temporal dysfunction in males was 7 years later than that for right-sided dysfunction, and the onset of right-sided dysfunction was 16 months later in females. Since the EEG abnormalities were typical of younger children, and since female brains are generally known to mature faster than male brains, Rey *et al.* (1949) interpreted their data as indicative of right hemispheric precocity.

Taylor (1969) studied patients that Rey *et al.* had eliminated from their survey (i.e., those with acquired rather than congenital lesions) and reported that, within the first 2 years of life, status epilepticus was most often associated with damage to the left temporal lobe of males. He argued that since vulnerability to febrile convulsions is correlated with cerebral immaturity, the left temporal lobe of a male must mature not only later than the right, but also later than either temporal lobe of a female.

Neither set of data just described require the conclusion that the right hemisphere develops more rapidly than the left hemisphere. Greater left-hemisphere vulnerability for either epilepsy or febrile convulsions could reflect a general vulnerability to insult rather than immaturity (see pages 85–86).

Indeed, some electrophysiological indices have been taken as evidence for left hemispheric precocity. For example, Fabiani and Favella (1975) recorded the EEG of full term infants during quiet sleep. Two phenomena were taken as signs of greater left hemispheric maturity: Spindle amplitudes were larger on the left than the right side, whereas the amplitude of slow activity was larger on the right side.

The important point for our purposes is that there may be growth spurts on the left versus right sides of the brain for different regions at different times. These may be accompanied by lateral shifts in motor control. This would be a fertile area for future research. For example, Geschwind has suggested that left-hemisphere growth may be slowed by high levels of testosterone and/or hypersensitivity to testosterone during fetal development (in Marx, 1982). Geschwind sees this as linked to the high incidence of left handedness in males. A 1983 study by Netley and Rovet is compatible with this notion. They observed 47 XXY males and compared them to an age-matched control group. The authors note that XXY males develop even slower than normal males, as indicated by bone age and rates of mitotic cell division. The incidence of left handedness in this slow-maturation population was twice that in the control group.

GENERAL RATE OF MATURATION

Taylor and Ounsted (1972) have suggested that the slower the nervous system develops, the more vulnerable it is to environmental influence.

Overall rate of neural development could therefore have implications for variability in motor asymmetries and could account for differences between the sexes. It is well known that the male nervous system develops more slowly than the female's. Thus, the more immature (male) brain as compared to the more mature (female) brain would be more vulnerable to brain damage, and it would be affected more by environmental variables. This perspective would lead to two specific predictions: First, greater vulnerability to damage in males as compared to females would result in a higher incidence of pathological left preference in males. Second, greater vulnerability to environmental influence during early development would result in greater variability across measures of lateral preference in young males than in young females. Each of these predictions is confirmed by empirical data (cf. McGlone, 1980).

STATE AND VARIABILITY OF STATE

State of arousal can affect the direction and extent to which behavior is lateralized. During infancy, the degree of rightward bias covaries with alertness (Michel & Goodwin, 1979) and degree of irritability (Liederman & Kinsbourne, 1980a; Reiser, Yonas, & Wikner, 1976). In the last study, a noxious olfactory stimulus was presented to either the left or right nostril. Although the neonates usually withdrew from the source of stimulation, their localization errors revealed a consistent rightward response bias. As agitation increased, the rightward response bias increased.

Hence, to the extent that state varies, lateral bias may vary. This could explain some of the exceptional variability that occurs in early infancy and may contribute toward the finding that children who are in poor physiological condition around the time of birth tend not to have a lateral preference (Fox & Lewis, 1982; Liederman & Coryell, 1981).

Note that even in adults, extreme state changes are associated with alterations in hand preference. Flor-Henry (1979) reviews cases in which depression interfered with left-hand dexterity and mania interfered with right-hand dexterity. For example, a patient who was 100% right-handed when asymptomatic, shifted to a 100% left-hand preference during manic episodes. Thus, fluctuations of state may change the functional organization of the brain and alter dominance relationships, resulting in instability of laterality measures across time.

Conclusions

This chapter has attempted to explain a central paradox in the developmental literature: that the proportion of children who are rightward-biased for a particular behavior increases only slightly across development, yet individual profiles reveal considerable inconsistency in lateral preference from one observation to another. The explanation for this inconsistent developmental profile is that lateral asymmetries can occur relatively independently within several systems. There are many factors that promote dextrality, but lateral preference, itself, is not mediated by a "unitary" system. Thus, any apparent unity in lateralization of motor behaviors is an epiphenomenon: Most behavior will be dominated by the left hemisphere–right hand—but this is due to the conjoint influence of many factors that themselves can operate relatively independently, rather than a single mechanism that reveals itself over time.

Acknowledgments

I wish to thank Rhoda Goodwin and Jane Coryell for providing me with access to their data.

References

Annett, M. (1967). The binomial distribution of right, mixed, and left handedness. *Quarterly Journal of Experimental Psychology* 19, 327–333.

Annett, M. (1973). Laterality of childhood hemiplegia and the growth of speech and intelligence. *Cortex, 9,* 4–33.

Annett, M. (1978). Genetic and non-genetic influences on handedness. *Behavior Genetics 8,* 227–249.

Bakan, P., Dibb, G., Reed, P. (1973). Handedness and birth stress. *Neuropsychologia 11,* 363–366.

Bolin, B. J. (1953). Left handedness and stuttering as signs diagnostic of epileptics. *Journal of Mental Science 99,* 483–488.

Braun, H. W., & Myers, R. E. (1975). Central nervous system findings in the newborn monkey following severe *in utero* partial asphyxia. *Neurology 25,* 327–338.

Braun, R., & Walton, J. (1969). *Brains' diseases of the nervous system* (7th ed.). London and New York: Oxford Univ. Press.

Bresson, F., Maury, L., Pieraut-Le Bonniec, G., & de Schonen, S. (1977). Organization and lateralization of reaching in infants: An instance of asymmetric functions in hands collaboration. *Neuropsychologia 15,* 311–320.

Brinkman, J., & Kuypers, H. (1973). Cerebral control of contralateral and ipsilateral arm, hand, and finger movements in the split-brain rhesus monkey. *Brain 96,* 653–674.

Bruning, J., & Kintz, B. L. (1968). *Computational handbook of statistics.* Glenview, Illinois: Scott, Foresman.

Carmon, A., & Gambos, G. (1970). A physiological and vascular correlate of hand preference: Possible implication with respect to hemisphere cerebral dominance. *Neuropsychologia 119,* 128.

Cermak, S. A., Quintero, E. J., & Cohen, P. M. (1980). Developmental age trends in crossing the body midline in normal children. *American Journal of Occupational Therapy 34,* 313–319.

Černáček, J., & Podivinský, F. (1971). Ontogenesis of handedness and somatosensory cortical response. *Neuropsychologia 9,* 219–232.

Chi, J. G., Dooling, E. C., & Giles, F. H. (1977). Left–right asymmetries of the temporal speech area of the human fetus. *Annals of Neurology 1,* 346–348.

Churchill, J. (1966). On the origin of focal motor epilepsy. Neurology 16, 49–58.

Churchill, J., Igna, E., & Senf, R. (1962). The association of position at birth and handedness. Pediatrics 29, 307–309.

Cobb, K., Goodwin, R., & Saelens, E. (1966). Spontaneous hand positions of newborn infants. The Journal of Genetic Psychology 108, 225–237.

Coren, S., & Porac, C. (1977). Fifty centuries of right-handedness: The historical record. Science 198, 631–632.

Coren, S., Porac, C., & Duncan, P. (1981). Lateral preference in preschool children and young adults. Child Development 52, 443–450.

Coryell, J., & Michel, G. (1978). How supine postural preferences of infants can contribute toward the development of handedness. Infant Behavior and Development 1, 245–257.

Crowell, D. H., Jones, R. H., Kapunai, L. E., & Nakawaga, J. (1973). Unilateral cortical activity in newborns—An early index of cerebral dominance? Science 180, 205–208.

Dennis, M. (1976). Impaired sensory and motor differentiation with corpus callosum agenesis: A lack of callosal inhibition during ontogeny? Neuropsychologia 14, 455–469.

DiFranco, D., Muir, D. W., & Dodwell, P. (1978). Reaching in very young infants. Perception 7, 385–392.

Eastman, N. J., Kohl, S. G., Marsel, J. E., & Kavaler, F. (1962). The obstetrical background of 753 cases of cerebral palsy. Obstetrics, Gynecology Survey 17, 459–500.

Fabiani, D., & Favella, A. (1975). Proceedings: Asymmetries of EEG and cerebral dominance. Considerations on sleep records in babies. Electroencephalography and Clinical Neurophysiology 39, 532.

Fleishman, E. A. (1972). On the relation between abilities, learning, and human performance. American Psychologist 27, 1017–1032.

Flor-Henry, P. (1979). Laterality, shifts of cerebral dominance, sinistrality and psychosis. In J. Gruzelier & P. Flor-Henry (Eds.), Hemisphere asymmetries of function in psychopathology. Elsevier: North Holland Biomedical.

Fox, N., & Lewis, M. (1982). Motor asymmetries in preterm infants: Effects of prematurity and illness. Developmental Psychobiology 15, 19–23.

Gazzaniga, M. S. (1970). The bisected brain. New York: Appleton-Century-Crofts.

Gesell, A., & Amatruda, C. (1967). Developmental diagnoses (3rd ed.). New York: Harper.

Gesell, A., & Ames, L. B. (1947). The development of handedness. Journal of Genetic Psychology 70, 155–175.

Goodwin, R. S., & Michel, G. F. (1981). Head orientation position during birth and in infant neonatal period, and hand preference at nineteen weeks. Child Development 52, 819–826.

Gordon, H. (1920). Left handedness and mirror writing especially among defective children. Brain 43, 313–368.

Hammer, M., & Turkewitz, G. (1974). A sensory basis for lateral difference in the newborn infant's response to somesthetic stimulation. Journal of Experimental Child Psychology 18, 304–312.

Harris, P., & MacFarlane, A. (1974). The growth of the effective visual field from birth to seven weeks. Journal of Experimental Child Psychology 18, 340–349.

Hécaen, H., & de Ajuriaguerra, J. (1964). Left handedness. New York: Grune & Stratton.

Heilman, K. M. (1979). The neuropsychological basis of skilled movement in man. In H. S. Gazzaniga (Ed.), Handbook of behavioral neurobiology (Vol. 3). New York: Plenum.

Hewitt, W. (1962). The development of the corpus callosum. Journal of Anatomy 96, 355–358.

Hicks, R. E. (1978). On the homogeneity of human handedness. The Behavioral and Brain Sciences 2, 299–300.

Hicks, R. E., & Kinsbourne, M. (1977). On the genesis of human handedness: A review. Journal of Motor Behavior 8, 257–266.

Hood, P. N., & Perlstein, M. A. (1955). Infantile spastic hemiplegia, II. Laterality of involvement. *Journal of Physiological Medicine 34*, 457–466.

Hurwitz, L. J. (1971). Evidence for restitution of function and development of new function in cases of brain bisection. *Cortex 7*, 401–409.

Ingram, D. (1975). Motor asymmetries in young children. *Neuropsychologia 13*, 95–102.

Kinsbourne, M., & Hiscock, M. (1976). Does cerebral dominance develop? In S. Segalowitz & F. A. Gruber (Eds.), *Language development and neurological theory*. New York: Academic Press.

Liederman, J. (1977). *Lateral head-turning asymmetries in human neonates: Hereditary, organismic, and environmental influences*. Unpublished doctoral dissertation, University of Rochester, New York.

Liederman, J. The incidence of head turning asymmetry and reflex asymmetry in newborn infants. Manuscript in preparation.

Liederman, J., & Coryell, J. (1981). How right-hand preference may be facilitated by rightward turning biases during infancy. *Developmental Psychobiology 145*, 439–450.

Liederman, J., & Coryell, J. (1982). The origin of left hand preference: Pathological and nonpathological influences. *Neuropsychologia, 20*(6), 721–725.

Liederman, J., & Kinsbourne, M. (1980a). The mechanism of neonatal rightward turning bias: A sensory or motor asymmetry? *Infant Behavior and Development 3*, 223–238.

Liederman, J., & Kinsbourne, M. (1980b). Rightward bias in neonates depends upon parental right-handedness. *Neuropsychologia 18*, 579–584.

Liederman, J., & Kinsbourne, M. (1980c). Rightward turning biases in neonates reflect a single neural asymmetry in motor programming. *Infant Behavior and Development 3*, 245–251.

Loria, C. (1980). Relationship of proximal and distal function in motor development. *Physical Therapy 60*, 167–172.

McDonnell, P. (1979). Patterns of eye–hand coordination in the first year of life. *Canadian Journal of Psychology 33*, 253–267.

McDonnell, P., Anderson, V. E. S., & Abraham, A. (in press). Asymmetry and orientation of arm movements in 3- to 8-week-old infants. *Infant Behavior and Development*.

McGlone, J. (1980). Sex differences in human brain asymmetry: A critical survey. *The Behavioral and Brain Sciences 3*, 215–263.

McGraw, M. B. (1969). *The neuromuscular maturation of the human infant*. New York: Hafner.

Marx, J. L. (1982). Research news: Autoimmunity in left-handers. *Science 217*, 141–144.

Michel, G. (1981). Right-handedness: A consequence of infant supine head orientation preference? *Science 212*, 685–687.

Michel, G., & Goodwin, R. (1979). Intrauterine birth position predicts newborn supine head position preferences. *Infant Behavior and Development 2*, 29–38.

Molfese, D. L., & Schmidt, A. L. (1978). Human laterality: Is it unidimensional? *The Behavior and Brain Sciences 2*, 307–308.

Moreau, T., Helfgott, E., Weinstein, R., & Milner, P. (1978). Lateral differences in habituation of ipsilateral head-turning to repeated tactile stimulation in the human newborn. *Perceptual and Motor Skills 46*,427–436.

Netley, C., & Rovet, J. (1983). *Handedness in 47 XXY males*. Manuscript submitted.

Peters, M., & Petrie, B. F. (1979). Functional asymmetries in the stepping reflex of human neonates. *Canadian Journal of Psychology 33*, 198–200.

Pollack, S. L. (1960). The grasp response in the neonate: Its characteristics and interaction with the tonic neck reflex. *Archives of Neurology 3*, 574–581.

Provine, R. R., & Westerman, J. A. (1979). Crossing the midline: Limits of early eye–hand behavior. *Child Development 50*, 437–441.

Reiser, J., Yonas, A., & Wikner, K. (1976). Radial localization of odors by human newborns. *Child Development 47*, 856–859.

Rey, J., Pond, D., & Evans, C. (1949). Clinical and electroencephalographic studies of temporal lobe function. *EEG Society Proceedings 152,* 891–904.

Saling, M. (1979). Lateral differentiation of the neonatal head turning response: A replication. *Journal of Genetic Psychology 135,* 307–308.

Satz, P. (1972). Pathological left-handedness: An explanatory model. *Cortex 8,* 121–135.

Satz, P. (1973). Left-handedness and early brain insult: An explanation. *Neuropsychologia 11,* 115–117.

Seth, G. (1973). Eye–hand coordination and "handedness": A developmental study of visuomotor behaviour in infants. *British Journal of Educational Psychology 43,* 35–49.

Silva, D., & Satz, P. (1979). Pathological left-handedness: Evaluation of a model. *Brain and Language 7,* 8–16.

Siqueland, E. R., & Lipsitt, L. P. (1966). Conditioned head turning in human newborns. *Journal of Experimental Child Psychology 4,* 356–377.

Sorrell, W. (1967). *The story of the human hand.* Indianapolis, Indiana: Bobbs-Merrill.

Steingruber, H. J. (1975). Handedness as a function of test complexity. *Perceptual and Motor Skills 40,* 263–266.

Subirana, A. (1964). The relationship between handedness and language function. *International Journal of Neurology 4,* 215–234.

Taylor, D. (1969). Differential rates of cerebral maturation between sexes and between hemispheres. *Lancet 2,* 140–142.

Taylor, D., & Ounsted, C. (1972). The nature of gender differences explored through ontogenetic analyses of sex ratios in disease. In C. Ounsted & D. Taylor (Eds.), *Gender differences: Their ontogeny and significance.* Edinburgh: Churchill Livingstone.

Teng, E. L., Lee, P., Yang, K., & Chang, P. (1976). Handedness in a Chinese population: Biological, social, and pathological factors. *Science 193,* 1148–1150.

Touwen, B. (1976). Neurological development in infancy. 38–45. *Clinics in Developmental Medicine 58,* London: S.I.M.P. with Hiveniann Medical.

Turkewitz, G. (1980). Mechanisms of a neonatal rightward turning bias: A reply to Liederman and Kinsbourne. *Infant Behavior and Development 3,* 239–244.

Turkewitz, G., Birch, H., Moreau, T., Levy, L., & Cornwell, H. (1966). Effect of intensity of auditory stimulation on directional eye movements in the human newborn. *Animal Behaviour 14,* 93–101.

Turkewitz, G., & Creighton, S. (1974). Changes in lateral differentiation of head posture in the human neonate. *Developmental Psychobiology 8,* 85–89.

Turkewitz, G., Gordon, E., & Birch, H. (1965). Head turning in the human neonate: Spontaneous patterns. *Journal of Genetic Psychology 107,* 143–158.

Turkewitz, G., Moreau, T., Birch, H., Herbert, G., & Crystal, D. (1967). Relationship between prior head position and lateral differences in responsiveness to somesthetic stimulation in the human neonate. *Journal of Experimental Child Psychology 5,* 548–561.

Viviani, J., Turkewitz, G., & Karp, E. (1978). A relationship between laterality of functioning at 2 days and at 7 years of age. *Psychonomic Science 12,* 189–192.

Weiffenbach, J. M. (1972). Discrete elicited movements of the newborn's tongue. In J. F. Bosma (Ed.), *Third symposium on oral sensation and perception.* Springfield, Illinois: Thomas.

Zaidel, D., & Sperry, R. W. (1972). Some long-term motor effect of cerebral commissurotomy in man. *Neuropsychologia 15,* 193–204.

5

Hemispheric Specialization
in Infancy

DENNIS L. MOLFESE
VICTORIA J. MOLFESE

Introduction

Evidence has accumulated rapidly in recent years to support the notion that hemispheric specialization for language functions begins in early infancy. Support for this view comes from a variety of studies employing different methodologies, including anatomical procedures, clinical case studies, dichotic listening techniques, and evoked potential electrophysiology. It now seems clear that the popular notion of hemisphere equipotentiality during infancy is not consistent with the accumulating evidence.

The equipotentiality theory, according to Lenneberg (1967), holds that the two hemispheres of the brain are equipotential for language during the first 2 years of life. Damage to either hemisphere during this time was thought to result in little or no long-lasting effects on the acquisition of language. Support for this view was based, in part, on research by Basser (1962). Lenneberg (1967) summarized Basser's work as demonstrating that "in roughly half of the children with brain lesions sustained during the first two years of life, the onset of speech development is somewhat delayed; however, the other half of this population begins to speak at the usual time. This distribution is the same for children with left hemisphere lesions as with right ones [p. 151]." According to Lenneberg, hemispheric specialization for language developed during later childhood could take several forms: (a) dominance of functioning in which the right hemisphere becomes decreasingly involved in language functions in favor of the left hemisphere; or (b) in the event that damage occurs in either hemi-

MANUAL SPECIALIZATION
AND THE DEVELOPING BRAIN

sphere, language functions develop normally in the undamaged hemisphere, whether it be left or right.

Research published since Lenneberg's writings has strongly challenged the notion of equipotentiality. One line of evidence arose from anatomical studies conducted in several different laboratories. Such work reported asymmetrical anatomical structures in areas thought to be involved in language functioning. Early work by Geschwind and Levitsky (1968) reported that the left-hemisphere temporal planum in adults is markedly larger than that in the right. Since this region corresponds approximately to the region called Wernicke's area, which is thought to mediate language functions, such anatomical asymmetries were interpreted as support for the functional asymmetry findings reported in behavioral research. Later work by Wada (1969; Wada, Clarke, & Hamm, 1975) examined the anatomical asymmetries in the brains of infants. Results of studies on over 100 infant brains (most between 29 gestational weeks to 2-months-old; mean: 48 gestational weeks) and 100 adult brains showed anatomical asymmetries in the infants that were similar to those found in the adults. In particular, the left temporal planum was found to be larger than the right in most of the infant and adult brains studied. These findings were later confirmed by Teszner, Tzavaras, Gruner, and Hécaen (1972) and Witelson and Pallie (1973). Wada et al. (1975) concluded that "the human brain possesses a predetermined morphological and functional capacity for the development of lateralized hemispheric functions for speech and language [p. 245]."

Evidence of Hemispheric Specialization

Clinical Populations

The presence of early anatomical asymmetries do not in themselves indicate that the two hemispheres are not equipotential for language processing, nor do they indicate that asymmetrical functioning is present at birth or soon after. Such evidence has been supplied from other lines of research. Researchers investigating the effect of cerebral damage in infancy and early childhood added new information. Contrary to the predictions of equipotentiality that cerebral damage in infancy to either hemisphere does not disrupt language acquisition and cognitive functioning, many researchers found evidence of disruption in young children who experienced cerebral damage in early infancy. For example, Annett (1973) found that children who experienced cerebral damage in either hemisphere prior to 13 months of age showed language impairments, although left-damaged children were more often impaired than those with right damage. A study by Dennis (1977) reports the results of studies with a group of three children who had undergone hemidecortication in early infancy (1 month–4.5 months). The one right-hemidecorticate child was more language proficient than the two left-hemidecorticates, who, in turn, were more proficient at visuospatial abilities.

Two studies (Dennis & Kohn, 1975; Kohn & Dennis, 1974) were conducted on adults who had undergone hemidecortication in late childhood, although their symptoms were noted in infancy. Although all subjects tested had similar verbal IQ scores, their language and cognitive abilities were related to the laterality of the lesion. Dennis and Kohn (1975) studied nine adults who had undergone hemidecortication in childhood (mean: 9.1 years for right hemicorticates; 11.5 for left hemidecorticates). Adults with only an intact left hemisphere were found to perform better and with shorter latencies on some language tasks (e.g., passive negative sentences) relative to adults with only a right hemisphere. Kohn and Dennis (1974) studied visuospatial abilities in a group of four adults who had undergone hemidecortication (mean age: 12.2 for right hemidecorticates; 14.0 for left hemidecorticates). They found that adults with only a right hemisphere evidence more age-appropriate visuospatial abilities than did adults with only a left hemisphere.

Each of the clinical case studies demonstrates that the two hemispheres are not equipotential for the acquisition of cognitive abilities after cerebral damage in infancy. The results show that, whereas either hemisphere can develop some level of cognitive competency, language functions are poorer in subjects with only a right hemisphere, whereas visuospatial abilities are affected in subjects with only a left hemisphere. These deficits are found even in children who have undergone hemidecortication in early infancy. There appear to be clear limits to cognitive–linguistic development when there is atypical lateralization.

Normal Populations

Early attempts to assess asymmetrical functioning in early infancy using normal samples have employed a variety of methodologies. Molfese (1972; Molfese, Freeman, & Palermo, 1975) used auditory evoked-potential response recording procedures to test for the presence of hemisphere differences. The subjects were infants 1 week–10 months (mean: 5.8 months), children 4–11 years old (mean = 6.0 years), and adults 23–29 years of age (mean = 25.9 years). Such techniques involve recording the auditory evoked response (AER, a temporally stable, reliable waveform that can be recorded at the scalp) in response to a series of sounds. Such waveforms have been found to be generated by mechanisms within the brain in response to specific external stimuli (Regan, 1972). Molfese recorded AERs generated over the left and right scalp regions in response to a series of speech syllables ([ba] and [dæ]), monosyllable words ([bɔi] and [dɔg]), a C-major piano chord, and a white-noise burst. Differences in the amplitudes of the auditory evoked responses from the left and right hemispheres were found at each age level, even in the young infants. The largest AER amplitude to speech stimuli occurred in the left hemisphere, whereas greater amplitude responses to the nonspeech stimuli occurred in the right hemisphere.

Other researchers employing these techniques have reported similar asymmetrical responding in young infants. Wada and Davis (1977) examined the AERs of 16 infants aged 2–10 weeks (mean: 5 weeks) to click and flash stimuli. These researchers sought to determine the comparability of infant responses to those of adults, who show greater left-hemisphere responsiveness to click stimuli and greater right-hemisphere responsiveness to flash stimuli. The results showed that 13 of the infants responded to click stimuli and 10 of the infants responded to flash stimuli in a lateralized manner similar to that found in adults.

Barnet, de Sotillo, and Campos (1974) also recorded AERs from infants in response to click stimuli as well as to speech stimuli (the infants' names). The subjects were normal and malnourished infants under 1 year of age. Only the normal infants showed larger amplitude left-hemisphere than right-hemisphere AERs to the speech stimuli. The malnourished infants failed to show greater left-hemisphere AER activity to the speech stimuli even after treatment for malnutrition. Interestingly, and contrary to the results reported by Wada and Davis (1977), both groups of infants showed greater AERs to the click stimuli in the right hemisphere. The cause of the discrepant findings of AERs to click stimuli is not clear, although the regions from which the recordings were made differed; Wada and Davis (1977) recorded from occipital and temporal regions, whereas Barnet *et al.* (1974) recorded from the parietal region. The use of different recording sites might, in part, account for such differences.

Three studies have employed the dichotic listening paradigm to examine hemisphere differences in responsiveness to speech and nonspeech stimuli in infancy. Entus (1977) reported finding hemisphere differences in groups of infants with mean ages of 43.3–100 days. The infants were tested using high-amplitude sucking (HAS) as the behavioral response. Pairs of either speech stimuli ([ma] and [ba], [da] and [ba], [da] and [ga]) or musical note stimuli executed on different instruments (piano and cello, piano and bassoon, and viola and bassoon) were presented through earphones while the infants sucked on a pacifier. After the continuous presentation of one stimulus pair for a period of time, the sucking rate decreased. When a prespecified decrement level in sucking was reached, one stimulus of the pair was changed. Entus found that the rate of sucking recovered faster if the changed stimulus was a speech sound presented to the right ear (left hemisphere) or a musical sound presented to the left ear (right hemisphere). Though these results seem to support the notion of early hemisphere differences, the failure of Vargha-Khadem and Corballis (1979) to replicate Entus's findings for speech using identical stimuli, response criteria, and equipment but a somewhat different procedure (the use of a mechanical arm to hold the pacifier in the infant's mouth) leaves the evidence of hemisphere differences based on HAS responses equivocal.

Glanville, Best, and Levenson (1977) also used a dichotic listening paradigm to study hemispheric differences in infants, but heart-rate habituation was used as the response measure. The stimuli were consonant–vowel syllable pairs (Set A: [ba], [da], [ga]; Set B: [pa], [ta], [ka]) and musical note pairs played on different instruments (Set A: piano, brass, reed; Set B: organ, string, flute). The sets were presented dichotically to infants 93–130-days-old. For 8 of the 12 infants greater recovery from heart-rate habituation occurred when novel speech stimuli were presented to the right ear (left hemisphere), whereas greater recovery occurred when novel musical stimuli were presented to the left ear (right hemisphere).

Hemisphere Differences in Response to Specific Stimulus Cues

The studies with infants that have been summarized thus far have demonstrated hemisphere differences in responsiveness to speech and nonspeech stimuli and may provide evidence of hemispheric specialization. However, little work has been conducted to determine the ways in which the mechanisms responsible for such hemisphere differences operate, what specific stimulus features the hemispheres are sensitive to, what the limitations of the cortical mechanisms are, or how such mechanisms are utilized by cognitive processes. In part, this failure has been due to the use of relatively gross stimulus features in the early studies. Most of the speech and nonspeech stimuli utilized in studies have differed along many dimensions. That is, the stimuli have differed in formant structure, number of formants, presence or absence of frequency transitions, and in the shift in frequency transitions. Consequently, although the magnitude and direction of hemisphere differences have been found to shift depending on the general type of stimuli presented, the specific stimulus characteristics responsible for the hemisphere differences cannot be identified.

In an attempt to isolate more specifically the cues that elicit early hemisphere differences, Molfese and his associates conducted a series of

Table 5.1
Electrophysiological Evidence of Speech Perception

	Adults	Infants and children
	Voicing contrasts	
Bilabial stop consonants [ba] 0 and +20 msec VOT; [pa] +40 and +60 msec VOT	Molfese (1978a) Electrode sites T_3, T_4 Task Identification Findings Right-hemisphere (RH) components reflect categorical discrimination Left-hemisphere (LH) components differentiate 0 and +60 from +20 and +40 msec stimuli	Molfese and Molfese (1979a) Age 2–5 months (M = 3.8 months) Electrode sites T_3, T_4 Findings RH component reflects categorical discrimination Bilateral components reflect categorical discrimination Molfese and Molfese (1979a) Age <24 hours full term Electrode sites T_3, T_4 Findings No evidence of categorical discrimination
Velar stop consonants [ka] 0 and +20 msec VOT; [ga] +40 and +60 msec VOT		Molfese and Hess (1978) Age 3.9–4.9 years (M = 4.5 years) Electrode sites T_3, T_4 Findings RH components reflect categorical-like discrimination Bilateral components reflect categorical-like discrimination
	Place of articulation contrasts	
CV syllables (consonants: [b,g]; vowel [æ]) with normal and sine wave formant bandwidth and phonetic and nonphonetic formant transitions	Molfese (1978b) Electrode sites T_3, T_4 Findings LH components differentiated phonetic from nonphonetic transitions Bilateral responses discriminate normal from sine wave formant stimuli	Molfese and Molfese (1979b) Age <24 hours full term Electrode sites T_3, T_4 Findings LH component differentiated consonants with normal formant structure Bilateral component

(continued)

Table 5.1   (Continued)

	Adults	Infants and children
		differentiated conso-nants with normal for-mant structure
		Molfese and Molfese (1980) Age: preterm infants 1–42.5 days ($M = 15$ days)
		Electrode sites T_3, T_4
		Findings LH components differentiated phonetic from nonphonetic transitions for both stimuli with normal bandwidth and differentiated nonphonetic [bæ] from [gæ] Bilateral component reflected formant structure differences
Synthetic normal and sine wave formant CV syllables: Consonants: [b, g] Vowels: [i, æ, ɔ]	Molfese (1980) Electrode sites T_3, T_4, T_5, T_6, P_3, P_4 Findings LH component discriminated [b] from [g] independent of vowel Bilateral component discriminated [b] from [g]	

studies with computer synthesized speech and nonspeech sounds. The work described next, from that laboratory, has centered on stop consonant perception involving voicing contrasts and place of articulation contrasts.

Voicing Contrasts

Voicing contrast or voice onset time (VOT) reflects the temporal relationship between laryngeal pulsing (e.g., vocal chord vibration) and consonant release (e.g., the separation of lips to release a burst of air from the vocal tract during the production of bilabial stop consonants such as [b, p]). Investigators have reported that when VOT was systematically manip-

ulated, adult listeners could discriminate changes in VOT only to the extent that they could assign unique labels to these sounds (Liberman, Cooper, Shankweiler, & Studdert-Kennedy, 1967). Listeners failed to discriminate between bilabial stop consonants with VOT values of 0 and +20 msec and identified both stimuli as [ba]. Stimuli with +40 and +60 msec VOT were both identified as [pa], and subjects failed to discriminate between the +40 and +60 msec stimuli. However, these adults could discriminate between, and assign different labels to stimuli with VOT values of +20 and +40 msec. The 20-msec difference in VOT between speech syllables was only detected when the VOT stimuli were from different phoneme categories. Consequently, changes in VOT appeared to be categorical. Such findings have been consistently reported with adults in identification and discrimination studies (Liberman, Delattre, & Cooper, 1958; Lisker & Abramson, 1964) as well as with young infants in studies that employed HAS procedures (Eimas, Siqueland, Jusczyk, & Vigorito, 1971; Trehub & Rabinovitch, 1972). The findings with infants indicate that VOT perception is present in infants as young as 1 month of age, long before the emergence of language development. This could suggest that at least some of the mechanisms that subserve language functions are innately specified from birth. However, given the severe limitations of behavioral techniques such as HAS with infants less than 1 or 2 months of age, no behavioral studies to date have successfully addressed the question concerning when the mechanisms for VOT perception first appear in development.

Additional questions which have not been addressed directly with behavioral procedures concern the localization of VOT mechanisms in the cortex and how such mechanisms change as the child develops into a sophisticated language-user. Since VOT is known to be an important speech cue, and speech processes have generally been thought to be controlled by the language-dominant hemisphere—generally the left hemisphere—most scientists have concluded that VOT perception is controlled by mechanisms within the left hemisphere. However, this question has never been systematically addressed. A final question concerns the nature of the VOT cue itself. Is VOT processed by specialized speech mechanisms or by more basic, acoustically tuned cortical mechanisms (Pisoni, 1977; Stevens & Klatt, 1974)?

Molfese and associates have utilized electrophysiological recording procedures as well as behavioral techniques to address these issues. The electrophysiological techniques involve the presentation of an auditory stimulus and the recording of the brain's AER that is triggered by this event. Various portions of the AERs have been found to reflect different stimulus properties. In the earliest electrophysiology study on adult VOT perception, Molfese (1978a) recorded AERs from the left and right temporal regions of 16 adults during a phoneme identification task. Subjects were presented with a randomly ordered series of synthesized bilabial stop consonants that varied in VOT with values of 0, +20, +40, and +60 msec. Subjects were asked to press one button after each stimulus presentation if they heard a [b] and a second button if they heard a [p]. Adults identified the consonant–vowel syllables with VOT values of 0 and +20 msec as [ba] approximately 97% and 93% of the time, respectively, whereas the consonant–vowel syllables with VOT times of +40 and +60 msec were identified 95% and 98% of the time, respectively, as [pa]. Auditory evoked responses to each stimulus were recorded during the identification task and then analyzed using standard averaging techniques. Subsequent analyses involving principal components analysis and analyses of variance indicated that two early AER components recorded from electrodes placed over the right hemisphere temporal region varied systematically as a function of the phoneme category of the evoking stimulus. Stimuli with VOT values of 0 and +20 msec elicited a different AER waveform from the right-hemisphere site than did the +40- and +60-msec stimuli. No differences in the AER waveforms were found between the VOT values within a phoneme category (i.e., no differences were found between the 0- and +20-msec responses or between the +40- and +60-msec responses). These AER patterns of responding were identical to the behavioral responses given by these subjects during the testing session. Components of the left-hemisphere responses reflected an ability of that hemisphere to differentiate between 0- and +60-msec stimuli and to differentiate 0- and +60-msec from +20- and +40-msec stimuli. The left hemisphere appeared responsive to the end boundaries of the VOT stimuli used but did not reflect the categorical discriminations shown by the right hemisphere.

Similar effects have also been found with 4-year-old children in a study in which velar stop consonants ([k,g]) were presented (Molfese & Hess, 1978). In this study, AERs were recorded from the left and right temporal regions of 12 nursery-school-age children (mean age = 4 years, 5 months) in response to a series of synthesized consonant vowel syllables that varied in VOT for the initial consonant (0, +20, +40, +60 msec). As with the adults, one AER component from the right-hemisphere electrode site was found to vary systematically as a function of phoneme category, but the AER components did not distinguish between VOT values within a phoneme category. A second and distinct (orthogonal) AER component also discriminated VOT values corresponding to phoneme categories. However, unlike that found for adults, this component was present in recording sites over both hemispheres.

This work was extended to include newborn and infant populations (Molfese & Molfese, 1979a). In one study, the four consonant–vowel speech syllables used by Molfese (1978a) were presented to 16 infants 2–5 months old (mean: 3 months, 25 days). Auditory evoked responses to each stimulus were recorded from scalp electrodes placed over the superior temporal regions of the left and right hemispheres. As was found for children, the results showed that one component of the cortical AER from the right-hemisphere site discriminated between VOT values from different phoneme categories. A second component of the AER that responded in a similar fashion was present over both hemispheres. In a separate study (Molfese & Molfese, 1979a), 16 newborn infants were tested in an attempt to determine the developmental onset of VOT discrimination as reflected in AERs. The same consonant–vowel speech stimuli and recording sites just described were used in the newborn study. Results were interpreted to indicate that, whereas both hemispheres were actively involved in the processing of the VOT stimuli, there was no evidence of any phoneme categorical-like VOT effect similar to that found with older infants, children, and adults. The ability to discriminate VOT stimuli along phoneme boundaries appears to be present in the early months of infancy but may not be present at birth. It may require some period of maturation or experience to develop or become functional.

Three general findings have emerged from this series of studies: (a) categorical perception of the VOT cue is controlled by several cortical processes—some of which are restricted to only the right-hemisphere site and some of which are common to both hemispheres; (b) there is a developmental pattern to the emergence of mechanisms related to VOT categorical perception; and (c) VOT perception at the cortical level occurs along phoneme boundaries.

Place of Articulation Contrasts

Several studies were undertaken to identify the electrocortical correlates of acoustic and phonemic cues that are important to the perception of consonant place of articulation information (Molfese, 1978b; Molfese, 1980; Molfese & Molfese, 1979b; Molfese & Molfese, 1980). In general, these studies indicated that multiple processing mechanisms (which include left-hemisphere and bilateral processes) are involved in the perception of such cues as second formant (F_2) transition and formant bandwidth. These findings agree with recent behavioral studies that utilized dichotic temporal processing procedures (Cutting, 1974). Cutting found that both bandwidth and transition cues influenced discrimination scores. Stimuli with speech formant structure or that contained an initial transition element were better discriminated by the right ear. Since the right ear is thought to have the majority of its pathways projecting to the left hemisphere, Cutting reasoned that such findings reflected differences in the processing capabilities of two cerebral hemispheres. He concluded that there are different cortical mechanisms involved in processing different cues.

Molfese (1978b) attempted to isolate and localize the neuroelectrical correlates of F_2 transition and bandwidth by presenting a series of computer-generated consonant–vowel syllables in which the stop consonants varied in place of articulation ([b,g]), formant structure (nonspeechlike formants composed of sinewaves 1 Hz in bandwidth or by speechlike formants with bandwidths of 60, 90, and 120 Hz for formants 1, 2, and 3, respectively), and phonemic versus nonphonemic transitions (the direction of the frequency changes for formant 1 and formant 3 were either rising so as to produce a phonetic transition in the sense that it could characterize human speech patterns, or these transitions were falling and therefore occurred in a manner not found in an initial position in human speech patterns). Using the principal components analysis to isolate major features of the AERs recorded from the left hemisphere and right hemisphere of 10 adults, Molfese found major AER components that accounted for 97% of the total variance. Analysis of variance on the gain scores for these factors resulted in the identification of these components as sensitive to the various stimulus and subject variables under investigation. One AER component unique to the left-hemisphere electrode site was found to vary systematically to changes in F_2 transitions.

In a replication and extension study, Molfese (1980) also found that the left hemisphere discriminated consonant place of articulation information. In this study, 20 adults were presented with a series of consonant–vowel syllables that varied in the initial consonant, [b,g], and the final vowel, [i, æ, ɔ]. Auditory evoked responses were recorded from three scalp locations over each hemisphere. Utilizing the analysis just outlined, one component of the brain's AER was found to reflect the ability of only the left hemisphere to differentiate between the consonants [b] and [g] independent of the following vowel, plus a bilateral component that differentiated [b] from [g].

The findings from this last study are important in terms of their implications for the problem of consonant invariance. Until the late 1970s, (Blumstein & Stevens, 1979; Stevens & Blumstein, 1978), acoustic scientists were unable to isolate a set of acoustic properties that are invariant for a particular consonant place of articulation. Although such invariance exists for vowels, acoustic cues for consonants change as a function of subsequent sounds. Consequently, speech scientists long assumed that consonant and vowel information were processed together as a unit. This electrophysiological study by Molfese (1980) represents the first direct indication that the brain may, in fact, respond to consonant sound configurations independent of vowel contexts. Further analysis of this data by Molfese and Schmidt (1983) supplements this report by identifying AER patterns that indicate both context-dependent as well as context-independent processing. Three components of the AERs were found that reflected consonant sound discriminations when those consonants occurred in combination with specific vowel sounds. Cortical processing of speech consonant sounds, then, may involve the perception and discrimination of *both* context-dependent *and* context-independent cues.

Two studies by Molfese and Molfese (1979b, 1980) attempted to determine at what point in development infants are able to differentially respond to such place-of-articulation contrasts. In the first study, AERs were recorded from 16 full term newborn infants in response to two stop consonants ([bæ] and [gæ]) that differed only in F_2 transition and formant bandwidth. As with adults, one AER component found only over the left hemisphere differentiated between consonants with normal formant structure (bandwidth). A second orthogonal AER component that occurred earlier in time and was recorded by electrodes over the left hemisphere and right hemisphere also distinguished between the stop consonants with normal formant structure.

The second study (Molfese & Molfese, 1980) sought to determine whether left-hemisphere processes are present in the responses of preterm infants and whether left-hemisphere mechanisms in infants are sensitive to phonetic and nonphonetic transitions. The subjects were 11 preterm infants with conceptional ages ranging from 32 to 37 weeks (mean: 35.9 weeks) who were tested 1–42.5 days (mean: 15 days) after birth. Auditory evoked responses to stimuli identical to those used by Molfese (1978b) were recorded again from the T_3 and T_4 electrode sites over the superior temporal regions of left and right hemispheres. As found with the full term newborns, a left-hemisphere process was identified in the AERs of the preterm infants that distinguished between transitions cues in stimuli with speech formant structure (bandwidth). An additional AER component recorded over the left hemisphere differentiated between only the nonphonetic stop consonants ([b] and [g]). This finding is similar to that reported by Molfese (1978b) with adults, except that the left-hemisphere process for adults was sensitive to both phonetic and nonphonetic stimuli. A final factor reflected general hemispheric responsiveness to formant structure differences. This effect was not found for the full term infants tested by Molfese and Molfese (1979b). It is interesting to note that stimuli with speechlike formant structure have yielded differential effects unique to the left hemisphere for infants (Molfese & Molfese, 1979b, 1980) but not for adults (Molfese, 1978b; Molfese, 1980). In the former case, the only lateralized effects noted occurred for stimuli with speech formant structure. Stimuli with sine wave formant structure produced no such effect. In the two adult studies, however, the place of articulation contrast effects were noted for stimuli with both speech and nonspeech formant structure. Only bilateral hemisphere effects were noted for formant structure differences. Intriguingly, this is a case where there are developmental changes in lateralized responses in which the early lateralized process appears to *disappear* with further development.

On the basis of the electrophysiological data collected to this time,

there appears to be some basic differences in the organization and localization of brain mechanisms that respond to the temporal information
contained in VOT stimuli and to place of articulation contrasts. Although
both contrasts involve both hemispheres (bilateral processes), they differ
in important respects. Voicing contrasts involve an additional right-hemisphere process, whereas place of articulation contrasts involve a left-
hemisphere process. These mechanisms also appear to develop at different times.

A Note on the Electrophysiological Procedures

As noted earlier, the hemisphere stimulus effects found with electrophysiological procedures have been very consistent across a large series of studies. Both place of articulation contrasts and voicing contrasts
are differentiated by electrical responses found over both hemispheres. In
addition, different lateralized responses to these two contrasts are also
noted: Place of articulation effects elicit differential left-hemisphere responses whereas voicing contrasts elicit differential right-hemisphere
responses.

These findings of interactions between hemispheres and certain stimulus characteristics allow the researcher to identify the specific manner in
which the hemispheres differentially respond to those stimuli. If only a
main effect for hemispheres is noted (without any interaction), the researcher can only conclude that the hemispheres somehow respond differently to the evoking stimuli but it is impossible to obtain more specific
information. Interactions between hemispheres and stimulus features
provide more information concerning the nature of these differences.

The lateralized effects reviewed earlier have been found over temporal
electrode leads in infants (i.e., T_3 and T_4 of the 10–20 system). It should
be noted that, because of volume conduction, the activity detected by
electrodes over the temporal sites does not originate from only neural
tissue in the temporal lobes but most likely is influenced by electrical
fields generated in adjacent regions. It is clear, however, that electrical
activity recorded over the left hemisphere will for the most part reflect
electrical activity originating from the left hemisphere. Subsequent research with adults (Molfese, 1980) and infants using more electrode sites
supports this view. For example, in a 4-year longitudinal study with 60
infants tested at 6-month intervals from birth, electrodes were placed over
temporal and parietal sites over each hemisphere (T_3, T_5, and P_3 over the
left hemisphere and T_4, T_6, and P_4 over the right hemisphere). Effects
identical to the left–right differences just described were found.

The evoked-potential effects, in addition to being reliable across leads
and studies, have also been robust. Even with the use of conservative p
levels ($p < .01$) and conservative posthoc statistics (Scheffé), the hemi-
sphere-by-stimulus effects continue to be noted.

Some scientists have noted that electrophysiological procedures are subject to contamination from motor artifacts. It is simple enough, however, to control for and eliminate these factors from the recording session. The use of a random stimulus order and varied interstimulus interval greatly decrease the likelihood of expectation and habituation. Moreover, the random stimulus order minimally should spread minor contamination equally across conditions, thereby increasing the variance somewhat, but not differentially by condition. Most electrophysiologists also test for motor artifacts by recording from additional electrode sites placed to detect head, eye, and other movements. If these motor actions occur during an evoked potential, the records are discarded and not used to build an averaged brain response. These procedures are usually augmented by monitoring the infant during the testing, both visually and electrically. During periods of increased activity, the test session is temporarily suspended until movements cease.

It should also be noted that early hemisphere effects in infants using electrophysiological procedures are consistent with findings from behavioral tests, as noted in the present volume. The first functional evidence for infant cerebral asymmetries came from the electrophysiological literature (Crowell, Jones, Kapuniai, & NaKagawa, 1973; Molfese, 1972; Molfese et al., 1975). Since that time, researchers using a variety of methodologies have continued to find comparable types of effects. Our own bias in the use of evoked potentials to study language and cognitive development is to employ these procedures if possible while behavioral measures are also recorded. Both the behavioral and electrophysiological measures are then used to interpret the findings. In situations where behavioral procedures would contaminate the brain activity with muscle artifacts, as in the case of young infants, we have chosen to use the electrophysiological procedures alone. However, in these cases, the evoked-potential findings must be compared to findings from behavioral studies, where possible. The strong case that is made today for the presence of early brain asymmetries does not, we believe, rest with any single methodology. Rather, the large number of studies employing so many different procedures such as head-turning, handedness, looking responses, anatomical studies, evoked potentials, EEG, and dichotic listening seem to make a far better case for such asymmetries than any single study or methodology. Science, after all, is, and should be, a cooperative and expansive enterprise.

Conclusions

The studies reviewed in this chapter provide converging evidence from a variety of different methodologies that argue against the notion of equipotentiality. It seems clear that the two hemispheres have anatomical differences and functional specializations that are evident from earliest infancy. There is also considerable evidence that early hemispheric specialization can be modified by need, as in the case of recovery from cerebral damage, and through normal developmental processes. Electrophysiological research has shown that different, perceptually important cues for speech perception are processed by a number of distinct mechanisms, some of which are bilaterally represented and some of which are lateralized to one cortical region. These mechanisms appear to change with development. For example, in infants, one mechanism responsive to the VOT cue along phoneme boundaries was found in both hemispheres, and a second mechanism restricted to the right hemisphere responded in a similar fashion. These two different mechanisms (one bilateral and one right-hemisphere lateralized) persist into early childhood, reflecting processes sensitive to phoneme boundaries. It is only in the cortical responses of adults that substantially different responses are noted. With adults, two distinct right-hemisphere mechanisms are found, but no bilateral VOT mechanisms. Apparently, between 4 years and adulthood either the bilateral VOT process becomes lateralized to the right hemisphere or it is replaced by a different mechanism that is restricted to the right hemisphere. In contrast to the VOT mechanisms, mechanisms sensitive to place of articulation contrasts were detected in the left hemisphere in infants under 30 hours of age. These mechanisms do not appear to change to any great extent with development into adulthood, except in the manner in which they interact with formant structure characteristics.

Perception of speech-relevant cues may depend on the presence and development of the basic acoustic mechanisms at the cortical level that are involved in language comprehension. Since these processes appear to change through development, the role they play in language functions could change over time. For example, the bilateral and right-lateralized mechanisms responsible for processing voicing contrasts that were found in infants and children, present interesting possibilities in cases of cerebral damage to one cortical region. Early-occurring damage might result in minimal effects due to the redundancy in the cortical mechanisms. In adulthood, however, this redundancy may be lost, with only lateralized mechanisms remaining. Damage at this stage to the lateralized process may find the remaining intact regions unable to interact with the damaged area and without comparable abilities. This change could be of importance in terms of recovery of functions following cerebral damage in adulthood.

References

Annett, M. (1973). Laterality of childhood hemiplegia and the growth of speech and intelligence. Cortex 9, 4–33.

Barnet, A., de Sotillo, M., & Campos, M. (1974). EEG sensory evoked potentials in early *infancy malnutrition*. Paper presented at the meeting of the Society for Neurosciences, St. Louis, Missouri, November.

Basser, L. S. (1962). Hemiplegia of early onset and the faculty of speech with special reference to the effects of hemispherectomy. *Brain 85*, 427–460.

Blumstein, S. E., & Stevens, K. N. (1979). Acoustic invariance in speech production: Evidence from measurements of the spectral characteristics of stop consonants. *Journal of the Acoustical Society of America 66*, 1001–1017.

Crowell, D. H., Jones, R. H., Kapuniai, L. E., & Nakagawa, J. K. (1973). Unilateral cortical activity in newborn humans: An early index of cerebral dominance? *Science 180*, 205–208.

Cutting, J. E. (1974). Two left hemisphere mechanisms in speech perception. *Perception and Psychophysics 16*, 601–612.

Dennis, M. (1977). Cerebral dominance in three forms of early brain disorder. In M. Blaw, J. Rapin, & M. Kinsbourne (Eds.), *Topics in child neurology*. Bloomington, Indiana: Spectrum.

Dennis, M., & Kohn, B. (1975). Comprehension of syntax in infantile hemiplegics after cerebral hemidecortication: Left hemisphere superiority. *Brain and Language 2*, 472–482.

Eimas, P. D., Siqueland, E., Jusczyk, P., & Vigorito, J. (1971). Speech perception in infants. *Science 171*, 303–306.

Entus, A. (1977). Hemispheric asymmetry in processing of dichotically presented speech and nonspeech stimuli by infants. In S. Segalowitz & F. Gruber (Eds.), *Language development and neurological theory*. New York: Academic Press.

Geschwind, N., & Levitsky, W. (1968). Human brain: Left–right asymmetries in temporal speech regions. *Science 161*, 186–187.

Glanville, B., Best, C., & Levenson, R. (1977). A cardiac measure of cerebral asymmetries in infant auditory perception. *Developmental Psychology 13*, 54–59.

Kohn, B., & Dennis, M. (1974). Selective impairments of visuo-spatial abilities in infantile hemiplegics after right cerebral hemidecortication. *Neuropsychologia 12*, 505–512.

Lenneberg, E. (1967). *Biological foundations of language*. New York: Wiley.

Liberman, A. M., Cooper, F. S., Shankweiler, D., & Studdert-Kennedy, M. (1967). Perception of the speech code. *Psychological Review 74*, 431–461.

Liberman, A. M., Delattre, P. C., & Cooper, F. S. (1958). Some cues for the distinction between voiced and voiceless stops in initial position. *Language and Speech 1*, 153–167.

Lisker, L., & Abramson, A. S. (1964). Across language study of voicing in initial stops: Acoustical measurements. *Word 20*, 384–422.

Molfese, D. L. (1972). *Cerebral asymmetry in infants, children and adults: Auditory evoked responses to speech and music stimuli*. (Doctoral dissertation, Pennsylvania State University, 1972). *Dissertation Abstracts International 33*. (University Microfilms No. 72–48, 394)

Molfese, D. L. (1978a). Neuroelectrical correlates of categorical speech perception in adults. *Brain and Language 5*, 25–35.

Molfese, D. L. (1978b). Left and right hemisphere involvement in speech perception: Electrophysiological correlates. *Perception and Psychophysics 28*, 237–243.

Molfese, D. L. (1980). The phoneme and the engram: Electrophysiological evidence for the acoustic invariant in stop consonants. *Brain and Language 9*, 372–376.

Molfese, D. L., Freeman, R. B., & Palermo, D. S. (1975). The ontogeny of brain lateralization for speech and nonspeech stimuli. *Brain and Language 2*, 356–368.

Molfese, D. L., & Hess, T. (1978). Hemispheric specialization for VOT perception in the preschool child. *Journal of Experimental Child Psychology 26*, 71–84.

Molfese, D. L., & Molfese, V. J. (1979a). VOT distinctions in infants: Learned or innate? In H.

A. Whitaker & H. Whitaker (Eds.), *Studies in neurolinguistics* (Vol. 4). New York: Academic Press.

Molfese, D. L., & Molfese, V. J. (1979b). Hemisphere and stimulus differences as reflected in the cortical responses of newborn infants to speech stimuli. *Developmental Psychology 15*, 505–511.

Molfese, D. L., & Molfese, V. J. (1980). Cortical responses of preterm infants to phonetic and nonphonetic speech stimuli. *Developmental Psychology 16*, 574–581.

Molfese, D. L., & Schmidt, A. (1983). An auditory evoked potential study of consonant perception. *Brain and Language 18*, 57–70.

Pisoni, D. B. (1977). Identification and discrimination of the relative onset time of two component tones: Implications for voicing perception in stops. *Journal of the Acoustical Society of America 61*, 1352–1361.

Regan, D. (1972). *Evoked potentials in psychology, sensory physiology and clinical medicine.* New York: Wiley.

Stevens, K., & Blumstein, S. (1978). Invariant cues for place of articulation in stop consonants. *Journal of the Acoustical Society of America 64*, 1358–1368.

Stevens, K., & Klatt, D. (1974). Role for formant transition in the voiced–voiceless distribution for stops. *Journal of the Acoustical Society of America 55*, 653–659.

Teszner, D., Tzavaras, A., Gruner, J., & Hécaen, H. (1972). L'asymetrie droit–gauche du planum temporale: A propos de l'étude anatomique de 100 cerveaux. *Revue Neurologique 126*, 444–449.

Trehub, S., & Rabinovitch, S. (1972). Auditory–linguistic sensitivity in early infancy. *Developmental Psychology 6*, 74–77.

Vargha-Khadem, F., & Corballis, M. (1979). Cerebral asymmetry in infants. *Brain and Language 8*, 1–9.

Wada, J. (1969). Interhemispheric sharing and shift of cerebral speech function. *Excerpta Medica International Congress Series 193*, 296–297.

Wada, J., Clarke, R., & Hamm, A. (1975). Cerebral hemispheric asymmetry in humans. *Archives of Neurology 32*, 239–246.

Wada, J., & Davis, A. (1977). Fundamental nature of human infant's brain asymmetry. *Le Journal Canadien des Sciences Neurologiques 4*, 203–207.

Witelson, A., & Pallie, W. (1973). Left hemisphere specialization for language in the newborn: Neuroanatomical evidence of asymmetry. *Brain 96*, 641–647.

6

How Many Lateralities Are There?

SIDNEY J. SEGALOWITZ

Introduction

The chapters in Part I of this volume are valiant efforts at finding some order in the tangle of results emanating from studies on hand preference and brain lateralization for speech and related processes in early infancy. Despite the temptation to find some theoretical link between hand preference and cerebral dominance for speech and language, the correlation between the two is actually very low. This is because although almost all right-handed adults have left-hemisphere control of language, so do most left-handers. We can calculate a correlation coefficient between hand preference and cerebral dominance for language where both are based on a left–right dichotomy (where bilateral language representation is considered to indicate some right-hemisphere control). Using the figures from Rasmussen and Milner (1977) (96% of right-handers and 70% of left-handers are left-hemisphere dominant for speech), we find that the correlation is far from perfect ($r = .34$, based on an incidence of right handedness of 90%). This correlation is highly significant, yet only accounts for about 11% of the variance. Clearly, other factors intrude on the relationship. Part of the difficulty in relating speech dominance and hand preference involves the definition of each. Is it the case that we are referring to a single construct when we talk of brain lateralization in general and of speech dominance in particular? Let us deal with speech dominance first.

When we refer to cerebral dominance for speech, we usually have in mind the strong correlation between left-sided brain damage and aphasic symptoms. Yet when we are discussing the infant's development of lan-

MANUAL SPECIALIZATION
AND THE DEVELOPING BRAIN

guage skills, are these the appropriate data? We may want to focus on phonological issues in speech perception and on pragmatic factors in communication instead of the semantic and syntactic processes so clearly tied to left-hemisphere functioning. Recent work in brain lateralization for phonological coding has raised a number of dilemmas. Traditionally, the dichotic listening literature has made it clear that when speech discrimination is being tested, the left hemisphere is superior. However, the recent use of different paradigms has brought this conclusion into question. For example, Molfese (1978, 1980) has found, using event-related potentials (ERPs), that the right hemisphere shows sensitivity to voice onset time (VOT) independent of the left. Segalowitz and Cohen (1982) also found a right-hemisphere sensitivity to the voicing cue by using different scalp sites, natural speech instead of synthetic speech, and a wider variety of vowel contexts. Using a dichotic listening paradigm, Cohen (1981) also found a right-hemisphere sensitivity to voicing cues. The aphasia literature agrees with this general result: Voicing cues are found to be significantly less disrupted in aphasia than are place-of-articulation cues (Miceli, Caltagirone, Gainotti, & Payer-Rigo, 1978; Perecman & Kellar, 1981). Given these results, we must allow that some aspects of speech perception may have a brain basis different from the usual unitary models.

There are other aspects of communication that are disrupted differentially in aphasia due to left-hemisphere damage: the appreciation of, and ability to make use of, various communicative functions including intonation, gesture, nonliteral use of words, and deixis (see Foldi, Cicone, & Gardner, 1983, for a review). We do not question the traditional model of left-hemisphere representation of semantic and syntactic abilities. Yet, when we consider the language functions most pertinent in infant development, we must consider that there may be a number of "lateralities."

This point is even more critical when we consider whether a unitary model of lateralization for language would account for the other cognitive functions so important for the neonate, such as recognition in visual perception, spatial mapping, and emotional processes. These functions have been linked to right-hemisphere activity in adults, yet this dependency is not necessarily contingent on left-hemisphere representation of language. In other words, we can ask whether or not the lateralization of language is related in an individual to the asymmetric representation of these other functions. This is the issue of complementarity, assumed, but not demonstrated, in neuropsychology. Bryden, Hécaen, and deAgostini (1982) have found that there is no statistical dependency between hemisphere dominance for language and for spatial skills (i.e., the hemisphere that subserves language does not necessarily not subserve spatial skills). Once again, we must be careful that when we speak of one form of laterality, we are not referring to the gamut.

We can also consider whether or not hand preference is a single construct. Young, Segalowitz, Misek, Alp, and Boulet (Chapter 2, this volume) review the literature suggesting that, even in early infancy, the two hands may specialize for different functions, suggesting that different forms of hand-preference exist. This notion is further supported if we expand our query to include bodily lateral preferences in general. For example, Porac and Coren (1981, p. 63) have found that although foot preference and eye preference are quite highly correlated, neither correlates very well with eye and ear preference ($r = .21$ and $.24$ for correlations with hand preference and $r = .29$ and $.32$ for correlations with foot preference, respectively), leaving much variance to be accounted for. Many normal individuals, then, have nondependent lateral preferences.

Developmental Considerations

Given, then, that the newborn child is destined (probabilistically speaking) to have at least several patterns of brain asymmetries for motor and cognitive behaviors, we can then ask whether or not the evidence points to a progressive development of lateralization. The alternative is a transformational development where asymmetries are present at an early stage and change their nature to become more like those we expect at maturity. The progressive lateralization model popular in the 1970s (Lenneberg, 1967), now has seen many arguments and much data to revise it (Kinsbourne & Hiscock, 1977; Segalowitz, 1983; Witelson, 1977). What researchers have found is that there very rarely is an interaction between the age of the subjects and the asymmetry in cerebral processing in whatever tasks are given. Thus, although younger children may perform more poorly on the various lateralization measures available compared to older children, they do not give evidence of a lesser degree of functional cerebral asymmetry. In Chapter 5 of this volume, Molfese and Molfese review a number of studies with infants who show evidence of asymmetries in cerebral processing of information. Most of the studies discussed in Molfese and Molfese utilize scalp-recorded ERPs, although a few using different measures have been reported (e.g., Segalowitz, 1980; Segalowitz & Chapman, 1980). It is interesting to note that despite the fact that not all of the studies succeed in detecting lateralized functioning, when an asymmetry is reported, it is always in the expected direction, no matter how young the infants (i.e.,favoring the left hemisphere when speech stimuli are used).

In Chapter 3 of this volume, Michel argues that we must treat these results with caution because they are based primarily on EEG data and most of these studies used temporal lobe placements. The danger here is that the standard temporal lobe placements, T_3 and T_4 in the International 10–20 system (Jasper, 1958), happen to be situated, in the adult, over brain tissue that is not symmetrical in the two hemispheres (Rubens,

1977). In these studies, we run the risk of recording over the upper part of the temporal lobe on the left side (directly over the auditory cortex) and over the center of the temporal lobe on the right. Any asymmetries found, Michel argues, could be due to differences in the areas generating the EEG rather than in the hemispheric coding of the stimuli. This is a possible difficulty with some of the data using T_3 and T_4 and not using nonspeech controls. However, the seriousness of this charge is mitigated since both Gardiner and Walter (1977), using P_3 and P_4 sites, and Barnet, Vicentini, and Campos (1974), using C_3 and C_4, found evidence for speech laterality in infants. It is also not clear that this objection holds generally. The infant skull has not been measured with respect to the 10–20 system, and therefore this problem may not obtain; also, it may be the case that the brain sites generating the ERPs in neonates are not cortical at all, but rather are much deeper, toward the brainstem (Molfese, personal communication). Of more concern for this criticism are the studies finding an interaction between stimulus (speech versus nonspeech) and hemisphere. If the electrode placement over the right hemisphere is such that poor auditory response should be found, then the same should hold for all auditory stimuli. This is not the case (e.g., Crowell, Jones, Kapuniai, & Nakagawa, 1973; Davis & Wada, 1977; Molfese, Freeman, & Palermo, 1975). Michel also argues that motor artifacts may confound the results of the EEG studies. It is certainly the case that motor artifacts are a confounded nuisance to EEG researchers, but as long as they are not temporally linked to a particular subset of the stimuli, they can only add variance to the results, not a significant interaction.

Could some developmental motor asymmetry such as head-turning, asymmetric tonic neck reflex (ATNR), or pointing account for brain lateralization for speech and other cognitive functions, as suggested by Michel and also by others (e.g., Kinsbourne & Lempert, 1979)? Considering the evidence that the various asymmetries are probably not linked in a direct fashion, it may be premature to speculate at this time. There may be, for example, a set of developmental gradients that predispose the development of certain asymmetries but not others. Such developmental processes may include those reviewed by Liederman in Chapter 4, this volume, concerning differing maturation rates for the two hemispheres, but may also include more dynamic inhibitory interactions that change over time (see Young, Bowman, Methot, Finlayson, Quintal, & Boissonneault, Chapter 7, this volume).

The Theorist's Problem

The considerable material presented in the chapters in this section allows us to see a variety of developmental constructs. Some are mutually exclusive. For example, a number of researchers suggest that there is a shift in hand preference in the early months from the left hand to the right. Others (e.g., Young et al., Chapter 2, this volume) argue that the results suggesting this are not in fact robust. Whatever the case, it seems that we have enough constructs to be able to account for a wide range of data. Another example is that greater maturity of one side over the other accounts for greater activity by the limb on that side (e.g., Caplan & Kinsbourne, 1976). On the other hand, greater maturity has also been used to account for a reduction (or a relative shift) in activity (Segalowitz & Chapman, 1980). Thus, both increase and reduction of activity can be seen as a sign of maturation. Clearly, the conclusion one comes to depends on the requirements of the particular manual activity and whether it reflects (among other things) control at the subcortical or cortical level. Given the multiplicity of lateralities (both motor and perceptual–cognitive) suggested in this volume, perhaps we can expect that explanatory developmental processes will not be successfully integrated for some time, no matter how tempting the exercise for all those concerned.

References

Barnet, A. B., Vicentini, M., & Campos, S. H. (1974). EEG sensory evoked responses (ERs) in early infancy malnutrition. Paper presented at the Society for Neuroscience, St. Louis, Missouri.

Bryden, M. P., Hécaen, H., & deAgostini, M. (1982). Patterns of cerebral organization. University of Waterloo, Waterloo, Ontario. (Mimeo)

Caplan, P., & Kinsbourne, M. (1976). Baby drops the rattle: Asymmetry of duration of grasp by infants. Child Development 47, 532–534.

Cohen, H. (1981). Hemispheric differences in the perceptual representation of speech sounds. Unpublished doctoral dissertation, Concordia University, Montreal, Quebec.

Crowell, D. H., Jones, R. H., Kapuniai, L. E., & Nakagawa, J. K. (1973). Unilateral cortical activity in newborn humans: An early index of cerebral dominance. Science 180, 205–208.

Davis, A. E., & Wada, J. A. (1977). Hemispheric asymmetries in human infants: Spectral analysis of flash and clicked evoked potentials. Brain and Language 4, 23–31.

Foldi, N. S., Cicone, M., & Gardner, H. (1983). Pragmatic aspects of communication in brain damaged patients. In S. J. Segalowitz (Ed.), Language functions and brain organization. New York: Academic Press.

Gardiner, M. F., & Walter, D. O. (1977). Evidence of hemispheric specialization from infant EEG. In S. Harnad, R. W. Doty, L. Goldstein, J. Jaynes, & G. Krauthamer (Eds.), Lateralization in the nervous system. New York: Academic Press.

Jasper, H. (1958). The 10–20 electrode system of the international federation. Electroencephalography and Clinical Neurophysiology 10, 371–375.

Kinsbourne, M., & Hiscock, M. (1977). Does cerebral dominance develop? In S. J. Segalowitz & F. A. Gruber (Eds.), Language development and neurological theory. New York: Academic Press.

Kinsbourne, M., & Lempert, H. (1979). Does left brain lateralization of speech arise from right-biased orienting to salient percepts? Human Development 22, 270–276.

Lenneberg, E. H. (1967). *Biological foundations of language.* New York: Wiley.

Miceli, G., Caltagirone, C., Gainotti, G., & Payer-Rigo, P. (1978). Discrimination of voice versus place contrasts in aphasia. *Brain and Language 6,* 47–51.

Molfese, D. L. (1978). Neuroelectrical correlates of categorical speech perception in adults. *Brain and Language 5,* 25–35.

Molfese, D. L. (1980). Hemispheric specialization for temporal information: Implications for the perception of voicing cues during speech perception. *Brain and Language 11,* 285–299.

Molfese, D. L., Freeman, R. B., & Palermo, D. S. (1975). The ontogeny of brain lateralization for speech and nonspeech stimuli. *Brain and Language 2,* 356–368.

Perecman, E., & Kellar, L. (1981). The effect of voice and place among aphasics, nonaphasic right-damaged, and normal subjects on a metalinguistic task. *Brain and Language 12,* 213–223.

Porac, C., & Coren, S. (1981). *Lateral preferences and human behavior.* New York: Springer-Verlag.

Rasmussen, T., & Milner, B. (1977). The role of early left-brain injury in determining lateralization of cerebral speech functions. *Annals of the New York Academy of Sciences 299,* 355–369.

Rubens, A. B. (1977). Anatomical asymmetries of human cerebral cortex. In S. Harnad, R. W., Doty, L. Goldstein, J. Jaynes, & G. Krauthamer (Eds.), *Lateralization in the nervous system.* New York: Academic Press.

Segalowitz, S. J. (1980). Developmental models of brain lateralization. Brock University, St. Catharines, Ontario. (Mimeo)

Segalowitz, S. J. (1983). Cerebral aymmetries for speech in infancy. In S. J. Segalowitz (Ed.), *Language functions and brain organization.* New York: Academic Press.

Segalowitz, S. J., & Chapman, J. S. (1980). Cerebral asymmetry for speech in neonates: A behavioral measure. *Brain and Language 9,* 281–288.

Segalowitz, S. J., & Cohen, H. (1982). *Right hemisphere sensitivity to speech.* Paper presented at the Canadian Psychological Association, Montreal, Quebec.

Witelson, S. F. (1977). Early hemisphere specialization and interhemispheric plasticity: An empirical and theoretical review. In S. J. Segalowitz & F. A. Gruber (Eds.), *Language development and neurological theory.* New York: Academic Press.

II

Theories of Lateralization Development

Hemispheric Specialization Development: What (Inhibition) and How (Parents)[1]

GERALD YOUNG
JAMES G. BOWMAN
CAROLE METHOT
MARY FINLAYSON
JANET QUINTAL
PAUL BOISSONNEAULT

Introduction

Goals

Novel hypotheses about both the organismic and experiential sides of the development of hemispheric specialization are presented in this chapter. The exact nature of hemispheric specialization remains an issue, with dichotomies continually suggested to help describe it (e.g., the sequential, serial, executive, verbal left hemisphere versus the holistic, parallel, subordinate, spatial right hemisphere). It has been suggested that there is probably not one major distinction between the hemispheres, but at least several of them that need not be related (e.g., Moscovitch, 1979). We try to show that, at the organismic level, what may characterize left-hemispheric specialization is one major function; in particular, a differential skill in controlling behavior through inhibition, either directly or in concert with activation. At the experiential level, the role of aspects of parental social behavior early in life is emphasized in the development of hemispheric specialization. The first part of this chapter describes some current models of manual and hemispheric specialization and shows how the inhibition—activation model that we propose is consonant with each of them. Also, it is emphasized that the model can concern social as much

[1]This research was supported by a Grant No. A7939 from the Natural Sciences and Engineering Research Council of Canada and by internal grants from Glendon and York. It was presented at conferences at the Centre Hospitalier Côte-des-Neiges, October, 1982, and Hôpital Sainte-Justine, December, 1982.

MANUAL SPECIALIZATION
AND THE DEVELOPING BRAIN

as manual and other behavior. The second part of the chapter presents research about the lateralized behavior of newborns and 1-month-olds that was derived from the inhibition–activation model of hemispheric specialization development.

Some Current Models of Hemispheric Specialization

Two reviews of the literature on hemispheric specialization in humans emphasize the superior sequential organization of the left hemisphere (Bradshaw & Nettleton, 1981a, 1981b; Moscovitch, 1979). Moscovitch points out that many dichotomies are used to qualify hemispheric differentiation, but that the sequential–nonsequential view is a predominant one. However, this model is not universally accepted. Poeck and Huber (1977) point out that there is more to language, the classic qualifier of left-hemisphere ability, than just reception (analysis) and production (speech) of temporal sequencing. Lexical (word) organization goes beyond sequencing operations. Moreover, some right-hemisphere skills, such as haptic finger exploration of objects and musical chord perception, are necessarily sequential. Nevertheless, one can argue that what counts is a relative balance between sequential and nonsequential operations, and that in this regard language demands fine-tuned sequential operations beyond integrating organization, whereas haptic and musical chord perception ultimately demand (spatial) integration beyond sequential information acquisition.

Moscovitch (1979) also shows how the left hemisphere's executive bent can lead it to try to control behavior even when this is not adaptive. He provides a modified version of Kinsbourne's (1970) attention model of hemispheric specialization by integrating it with the structural model. The structural model stipulates that perceptual asymmetries result from the more direct access of stimuli in one sensory field to the contralateral hemisphere specialized in their processing, as compared to those stimuli presented to the opposite field. The attention model states that a hemisphere can be selectively primed (e.g., by expectation), thus channeling selective attention to the contralateral sensory field. Klein, Moscovitch, and Vigna (1976) suggest an interactive model where priming, direct access, and the specialized skills of a hemisphere can facilitate quicker and/or more accurate activation or processing in one hemisphere.

However, there are some findings that the model would not have predicted according to Moscovitch. Marin and Saffran (1975), for example, studied a patient who tried to use the damaged left hemisphere, leading to task failure. Only when the individual performed simple activities that presumably occupied the left hemisphere, such as counting aloud, could the intact right hemisphere take control in guiding behavior in the more complex task. Other studies show that the left hemisphere will not necessarily relinquish its executive control to the right, even if it can less ably perform the particular task involved (e.g., Cohen, 1975). In short, the executive volitional nature of the left hemisphere seems at times even a more powerful determinant of its use than priming, its specialized sequential skills, or direct access (Nottebohm, 1979; Oldfield, 1969; see Jackson, 1874/1915, for historical interest).

A similar conclusion can be derived from examining Bradshaw and Nettleton(1981a, 1981b), who emphasize sequencing in time in their review of the differentiation of the hemispheres. The left hemisphere's chief characteristic seems to be its use of the strategy of segmenting features, especially where there are rapid, dynamic,complex changes(e.g.,concerning durations, rhythm) in sensorimotor coordination based on kinesthetic feedback. That is, the left hemisphere excels in relating individual components in fine sequential movement to internalized schemes of target and body. In contrast, the right performs simpler, unmonitored activities such as determining gestalt configurations between features. Thus, it maps the space in which movement is taking place and guides movement in space when it is ballistic and automatic. Bradshaw and Nettleton do not address the concept of greater executive control from the left hemisphere, but the responses of both Corballis (1981) and Nottebohm (1981) to Bradshaw and Nettleton's work mention the planned, purposive, executive decision making involved in commencing and in continuing a movement sequence.

There is an area of research on hemispheric specialization in adults that also emphasizes both manual efficiency and decision making in manual behavior as specializations of the left hemisphere. When simple manual reaction times to unpatterned visual stimuli presented to the hemifields of adults are analyzed, the right hand emerges superior not only in movement times, but also in decision times (Bashore, 1981; Malfara & Jones, 1981). Thus, here too, the left hemisphere seems to be specialized for an aspect of performance per se and the executive decision underlying that performance.

An Inhibition–Activation Model of
Hemispheric Specialization

The fine sequential and executive models of left-hemisphere specialization are not as different as they first seem, for they appear to be linked through the common bond of better inhibitory control of ongoing behavior and processes in the left hemisphere.

If the left hemisphere is better at organizing sequential activity, then it is better at organizing series of relevant units (muscular movements and/or other processes) by coordinating successive activation and inhibition of these units. Moreover, it is also better at inhibiting possible parallel series of similar but inappropriate interfering movements and/or processes. Finally, if the left hemisphere is better at exercising executive voluntary control than the right, then it is not only better at activating appropriate behavior but also better at inhibiting competing behavior quite different from the appropriate one. That is, the left hemisphere seems to excel in at least two kinds of inhibition—(a) coordination with activation to produce smooth, sequential, goal-appropriate behavior; and (b) control of gross, secondary, competing behavior distinct in nature from the appropriate behavior, and fine-tuned, interfering, parallel behavior similar in nature to the appropriate behavior.

The infant trying to reach gives us the perfect example. Not only does reaching by the chosen arm have to occur by itself in isolation from other behaviors and activity by the other arm, but also the fine coordination of arm, wrist, hand, and finger muscles requires an intricate series of activation and inhibitory commands for success. If we imagine the infant moving through the various phases of target-related activity, we can see that the type of left-hemisphere sensorimotor coordination hypothesized by Bradshaw and Nettleton (1981a, 1981b) fits very well here. Each movement segment must not only be activated just at the right time, but also must be inhibited just at the right time in order for each appropriate movement to fit smoothly into a sequence. Moreover, the complex sequencing, coordination, feedback, and schema comparisons leading to successful grasping and exploration by the fingers requires that the segmented components of activity at each instance of time be free from contaminating movements. For example, at one point it may be appropriate for two fingers to move, each in a slightly different direction, one after the other—something only possible if a certain sequence of muscles are activated while all other muscles are fully inhibited.

In summary, some of the more powerful, seemingly different, models of manual and hemispheric specialization currently in vogue could be subsumed under one model that emphasizes the superior ability of the left hemisphere not only to be involved in certain kinds of activation of behavior or processes, but also in intra-hemispheric inhibition and in the interweaving of activation with inhibition. In formulating this model, we felt that the emphasis on inhibition was a novel feature. However, the following quote illustrates once more that many of the contempory concepts about manual and hemispheric specialization have preliminary forms in earlier eras of scientific inquiry (Harris, Chapter 10, this volume): "A greater cortical control ('inhibition') of the movements of the so-called dominant side . . . is only a counterpart of the more highly perfected coordination of movement on this side [Jasper & Raney, 1937, p. 161]."

At this point, we remind the reader that whatever theory of left-hemisphere specialization eventually emerges, it should ultimately consider factors such as the right hemisphere, the left-hander, individual differences, and pathology, unlike the case here.

Research Supportive of the Model

Work on the specific nature of motor control in the left hemisphere supports this idea of differential inhibition skills in the hemispheres, even though it was not undertaken to directly test this idea. Annett, Annett, Hudson, and Turner (1979) examined performance of the hands on a pegboard task in mostly right-handed adults. Pegs had to be transferred from one row to another nearer the body as quickly as possible. A frame-by-frame analysis of four filmed subjects familiar with the task showed that the last part of the peg transport, positioning to get the peg in the hole, was especially difficult for the nonpreferred hand, as it required much more subtle corrective movements to get the peg into the hole; no other quality of the movement (e.g., speed of a single corrective movement) differed across hands. Since the speed of corrective movements was just as fast with both hands, information transmission—sensory feedback differences between hands, either after (Flowers, 1975) or during movement, seem precluded as part of an explanation of their difference. Rather, according to Annett et al. (1979), the preferred hand seems to excel in reducing noise or variability in the open-loop, neural–muscular–mechanical mechanism for initiating and controlling accurate movement production. In other words, it seems that inhibition seems to differentiate the preferred and nonpreferred hands.

Kimura's (1980) model of left-hemisphere specialization and the research she and her colleagues performed in support of it provides the best evidence for the model described in this chapter. First, she argues that apraxia, a movement disorder associated with left-hemisphere damage in normal hearing people, is more than a disorder of symbolic or language comprehension, as Liepmann argued in 1908. The patient does not correctly answer verbal requests for demonstration of the use of absent objects or the performance of movements such as saluting, thus supporting the symbolic hypothesis. However, Liepmann (1908) showed that such patients could not imitate these movements. Further evidence against the symbolic hypothesis is Kimura and Archibald's (1974) demonstration that the imitation of meaningless arm movements per se was also impaired in left- more than right-hemisphere-damaged patients. Similarly, Kimura, Battison, and Lubert (1976) showed that a deaf patient with left-hemisphere damage that impaired his signing could not imitate meaningless arm movements. In order to determine whether meaningless vocal movements are also implicated in left-hemisphere damage, Mateer (1978) and Mateer and Kimura (1977) tested right-hemisphere-damaged patients and both aphasic (language impaired) and nonaphasic left-hemisphere-damaged patients on complex sequential nonverbal, oral, and verbal imitation tasks and on simple sequential nonverbal oral-imitation tasks. Patients with left-hemisphere-induced aphasia were impaired not only on complex verbal sequence imitation, but also on complex nonverbal sequence imitation.

Together, these results lay to rest the symbolic impairment hypothesis of left-hemisphere damage. The left hemisphere is not in control of verbal or representational movements alone. But what kind of movement does it control relative to the right hemisphere in Kimura's research? To answer this question, the kinds of errors made in the nonverbal task of the previous study were analyzed. Also, another study used an apparatus that required direction changes in upper-limb position and posture, and subjects were either given directions to go as quickly as possible or not (Kimura, 1977). In all cases, left-hemisphere-damaged patients were not deficient in sequencing per se but manifested perseverative errors, unnecessarily repeating hand postures or nonverbal oral movements within the sequences. In addition, in the manual sequencing task, left-hemisphere patients exhibited many movements unrelated to the task at hand. Also, copying a single hand posture (Kimura & Archibald, 1974) and simple or complex repetitive movements (e.g., finger-tapping, rotating a screw, saying ba-ba-ba [Kimura, 1977]) were not differentially affected by left- or right-hemisphere damage. Moreover, other evidence excludes a somatosensory component. From this, Kimura (1980) suggests that the left hemisphere is primarily specialized not for all sequencing, but by the formation of an accurate representation of body movement, a superior capacity for selection and/or efficiency of execution of changes in position and/or posture involving the proximal and/or distal musculature.

In short, Kimura's left-hemisphere-damaged patients manifested perseverative errors within sequences, indicating a relative lack of control of subtle rapid-movement changes most probably due to a problem in appropriately balancing inhibition and activation during such behavior. Moreover, the manifestation of irrelevant movements in her left-hemisphere patients suggests that the second kind of inhibition described in this chapter is important in left-hemisphere specialization as well.

Are these the only types of inhibition involved in hemispheric specialization? Perhaps not, since Kimura describes other left-hemisphere motor systems not involving such complex motor plans, each in separate cortical regions. This suggests that the left hemisphere may be specialized for a variety of as yet undetermined inhibitory-related skills in the context of behavioral organization relative to the right hemisphere. In this regard, although inhibitory components of left-hemisphere movement control were apparently affected in Kimura's patients, such inhibition may not have been totally disturbed. Motor plans were ultimately seen to their

end, possibly by other control centers of movement in the right hemisphere, subcortical areas, and/or undamaged portions of the left hemisphere.

Social Factors and the Inhibition–Activation Model

Hemispheric specialization is often described in terms of factors related to sociality (e.g., communication, language, emotion), and its development may be influenced by experiences that can be considered social
(e.g., socioeconomic status). However, the underlying functions differentiating the hemispheres are never phrased in direct social terms, nor are
the experiences posited to influence hemispheric specialization. Is it not
possible that the underlying adaptive significance of hemispheric specialization relates to the facilitation of social interchange and that direct
social experiences acquired in such encounters affect the development of
hemispheric specialization, which in turn may affect the quality of social
experience?

I have previously implied that the respective information-processing–organizing skills of the hemispheres (especially their sequential–spatial distinction) may have evolved in protohominids to provide as
much as anything else the substrate for better understanding and controlling the intricate subtle sequence of complex multimodal gestalts comprising the chain of social interaction (Young, 1977). Similarly, Jaffe
(1978) speaks of the face-to-face social context as the one in which lateralization of brain function evolved. Campbell's (1982) review of the lateralization of the emotions supports this position, for positive emotions are
seen as perhaps more lateralized in the left hemisphere, and negative ones
as more lateralized in the right hemisphere. Similarly, Davidson and Fox
(1982) found that 10-month-olds showed greater left frontal region activation in response to spontaneous, happy facial expressions. Since positive
emotional expression is an intricate part of subtle sequential social interaction, then a social emphasis in the "sequential" left hemisphere can
be inferred. The hypothesis that hemispheric specialization evolved as
much for social as other adaptations in protohominids suggests that animal models apply especially to subcortical, not cortical, levels in the
human. (See Ledoux, 1982, for a similar view, and Peters, Chapter 8, this
volume, for a discussion of the evolution of subcortical specialization).
Clearly, much research, especially with face-to-face interaction, is needed
to test these ideas. In this regard, Saling (1978) found that compatability of
the sides of neonatal head orientation and maternal cradling was associated with adequate breast-feeding, presumably because it enhanced face-
to-face interaction (see Harris, Chapter 10, this volume, for a review of
similar studies).

Is the argument that hemispheric specialization can be best understood if inhibition is taken into account orthogonal to the present concern with the role of social interaction in its function and development? Not at all, since our argument is that social behavior and processes became so complex in its coordinated gestalt sequences that only a specialization along the lines proposed could cope with it. That is, like more basic motor behavior such as reaching in 1-month-olds, at one level, social processes are movements or other sequences organized internally not only by coordinated activation but also by interwoven inhibition commands of the relevant muscles or units. In this scheme, evolutionary pressures led to specialization in the hemispheres of complex social behavior organized in terms of differential inhibition and/or its interweaving with activation, and any other process, behavioral or otherwise, social or not, could profit from the cerebral organization involved if it could successfully map onto it, and any experience, even if not complexly social, could influence the cerebral organization in its development if it related to the specialized skills of the hemispheres.

Vygotsky (1962) has described how the child gradually develops internalized control or inhibitory influence over motor output and behavior in general. For our purposes, it is important to note that early in life such inhibitory control may often be exercised by the parent. May we suggest that the point at which the various concepts being presented in this chapter relate is here, for could it not be that the more the parent manifests social behavior relevant to the infant's developing left, compared to right hemisphere, whether the behavior be of an activation and/or an inhibitory variety, the more the infant's left hemisphere will be differentially developed and affect behavior in turn? The following section concerns research with 1-month-olds that examines some of these hypotheses using correlation techniques.

Hierarchies of Inhibition–Activation

In conclusion, relatively novel hypotheses about what is specialized in the hemispheres (differential inhibition skills) and how hemispheric specialization develops (through aspects of parental social, as much as other, experiences) have been presented. Eventually, a picture should emerge of the left hemisphere as a superb, hierarchically organized entity, among other things. In choosing the appropriate response or process (its executive nature) and inhibiting irrelevant interfering ones, one macropath in a multichanneled system is followed. In ensuring successful sequencing in that path through its skill of appropriately interweaving activation and inhibition, one micropath among a large number of possibilities is followed. In helping to interrelate humans in dynamic social interchange, the hierarchy expands to include the personal path of the individual. In other words, one hierarchic motor, verbal, processing, or social plan is chosen and skillfully descended via a specific node pathway, with nodes often being subhierarchies, looping subsystems, etc., while other hierarchies and nodes within the chosen hierarchy are inhibited in order to minimize interference. This view would seem to account for Goldberg and Costa's (1981) characterization of the left hemisphere as a better utilizer (processing, manipulating, etc.) of well-routinized descriptive code systems, perhaps because of a better interregional connectivity.

How much of left-hemisphere specialization can be explained by using the idea of inhibition remains to be determined. For example, the applicability of the model in partially explaining effects of left-hemisphere insult may be worth pursuing. Does the motor, vocal, social, and/or processing activity in the patient suggest one inclusive model where there is an inability to select the appropriate hierarchy and/or to descend it (e.g., looping at a node or repeating it) and/or to exclude irrelevant parallel, lower, or higher nodes within a hierarchy, and/or to exclude nodes of unrelated hierarchies? Does the extent of recovery reflect reintegration in part along these lines? And so on.

Predictions

Studies with 2-day-olds and 1-month-olds have been undertaken in order to show that (a) left-hemisphere specialization very early in life can be revealed both by behavioral effects where a smooth balance of inhibition and activation is required and by purely inhibitory effects, and (b) that the more the parent interacts with behavior presumably processed in the left hemisphere of the infant, the more the infant's left hemisphere will be differentially developed and manifest in appropriate daily activity.

In order to examine hypothesis (a), 2-day-olds were presented with speech and music stimuli from behind at the midline and the direction of head-turning was measured. It was predicted that the neonate would manifest a pattern of hemispheric specialization analogous to that of the adult. Molfese and Molfese (Chapter 5, this volume), with electrophysiological measures, and Hammer (1977), with eye-turning, have shown that already in the neonatal period, speech stimuli are differentially processed in the left hemisphere and music stimuli in the right. Thus, we expected that neonates would turn their heads more to the right when listening to speech sounds, indicating left-hemisphere activation, and would not turn as much to the right when listening to music sounds, indicating a right-hemisphere contribution. Since neonates have a spontaneous head-turning preference to the right (Saling, 1982), we did not predict that head-turning when listening to music would necessarily be a

left-side activity. It was also predicted that, when listening, the left, relative to the right, hemisphere, can more effectively inhibit secondary simultaneous manual activity (e.g., chair–body contact).

As for the 1-month-olds, three-dimensional objects were suspended
just within reaching distance at the midline, the left, and the right, and the
hand used to reach toward and touch the object was scored. Young,
Segalowitz, Misek, Alp, and Boulet (Chapter 2, this volume) review suggests that the young infants' left hemisphere, in particular, can already
bilaterally control, either directly or indirectly, right and/or left upper-
limb activation of almost any variety, consonant with the adult model
(Geschwind, 1975; Peters, 1981). Thus, it was predicted that, especially
for right and midline presentation, the left hemisphere (right hand) would
be relatively more involved in reaching and contact because of the sequential, exploratory, fine motor coordination (i.e., inhibition–activation
interweaving demanded) in such behavior early in life. It was also predicted that when hand opening just before and during reach–touch behavior was examined, a pattern suggesting not only better left-hemisphere
inhibition–activation interweaving of the contralateral hand in target-
related activity, but also better inhibition of irrelevant movements of the
ipsilateral hand would be found. That is, the left hemisphere should not
only be able to better coordinate opening and reaching–touching of the
contralateral hand, it should also be better able to inhibit irrelevant opening of the ipsilateral hand not in use while the other hand reaches.

In short, because of a presumed superior bilateral control of upper-limb
behavior early in life, the left, compared to the right, hemisphere should
not only better contralaterally control coordination of the reaching upper
limb, it should also better ipsilaterally inhibit the nonreaching upper
limb. This should lead to a right-hand superiority in target-directed behavior such as reaching or coordinating reaching and hand opening, and a
left-hand superiority in inhibiting the hand during nonreaching (e.g.,
keeping it closed). Thus, the right hand, compared to the left, should be
proportionately more open not only during reaching–touching behavior,
but also during nonreaching–touching behavior (i.e., of the hand not in
use while the other reaches). Needless to say, it was not expected that this
pattern of results would be obtained when the toy was positioned to the
left (i.e., a Hand × Position interaction was predicted.).

Hypothesis (b), concerning the role of social factors in the development
of left-hemisphere specialization, was examined in the 1-month-olds. Infants interacted with each of their mothers and fathers, and we calculated
the correlation of adult verbal and related oral behaviors in the parent-
interaction situations with the degree of right-hand target-directed activity in the previously described object presentation situations. It was
predicted that the more the parents manifested verbal and related behavior presumably differentially processed in the left hemisphere, the more

the infants would manifest behavior indicative of left-hemisphere activity (e.g., right-side reaching-related behavior, indicative of left hemisphere inhibition–activation interweaving, and left-side closing of the hand during nonreaching–touching behavior, indicative of left-hemisphere inhibition). At a more specific level, parent oral (e.g., verbalization) behavior would positively correlate with the degree of infant right-hand-directed behavior (inhibition–activation balance index) and with the degree of infant right-hand opening in regard to the nonreaching–touching hand (inhibition index).

Research on Hemispheric and Manual Specialization Development

A Study of Two-Day-Olds

METHOD

Tapes of the first 22 of 47 neonates ($M = 58.2$ hours, range: 20–101) have been partially decoded for some of the behaviors of interest to us. All infants were full term, healthy, 10 were males, 12 were females, most were second- or third-born (except for 4 first-borns), and the average birth weight was 3425 gm ($SD = 470.36$). Only 3 of the neonates had a left-handed or ambidextrous parent, as determined by Bryden's (1977) suggested revision of Crovitz and Zener's (1962) questionnaire.

The study was conducted in a quiet room beside the hospital nursery. Neonates were videotaped while sitting in an infant seat that had been angled at 30° and placed in a symmetric white hut. Head rests and a seat belt were employed to obtain symmetry in body position. A bar attached to the seat was positioned horizontally over the waist at shoulder level. A speaker was positioned behind the seat at the midline. At the level of the neonates' ears, background noise was consistently 60 dB SPL and stimuli were played at 61.5 ± 1 dB. Up to 20 2-sec speech and music stimuli were presented in quasi-random order at intervals of 6–8 sec. The speech stimuli were composites of five consonant–vowel syllables spoken by a male (e.g.,[BA]), and the music stimuli were composites of five computer-generated tones (e.g., A_2 at 110 Hz). The steady-state portion of all stimuli were equated for root-mean-square amplitude corresponding to linear (C) weightings within the frequency range used.

When alert, the neonates were placed in the seat and their hands were symmetrically held on the bar by an experimenter standing behind the seat. Two seconds after the experimenter removed his or her hands, the audiotape began to play. The experimenter started the procedure again if the neonates stopped being alert or if they neither touched the bar nor moved their upper limbs for 6 sec.

Each of two trained observers naive to the area of research and to the hypotheses, coded each 2-sec period (during the stimulus, 0–2 sec after, 2–4 sec after) of each subject in terms of the presence or absence of head movements away from the midline, hand–finger movement on the bar, and other (seat, body) contact. Percentage of agreement was 75%, 70%, and 72%, respectively. Disagreements were resolved by conference in every case, producing a situation where two observers ultimately concurred on each observation in the data. Frequencies, adjusted for periods of nonalert activity, were subjected to four-way ANOVAs (Sex, a between factor, × Stimulus × Side × Period, within factors).

RESULTS

Main effects for stimulus and side revealed more head-turns to speech and the right, respectively (F [1, 20] = 4.76, p < .05, M speech = 2.31, M music = 2.01; F [1, 20] = 24.70, p < .001; M right = 3.28, M left = 1.04). Figure 7.1a shows that the significant interaction effect supports the prediction that there would be relatively more right head-turns to speech (F [1, 20] = 4.76, p < .05). The results were comparable in each of the three phases.

The manual behavior data did not conform to predictions. No significant results emerged for movement on the bar, whereas only a Side × Period interaction was found for other contact (see Figure 7.1b). The right hand was less active during stimulus presentation, but switched to being more active 2–4 sec afterward (F [2, 40] = 5.31, p < .01). This pattern was obtained for both types of stimuli.

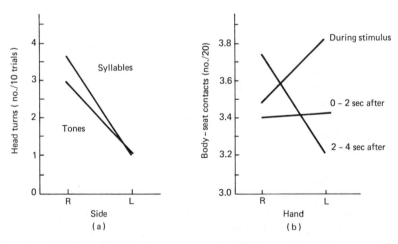

Figure 7.1. (a) Right and left head-turns to speech syllables and music tones in 2-day-olds. (b) Right and left body–seat contacts during the stimuli, 0–2 sec after, and 2–4 sec after.

A Study of One-Month-Olds

METHOD

Healthy, first-born, full term 28-day-olds (±4 days, eight of each sex) from middle-class backgrounds were observed. Of the sixteen infants, only four had a left-handed parent, as according to Bryden's (1977) suggested questionnaire.

Observations took place in the home. For the object situations, an infant chair was positioned at an angle of 30° on the floor. Head supports, a waistband, and lack of side supports permitted a symmetric posture and free arm movements. Objects were three-dimensional 20-cm felt head-shaped objects with a regular or scrambled facial pattern (Freedman, 1975, p. 30) and bells sewn on. The objects were suspended 20–25 cm in front of the infant at shoulder height. As for the parent interactions, a chair was positioned before a table on which was placed a mirror oriented to permit videotaping from the center, 1 m away.

The study involved four situations, two with parent and two with toy, and each began only when the infant and the parent were comfortable. First, there was one 3-min parent situation (which one was randomly determined), then one of the two toy situations (randomly determined). The remaining parent and toy situations followed in random order. Each toy situation consisted of six 30-sec trials (two midline, two right at 60°, two left at 60°, in random order). Data from only the first 25 sec of each trial are reported since objects were moved from position to position by an experimenter sitting out of view in the last 5 sec (leaving a total of $2\frac{1}{2}$ min per object presentation per subject). In the interaction situations, the parents held the infants on the left side while seated (the left side was considered more natural by pretest parents), and they interacted as they "normally would." One min of alert activity had to be obtained in each of the four situations in order for the infant to be retained as a subject (9 infants did not meet this criterion and were dropped from the study).

An extensive behavioral catalogue was used in decoding (Table 1 in Young, Finlayson, Quintal, & Methot, in press). A primary observer coded all behaviors during each situation, while another observer coded a randomly selected 30 sec segment from each situation of each subject ($\frac{1}{6}$ of the data) for the purpose of checking interobserver reliability. Each randomly selected 30 sec segment was chosen without the knowledge of the primary coder. Kappa, which accounts for chance agreement independent of the frequency of occurrence, was calculated. A value of .6 was used as the criterion of acceptability for each category within each situation (following Hartmann, 1977). This criterion was met not only for the group as a whole but also for each subject. Observers failed to meet the criteria only once. The category involved was entirely recoded, and the criterion was met. Data were not considered where four or fewer subjects manifested a behavior in any one pair of situations (parents, toy). The duration of each remaining behavior in each trial was calculated, adjusted for missing data due to nonalert activity. Data were collapsed across order and toy since visual inspection revealed no effect of these variables on differential manual behavior. Then the following behaviors, some of which were composites of others, were analyzed for the purposes of the present chapter.

Reaching was defined as target-directed arm movement, touch as hand or finger contact of the target, and nondirected arm movements as a composite of body-oriented and other nondirected movements. Infant vocal behavior was a composite of neutral, rhythmic, and coo sounds; infant mouth movement was a composite of wide-open mouth, smile, lateral lip movement, suck, tongue out, and other lip–mouth–tongue activities; adult verbal–vocal behavior was a composite of verbal utterances, nonverbal sounds, laughter, and imitation, and adult mouth behavior was a composite of lips moving, sucking, smiling, kissing–biting–sucking, and imitating.

Finally, the data were analyzed second by second to determine whether just before or during a reaching and/or touching sequence in the object situations, the reach–touch hand and the other hand were fully or partly open (at least one finger extended or thumb opposed). In selecting reach–touch sequences for further analysis, isolated 1-sec periods of non-reach–touching within a reach–touch sequence were preserved. Once the duration of each reach–touch sequence was calculated, the onset and offset of before-period intervals were established as well, since their durations were set as equivalent to their associated reach–touch behavior durations. Where a particular time segment could be classified two ways (e.g., as behavior prior to reach of either reaching or nonreaching hand) because relatively lengthy reaching–touching behavior sequences occurred close in time, the segment was usually split proportionately according to the durations concerned. Since the frequency of reaching–touching per se was not of concern in this analysis, the proportion of right- and left-hand-opening activity to total reach–touch and non-reach–touch duration was calculated. This was done separately in each toy trial.

A MANOVA using Wilk's lambda criterion and Rao's approximate F test was employed to analyze together the reach and touch data, whereas an ANOVA alone was employed to analyze nondirected arm activity (3-way designs: Sex, a between factor, × Hand × Position, withins). A 4-way ANOVA was used to analyze the open-hand data (Sex × Hand × Position, as before, and an extra within factor, opening of the reach–touch versus the nonreach–touch hand). Univariate F tests were used to decompose significant interactions since, as we shall see, only factors with repeated measures (2 × 3; Hand × Position interactions) were involved, and different error terms need to be used for each relevant comparison in such cases

(Winer, 1971). Manual behavior on midline trials was used to create a laterality coefficient $(R - L)/(R + L)^{\frac{1}{2}}$ that was correlated with the parent and infant oral behaviors.

RESULTS

The MANOVA revealed a main effect for sex $(F[2, 13] = 5.23, p < .05)$ that seemed especially due to reaching (ANOVA $F[1, 14] = 19.98, p < .001$). Males reached three times longer than females $(M = 2.20$ versus .76 sec per 25-sec trial), replicating Bower's findings (cited in Shucard, Shucard, Cummins, & Campos, 1979) with 2-week-olds.

Nondirected arm activity was the only activity to show a main effect for hand (ANOVA $F[1, 14] = 5.37, p < .05$). This frequent activity was performed more by the left hand $(M = 17.39$ versus 15.62 sec; left hand preferred [50% of the time] by most [13] infants).

The predominant finding in the study was the predicted Hand × Position interaction, seen in all behaviors analyzed (see Table 7.1; the MANOVA result for reach and touch: $F[4, 54] = 4.05, p < .01$). The 2 × 2 F tests help specify that the right hand was preferred for reach, touch, and hand open when the object was at the right and at the midline, whereas the left hand was preferred when the object was at the left. The opposite pattern was found for nondirected arm activity. In terms of the number of lateralized subjects in each of the right, middle, and left positions, the trends follow the pattern just given. For reach, all 13 lateralized subjects in the right position were right-handed. Corresponding data for the middle and left positions were 7 of 11 and 2 of 12, respectively. Corresponding data for touch were 6 of 7, 4 of 4, and 0 of 5, respectively; for nondirected arm activity 3 of 16, 8 of 16, and 10 of 16, respectively; and for hand open, 13 of 14, 10 of 14, and 1 of 12, respectively. For hand opening of the reaching–touching hand alone, the data were 13 of 14, 8 of 12, and 0 of 12, respectively; whereas for hand opening of the nonreaching–touching hand, the data were 13 of 13, 10 of 14, and 1 of 12, respectively. The absence of an effect involving the factor whether the open hand was the reaching–touching or the other one fits the predictions that the right hand would be more open even when it was the nonreaching–touching one (at least for midline and right-side object presentation).

In determining correlations of right-lateralized 1-month object-directed activity at the midline with parent verbal–vocal and other behavior, touch could not be used since too few subjects used it in the midline position. Also, nondirected arm activity was subtracted from directed reaching in order to balance subordinate with executive activity (see Table 7.2). As predicted, the more the parents verbalized–vocalized, the more the infants were right-lateralized in directed arm activity. Infant mouthing behavior was also positively correlated with right lateralization in directed arm activity. Right lateralization of nonreaching hand opening was also

Table 7.1

Reaching at One Month: Means, 3 × 2 Hand × Position Interactions, and 2 × 2 F Tests Decomposing Them

Behavior	Position	Hand R	Hand L	Interaction (F;df)	L versus M	L versus R	M versus R	(L + M)/2 versus R	(L + R)/2 versus M	(M + R)/2 versus L
Reach to target	R	2.34	.23	9.81; 2,28 ***	6.39; 1,15 *	17.93; 1,15 ***	2.72; 1,15	18.41; 1,15 ***	1.16; 1,15	12.11; 1,15 **
	M	1.92	1.05							
	L	.53	2.80							
Touch target	R	.45	0	4.74; 2,28 *	4.09; 1,15 $p = .06$	8.66; 1,15 *	0.03; 1,15	7.59; 1,15 *	2.07; 1,15	6.08; 1,15 *
	M	.51	0							
	L	0	.85							
Nondirected-arm movement	R	13.37	17.86	4.08; 2,28 *	1.62; 1,15	10.87; 1,15 **	2.53; 1,15	9.74; 1,15 **	0; 1,15	5.78; 1,15 *
	M	14.90	16.66							
	L	18.58	17.66							
Reach–touch hand open[a]	R	.47	.04	31.45;[c] 2,26 ***	23.10; 1,14 ***	62.01; 1,14 ***	7.17; 1,14 *	41.88; 1,14 ***	2.33; 1,14	49.20; 1,14 ***
	M	.40	.29							
	L	.04	.49							
Nonreach–touch hand open[b]	R	.47	.02							
	M	.45	.24							
	L	.05	.42							

Note: R = Right; L = Left; M = Middle. First three behaviors in sec/25-sec period.
[a]During or just before reach and/or touch, proportion hand at least partly open.
[b]During or just before reach and/or touch, proportion nonreach–touch hand at least partly open.
[c]Results concern average of behaviors in a and b, since no significant results associated with whether the open hand is the reaching one or not.

*p < .05
**p < .01
***p < .001

134

Table 7.2

Correlation (Pearson r) of Relative Right-Hand Directed-Arm Movements at One Month[a,b] with Oral Behavior When with the Parent and Toy, Family Handedness, and Eighteen-Month Laterality[b]

Oral behavior with toy			Family handedness		
Behavior	N	r	Item	N	r
Vocalize when before toy	16	.13	Mother's handedness questionnaire	16	−.29
Mouth when before toy	16	.62***	Father's handedness questionnaire	16	−.08
			Mother's family handedness	8	.22
			Father's family handedness	9	.30

Oral behavior with parent			Eighteen-month laterality		
Behavior	N	r	Behavior	N	r
Vocalize when with mother	16	−.25	Grasp reached for toy	9	−.05
Vocalize when with father	16	−.56	Manipulate reached for toy	9	.72**
Mouth when with mother	16	.47**	Tap 1 baton on another	4	.90**
			Tap xylophone—unimanual trials	7	−.34
Mouth when with father	16	.64***			
			Tap xylophone—bimanual trials	7	.56*
Verbalize–vocalize by mother	16	.53**			
			Hand move on toy—unimanual	5	−.45
Verbalize–vocalize by father	16	.59***			
			Hand move on toy—bimanual	8	.09
Mouth by mother	16	−.15			
			Imitate gesture—unimanual	2	—
Mouth by father	16	−.26	Imitate gesture—bimanual	6	−.66*

[a]Directed-arm movement = (reach to target−nondirected-arm movement) at midline position.
[b]Relative right-hand laterality = $(R - L)/(R + L)^{1/2}$.
*$p < .10$
**$p < .05$
***$p < .01$, 1-tailed test.

correlated with parent behaviors. As predicted, the more the parents mouthed, the more the infants were right-lateralized in nonreaching–touching hand opening ($r = .48$, $N = 14$, $p < .05$ for the father; $r = .39$, $N = 14$, $p < .10$ for the mother). No other significant results were obtained for hand opening of the nonreaching–touching or reaching–touching hand, except that the former was positively correlated with mouth when with mother ($r = .68$, $N = 12$, $p < .01$).

The validity of the lateralized directed arm activity measure is shown by the correlations between it and data gathered longitudinally (see Table 7.2) at 18 months of age for nine of the sixteen infants; 1-month right-lateralized directed arm activity correlated positively not only with right lateralization of manipulation of a toy after reaching for it at 18 months, but also with tapping measures, taken to be indices of hemispheric specialization (Ramsay, Chapter 9, this volume). Moreover, as one would predict, 1-month, right-lateralized, directed-arm activity correlated negatively with an 18-month left-lateralized spatial activity measure (imitate gesture, bimanual presentation; $p < .10$). Family handedness did not correlate with 1-month right-lateralized directed-arm activity.

Conclusions

The 2-day-old head-turning data, showing more right turns especially with respect to speech stimuli, suggest that from this very early period, the left hemisphere seems specialized for receptive speech functioning and/or the right hemisphere contributes to receptive music functioning. This confirms previous findings (especially Hammer, 1977; Molfese & Molfese, Chapter 5, this volume) that early hemispheric specialization approximates the adult model. The 1-month reaching data only adds to this impression; the right hand was used more in reaching and touching, especially when the object was at the midline or right side, whereas non-directed activity showed the opposite pattern. Young et al. (Chapter 2, this volume) have shown that these results fit the predominant trend in the literature (e.g., von Hofsten, 1982, with 2-week-olds) and how McDonnell's (1979) findings, which apparently contrast with this pattern, do not really concern directed reaching.

What is lateralized in the left hemisphere even so early in life may concern inhibition skills as much as any other kind. In the 1-month-olds, the right hand is relatively more open when the object is at the midline and at the right, not only if it is reaching, but also if the left hand is reaching. Thus, the left hemisphere compared to the right may both (a) better organize the contralateral hand in coordinated activity that presumably demands a balance of inhibition and activation; and (b) better inhibit the ipsilateral hand in irrelevant activity (see pages 121–123). Even in the study of 2-day-olds, there is a sign of effective left-hemisphere inhibition of secondary activity. During the stimulation period, where the head-turning data suggested that the left hemisphere was more involved in listening even for music, secondary body–seat contact occurred less with the right hand, which was not the case 2–4 sec after stimulation. These data suggest a contralateral inhibition by the left hemisphere of secondary manual activity during listening, followed by a right-hand preference for this behavior well after the stimuli have terminated.

We are not suggesting that because we find data analogous to that found with the adult hemispheric specialization does not develop. What is lateralized, the degree and stability of lateralization, and the proportion of lateralized individuals in a population may change over age even if the modal direction of lateralization does not. This point is illustrated by our finding that degree of parent verbalization–vocalization to the infant at 1 month of age is positively correlated with the degree of right lateralization in directed arm activity, an apparent index of left-hemisphere balancing of inhibition and activation, and our finding that the degree of parent mouthing behavior positively correlated with the degree of right lateralization in nonreaching hand opening, an apparent index of left-hemisphere inhibition of irrelevant activity. Other behaviors (e.g., look) not particularly associated with the left hemisphere more than the right did not show this pattern, fitting with the idea that the more the infant receives active social behaviors that are presumably processed in the left hemisphere, the more that hemisphere will develop its specialization, whether of an inhibition–activation or inhibition variety, and be used in situations appropriate to its specialization. The positive correlation of right-lateralized, directed-arm activity with infant mouthing, akin to prespeech, both when with object or parent, suggests that the parent may respond more vocally–verbally with an "active left hemisphere" in dialogue with intrinsically more "left-hemisphere active" infants, accounting in part or in full for the positive correlation between parent verbal–vocal behavior and infant right lateralization in directed arm activity. However, the lack of similar correlations for the nonreaching hand-opening measure suggests that an interpretation of these correlations that stresses a role of parental oral behavior in fostering left-hemisphere development is a plausible one, notwithstanding the multiple interpretations one can ascribe to any correlation.

There seems to be an effect of modality in the possible relationship of parent oral behavior and infant hemispheric specialization. The parent verbal–vocal measure correlated positively with the apparent inhibition–activation measure of the infant, whereas the parent mouth measure correlated positively with the apparent inhibition measure of the infant. It could be that the more overt the presumably left-hemisphere-oriented behavior in the parent, the more the effect on the infant's left-hemisphere development results in more overt behavior, and/or it could be that the more the parent's behavior demands subtle attention, as in mouth movements without sound, the more concomitant manual behaviors are inhibited in order to attend, and the more the left hemisphere's ability to inhibit irrelevant manual activity in general is increased.[2]

[2]The lack of correlation of infant vocalization with any of the measures is not emphasized here because this behavior was infrequent. An important role in early development for the father, as well as the mother, will probably be specified by such research if the pattern suggested by the present correlations continues to involve both parents. However, the lack of correlation of family handedness with 1-month, right-lateralized, directed-arm activity is contrasted with the significant positive correlation found between the mother's right-handedness and infant right-hand opening ($r = .69$, $r = .62$, for reaching/touching and other hand, respectively). These correlations do not allow us to determine whether the mother contributes more to lateralization development as they seem to suggest at first glance.

Finally, the longitudinal correlations between 1-month directed-arm activity and 18-month lateralized behavior not only on a reaching task but also in tapping, in particular, suggests that the 1-month measure used in the present chapter may be a valid, powerful, predictive index of laterality. There may be a critical period early in life in the development of hemispheric and/or manual specialization in which parental social experience conducive to left-hemisphere processing by the infant has long-lasting effects on the development of the specializaton of the hemispheres and, in turn, the behavior of the parents and the infant's development in other areas. This may apply to what the hemispheres do, what they prevent from being done (inhibition), and how these two factors interweave in a balancing of activation and inhibition.

This concept of parental left-hemisphere-oriented activity needs to be refined. It could be that only certain speech characteristics of the voice are involved (e.g., phoneme contrasts). Or perhaps not only (specific) speech characteristics but also nonverbal social phenomena are involved. That is, if the hypotheses just presented regarding the social nature of the left hemisphere are valid, the dynamic social interchange that the parent structures for the neonate and young child may be what actually best stimulates left-hemisphere development, especially if this interchange includes verbal–vocal behavior. Also, there may be sex differences in the sensitivity to early parental stimulation, with girls more effected in the long-term, in particular (Young et al., in press). It seems worthwhile to add that the role of right-hemisphere and general stimulation in the development of lateralization of brain function needs to be investigated, as does the role of any stimulation in interhemispheric interaction and in the lateralized brain development of the left-hander. Finally, there may be a distinction between short-term and long-term effects of these types of stimulation on early brain development.

Acknowledgments

Many thanks are due to Carl Corter and Sid Segalowitz for their incisive comments and to Yves Joannette, André Roch Lecours, and David Caplan for pointing out relevant material. The writing of this chapter was completed while the first author was on sabbatical at the Laboratoire Théophile Alajouanine, Centre de Recherche, Centre Hospitalier Côte-des-Neiges, Montréal, Québec.

References

Annett, J., Annett, M., Hudson, P. T. W., & Turner, A. (1979). The control of movement in the preferred and nonpreferred hands. *Quarterly Journal of Experimental Psychology 31*, 641–652.

Bashore, T. (1981). Vocal and manual reaction time estimates of interhemispheric transmission time. *Psychological Bulletin 89*, 352–368.

Bradshaw, J., & Nettleton, N. (1981a). Double trouble: An evolutionary cut at the dichotomy pie. The Behavioral and Brain Sciences 4, 79–85.

Bradshaw, J., & Nettleton, N. (1981b). The nature of hemispheric specialization in man. The Behavioral and Brain Sciences 4, 51–63.

Bryden, M. (1977). Measuring handedness with questionnaires. Neuropsychologia 15, 617–624.

Campbell, R., (1982). The lateralization of emotion: A critical review. International Journal of Psychology 17, 211–229.

Cohen, G. (1975). Hemispheric differences in the utilization of advance information. In P. Rabbitt & S. Dornic (Eds.), Attention and performance (Vol. 5). New York: Academic Press.

Corballis, M. (1981). Toward an evolutionary perspective on hemispheric specialization. The Behavioral and Brain Sciences 4, 69–70.

Crovitz, H., & Zener, K. (1962). A group-test for assessing hand- and eye-dominance. American Journal of Psychology 75, 271–276.

Davidson, R., & Fox, N. (1982). Asymmetrical brain activity discriminates between positive and negative affective stimuli in human infants. Science 218, 1235–1237.

Flowers, K. (1975). Handedness and controlled movements. British Journal of Psychology 66, 39–52.

Freedman, D. (1975). Human infancy: An evolutionary perspective. Hillsdale, New Jersey: Erlbaum.

Geschwind, N., (1975). The apraxias: Neural mechanisms of disorders of learned movement. American Scientist 63, 188–195.

Goldberg, E., & Costa, L. (1981). Hemispheric differences in the acquisition and use of descriptive systems. Brain and Language 14, 144–173.

Hammer, M. (1977). Lateral differences in the newborn infants' response to speech and noise stimuli. Unpublished doctoral dissertation, New York University.

Hartmann, D. (1977). Considerations in the choice of interobserver reliability estimates. Journal of Applied Behavior Analysis 10, 103–116.

Jackson, H. (1915). On the nature of the duality of the brain. Brain 38, 80–103. (originally published, 1874.)

Jaffe, J. (1978). Parliamentary procedure and the brain. In A. W. Seigman & S. Feldstein (Eds.), Nonverbal behavior and communication. Hillsdale, New Jersey: Erlbaum.

Jasper, H. H., & Raney, E. T. (1937). The physiology of lateral cerebral dominance: Review of literature and evaluation of the test of simultaneous bilateral movement. Psychological Bulletin 34, 151–165.

Kimura, D. (1977). Acquisition of a motor skill after left hemisphere damage. Brain 100, 527–542.

Kimura, D. (1980). Neuromotor mechanisms in the evolution of human communication. In H. D. Steklis & M. J. Raleigh (Eds.), Neurobiology of social communication in primates. New York: Academic Press.

Kimura, D., & Archibald, Y. (1974). Motor functions of the left hemisphere. Brain 97, 337–350.

Kimura, D., Battison, R., & Lubert, B. (1976). Impairment of nonlinguistic hand movements in a deaf aphasic. Brain and Language 3, 566–571.

Kinsbourne, M. (1970). The cerebral basis of lateral asymmetries in attention. Acta Psychologia 33, 193–201.

Klein, D., Moscovitch, M., & Vigna, C. (1976). Attentional mechanisms and perceptual asymmetries on tachistoscopic recognition of words and faces. Neuropsychologia 14, 55–56.

Ledoux, J. (1982). Neuroevolutionary mechanisms of cerebral asymmetry in man. Brain, Behavior and Evolution 20, 196–212.

Liepmann, H. (1908). Drei Aufsätze aus dem Apraxiegebiet. Karger, Berlin.

McDonnell, P. M. (1979). Patterns of eye–hand coordination in the first year of life. *Canadian Journal of Psychology 33*, 253–267.

Malfara, A., & Jones, B. (1981). Hemispheric asymmetries in motor control of guided reaching with and without optic displacement. *Neuropsychologia 19*, 483–486.

Marin, O. S. M., & Saffran, E. M. (1975). Agnosic behavior in anomia: A case of pathological verbal dominance. *Cortex 11*, 83–89.

Mateer, C. (1978). Impairments of nonverbal oral movements after left hemisphere damage: A followup analysis of errors. *Brain and Language 6*, 334–341.

Mateer, C., & Kimura, D. (1977). Impairment of nonverbal oral movements in aphasia. *Brain and Language 4*, 262–276.

Moscovitch, M. (1979). Information processing. In M. S. Gazzaniga (Ed.), *Handbook of behavioral neurobiology* (Vol. 2): *Neuropsychology.* New York: Plenum.

Nottebohm, F. (1979). Origins and mechanisms in the establishment of cerebral dominance. In M. S. Gazzaniga (Ed.), *Handbook of behavioral neurobiology* (Vol. 2): *Neuropsychology.* New York: Plenum.

Nottebohm, F. (1981). Does hemispheric specializaton of function reflect the needs of an executive side? *The Behavioral and Brain Sciences 4*, 74.

Oldfield, R. (1969). Handedness in musicians. *British Journal of Psychology 60*, 91–99.

Peters, M. (1981). Handedness: Coordination of within- and between-hand alternating movements. *American Journal of Psychology 94*, 633–643.

Poeck, K., & Huber, W. (1977). To what extent is language a sequential activity? *Neuropsychologia 15*, 359–364.

Saling, M. (1978). The significance of lateral compatibility for the early mother–infant relationship. *South African Journal of Psychology 8*, 35–42.

Saling, M. (1982). *Determinants of lateral organization in neonates.* Unpublished doctoral dissertation, University of the Witwatersrand, Johannesburg.

Shucard, J., Shucard, D., Cummins, K., & Campos, J. (1979). *Auditory evoked potentials and sex related differences in brain development.* Paper presented to the Society for Research in Child Development, San Francisco, California, March.

Winer, B. (1971). *Statistical principles in experimental design* (2nd ed.). New York: McGraw-Hill.

von Hofsten, C. (1982). Eye–hand coordination in the newborn. *Developmental Psychology 18*, 450–461.

Vygotsky, L. (1962). *Thought and language.* Cambridge, Massachusetts: The M.I.T. Press.

Young, G. (1977). Manual specialization in infancy: Implications for lateralization of brain function. In S. Segalowitz & F. Gruber (Eds.), *Language development and neurological theory.* New York: Academic Press.

Young, G., Finlayson, M., Quintal, J., & Methot, C. (in press). Parent interaction and reaction to objects with facial patterns in 1-month olds: Sex differences. *L'Actualité Medicale.*

8

Differentiation and Lateral Specialization in Motor Development

MICHAEL PETERS

Introduction

Efforts to study the development of handedness have largely focused on several empirical questions: Are there indicators of lateral preference early in life, when do such preferences emerge, and what kinds of movements are involved (McDonnell, 1979; Young, 1977)? Thus, researchers are still struggling to document the facts of motor asymmetry early in life, and it is not surprising that some important developmental questions have been relatively neglected. With reference to the neonate, such questions center on the meaning of lateral biases to the brain in which much of the machinery that guides skilled movement in the adult has not yet fully differentiated. The substantial differences between the neural substrates guiding movement in the newborn and in the adult suggest that the meaning of lateral asymmetries must differ early and later in life. This, in turn, raises questions about the nature of the transforming processes that link early and late asymmetry. Such transforming processes represent the essence of development; *development* does not denote a unidimensional progression along a maturational gradient, but rather an interactive process where the results of differentiation feed back on the very substrate that is differentiating, to bring about further change in form and function. This chapter will focus on the way in which differentiation of executing motor structures interacts with higher-order processes involved in the planning and guidance of movement to yield ever more powerful sources of lateral bias in movement (the ontogenetic perspective). However, there will also be a brief discussion of the search for more general principles of

141

function that allow an understanding of handedness in a broader evolutionary sense (the phylogenetic perspective).

Throughout this chapter, little attention will be paid to the question of
how the direction of lateral specialization becomes fixed (Corballis &
Morgan, 1978). Once lateral specialization has proven to confer a selective
advantage, processes of selection will tend to work toward a fixation of
the direction of asymmetry that allows the best exploitation of the various
processes that need to be lateralized for optimal functioning. By what
mechanism this fixation occurs is considered a peripheral question here.

The Phylogenetic Perspective

MacLean (1964) has proposed that the brainstem and midbrain region
of the human brain are homologous to the corresponding regions of the
reptile brain and that these regions contribute to the same behavioral
functions in humans as they do in reptiles. MacLean speaks, meta-
phorically, of the "reptile brain" within the human brain when he refers
to these structures. There are obvious problems with MacLean's argument. First, there is the dispute as to what parts of the reptile brain may be
considered homologous to human midbrain structures (Webster, 1979).
Second, and more important for the present discussion, there is the question as to the nature of the behavioral functions that these structures are
said to guide. After all, the behavior of adult reptiles is highly differentiated, and the problem is not solved if reference is made to the behavior of
young reptiles, ancestral or present: Reptiles show highly differentiated
behavior at the time of birth, or hatching. The argument, if there is to
remain any validity to MacLean's model, leads back to a position that
biologists have reached with regard to the concept of recapitulation as it
relates to morphological features: During ontogenetic development, the
morphological features of the embryonic stages of ancestral species (and
not the features of their adult forms) are recapitulated (Gould, 1977).
Applied to behavior, if there is any phylogenetic link between the behavior of reptiles and humans, it would have to be restricted to the recapitulation by humans, in the very early neonatal period, of undifferentiated
"embryonic" reptile behavior. MacLean's model is interesting since it
suggests that the behavior of the human neonate is essentially undifferentiated reptile behavior; presumably, the "reptile brain" matures early during development and guides behavior until the "other brains" superimpose their function.

Another, more general, way of looking at the same question has been
offered by Jerison (1976). Jerison suggests that the "basic vertebrate brain"
has remained quite stable in terms of its major anatomical components
and their relations to each other, and he feels that the brains of fish,

amphibians, and reptiles can all be considered "basic vertebrate brains." In terms of function, Jerison (1976) has a conservative interpretation, "It is likely that the nervous system is conservatively organized in the sense that a particular input–output relationship (function), once established in particular networks, will probably be performed by homologous networks in descendant species in an evolutionary series [p. 12]." In other words, functions that are mediated by the "basic vertebrate brain" continue to be mediated by homologous regions in the brains of mammals in general.

Jerison's interpretation converges with that extrapolated from MacLean's view: At birth, much of the functioning part of the brain can be labeled as equivalent to the "basic vertebrate brain." The question is whether behavioral asymmetries can be considered a feature of the basic vertebrate brain and, if so, what is their functional significance? An answer to this question will have to consider the structural basis for any possible asymmetries in behavior.

All vertebrates possess a brain that, at least superficially, shows bilateral symmetry, and the two halves appear functionally equivalent. However, the output from the two brain halves has to be integrated and, if need be "when incompatible decisions are simultaneously formulated, one brain half overrides the other and commands the bilateral musculature [Kinsbourne, 1974, p. 230]." Kinsbourne suggests that the process whereby one system overrides the other is simple reciprocal inhibition. At another level, the organism has to integrate the two separate systems into a unitary acting self (Trevarthen, 1974). The basic vertebrate brain must, in the normal initiation of movement, act as a unitary system. According to Corballis and Beale (1976), unity in function presupposes structural asymmetry, and such asymmetry must be a feature of the "basic vertebrate brain." Supporting evidence for this statement is scarce, not for the reason that it is untrue, but rather because researchers do not, at this point, know where to look for asymmetry in subcortical structures. In some isolated cases (Morgan, 1977), obvious anatomical asymmetries in "basic vertebrate brains" have been documented, but such asymmetries may also be based on different distributions of transmitters. Such a possibility is raised by the research of Glick, Jerussi, and Zimmerberg (1977), who observed that rotation to the left and right in rats is related to an asymmetry in the distribution of dopamine in the nigrostriatal system. Such rotation tendencies underlie spontaneous orienting behavior and represent directional biases in the attention to left and right hemispace. Recent evidence on the asymmetrical distribution of norepinephrine in the somatosensory transmission nuclei (Oke, Keller, Mefford, & Adams, 1978) of humans is another example of a subtle asymmetry that cannot be identified with gross anatomical methods.

In summary, the "basic vertebrate brain" is capable of asymmetry in function. Assuming that Jerison's dictum about the preservation of function in homologous structures is correct, subcortical structures continue to play a role in the expression of behavioral asymmetries even when cortical structures are involved as well.

It had been stressed previously that the demand for functional asymmetry arises out of the problem of how to make separate systems act as one. The importance of asymmetry at this level does not lie in the quality of the movement that is to be guided, but rather in the decision as to which of two systems, equally capable of initiating movement, is to be activated first. Asymmetry, then, refers at this level to the bias that is expressed when events in the environment are attended to, or when the direction of goal-directed behavior is determined. Implicit in this view is that motor and sensory function cannot be separated in terms of priority; it cannot be said that asymmetry of one leads to asymmetry in the other. Rather, the dictates of functional adaptiveness of behavior demand an interaction: Movement has meaning only in its relation to the environment, and sensory stimuli have meaning only in terms of potential response.

The analysis of lateral specialization in terms of phylogenesis leads to two major conclusions about the nature of lateral specialization in the neonate. First, the structural basis for functional asymmetry must lie at the subcortical level. Full cortical participation depends on further structural and functional differentiation during ontogeny. Second, the expression of lateral specialization in the neonate is more aptly described in terms that relate to the allocation of attention and the decision to move rather than in terms that relate to the specifics of movement execution.

Beyond this, the phylogenetic approach is not very helpful in predicting what form lateral specialization will take in the course of ontogeny. The processes of differentiation that lead from the expression of lateral specialization in the neonate to its final manifestation as hand preference in skilled motor behavior are best discussed alone. This will be done in the following section.

The Ontogenetic Perspective

Differentiation in the motor domain proceeds both centrally and peripherally. We will show how lateralization can be manifested at the central and the peripheral levels and how the interaction between the levels determines the nature and extent of lateralization over the course of development.

Differentiation at the Peripheral Level

A marked, although not unique, feature of the human neonate is the lack of development of the neuromuscular apparatus. During the first few weeks and months of life, changes take place both in peripheral nerves and muscles that represent not only qualitative modifications, but also qualitatively different principles of function. Some of these changes have a bearing on lateral specialization and are therefore pertinent to the present discussion. During ontogeny, muscle fibers differentiate into two principal types (although presence of fibers with intermediate characteristics is likely)—slow and fast fibers. Slow fibers have slow contraction speeds, low activation thresholds, and good endurance. Fast fibers contract quickly, have high activation thresholds, and fatigue more easily. Within a muscle group, fast and slow fibers intermingle, and their ratio differs among particular muscle groups and among individuals. The factors which determine the differentiation of muscle fibers into one or the other type are not well understood at present. However, there is an intriguing suggestion that the nature and extent of activity in muscle partially determines the differentiation into the two muscle types. An experimental study by Guth and Yellin (1971) in which activity in one muscle group was experimentally manipulated suggests that marked and sustained activity might promote differentiation into the slow fiber type.

Superimposed on the process of differentiation of muscle fibers into different types is a general trend toward increasing contraction speed during development that affects both slow and fast muscle fibers. In human infants, muscles contract relatively slowly. This might permit feedback control of movement, which would be an important factor in the acquisition of central motor programs. However, slowness of movement in itself does not guarantee the conditions for feedback control; early in life, the axons of motor neurons at the peripheral level conduct impulses much more slowly than they do in the adult, and afferent nerves may show a similar trend (Hildebrand & Skoglund, 1971). Nevertheless, this slowness is counterbalanced, to some extent, by the shorter distances that nerves travel in the infant as compared to the adult.

Another process of differentiation at the peripheral level is observed in patterns of muscle fiber innervation. In a variety of mammalian young (Jacobson, 1978, p. 311), a single muscle fiber receives several different motor neuron inputs. However, in the adult of the species, each muscle fiber receives input only from one single neuron. During development, there must therefore be a progressive elimination of multiple innervation until only one input survives.

In functional terms, the early pattern of multiple innervation means that the output of a motor neuron results in a more diffuse and less specific activation of its target musculature than is the case after competing multiple inputs to muscle fibers have been eliminated. Thus, if there is any feedback of results of motor neuron activation in the first few weeks of life, this feedback cannot be very precise.

It is not entirely clear how multiple inputs to a single muscle fiber are eliminated, but it is likely that such elimination depends, to some extent, on patterns of activation. In other words, the processes of differentiation at the peripheral level, both in terms of the type of muscle fiber that forms and in terms of the nature of innervation, likely depend on activity in the efferent nerves (Jacobson, 1978, p. 316 ff.).

As a result, a very complex picture emerges. The substrate on which the output acts is changing continuously over the course of development, and the central representation of the relation between output and response must take into account the plastic nature of the response apparatus. It is also clear that movement—any movement—must play an important role in the differentiation of the response apparatus.

If movement—spontaneous or otherwise—does substantially affect the differentiation of peripheral nerves, their innervation of the muscle fibers and the nature of muscle fibers, then any early bias in the mere amount of movement in a given arm or leg is liable to result in different rates of differentiation. This would affect further output to the extent that the central representation of the more clearly differentiated peripheral apparatus is more accurate. It is suggested here that an initial and very mild bias can result, in the end, in a rather strong asymmetry, since the results of the bias will tend to reinforce the bias in a positive feedback manner.

Differentiation at the Central Level

The differentiation of motor processes at the central level is, of course, a vast area and can only be treated in a sketchy way. To introduce some of the more intriguing points of the ontogeny of motor control, a hierarchical model of the motor system will be adopted. At the basis of the hierarchy are the motor neurons of the spinal cord (and the corresponding motor neurons of the cranial nerves). In the basic vertebrate and in the human neonate, these neurons are interconnected so as to allow functional movements—the reflexes. In its original meaning, the term *reflex* denotes something that reflects back on itself and, as applied to movement, the term is a metaphor for a response that reflects back on the agent that elicits it. In keeping with its original meaning, the term has acquired the connotation of immutability and automaticity, and "reflexive" behavior is often contrasted with "voluntary" behavior.

This view, however, fails to take into account the flexibility of spinal processes. Much of the spinal cord is taken up not by simple input and output elements, but by a great number of intercalated structures that mediate between input and output. The reticular formation is, in fact, not an emergent structure, but represents a continuation of the diffuse nerve nets in the center of the spinal cord that allow a great deal of processing at the spinal level. In the normally developing neonate, reflexes are notoriously fickle. Often, reflexes do not appear when the adequate stimulus is present, and their topography is variable in its expression. They are sensitive to the general state of the infant and easily affected by changes in the internal and external environment. This contextual sensitivity is indicative of supraspinal influences that are of great importance even in the neonate. An illustration of this is given by pathological reflexes in adults. After certain brainstem and midbrain damage, adults may show a very marked and persistent forced grasp response (Twitchell, 1965). In the neonate, this response is far more variable and flexible. A further illustration of the openness of spinal cell assemblies underlying reflexive behavior of neonates is given by the way in which experience can modify the context in which reflexes are elicited or the ease with which reflexes can be activated. Examples are the rapidly acquired operant control of the sucking response by infants who can influence certain events with their sucking (Bruner, 1969) and the delay in the disappearance of the stepping reflex after extended practice with stepping movements (Zelazo, 1976).

Evidence of this kind leads to a different understanding of the nature of hierarchical models of the motor system. For example, Kots (1977) visualizes the motor hierarchy as a system in which "each underlying level is not merely a slave relay for the undistorted transmission of signals originating at a higher level, but is in large measure an active integrative component of the system as a whole [p. 214]."

Once reflexes are seen as an integral part of an interacting motor system, their role in the differentiation of motor function can be seen in a wider perspective, one that relates both to the ontogeny of voluntary movement and to the formulation of motor plans in general.

THE ROLE OF REFLEXES IN VOLUNTARY MOVEMENT

Current views, in accordance with Kots' (1977) suggestion, stress the role of reflexes within voluntary behavior (Easton, 1972; Evarts, 1980) rather than recognizing reflexive and voluntary movement as separate categories. The current conceptions of reflex movement suggest that most movements that are initiated from supraspinal structures depend on functional cell assemblies in the spinal cord. Descending commands, therefore, do not normally "compose" the detail of the topography of a movement, but address entire cell assemblies that issue functionally meaningful movements. In principle, there is little change over the course of development in this; the activation of interconnected cell assemblies continues to form the basic substrate of movement—voluntary or otherwise—in the neonate and in the adult. What does change over the course of development is the way in which the spinal cell assemblies that spell out reflexes can be accessed by supraspinal structures. One of the manifestations of differentiation in movement control is the ever-widening range of conditions under which the spinal cell assemblies can be activated.

An advantage of seeing reflexes as an important part of skilled and voluntary behavior in the adult (Easton, 1972) is that a conceptual link between manifestations of lateral asymmetry in the infant and handedness in the adult can be established. This link is explored a little later.

When the neonate clenches its fingers into a fist, a number of spinal motor neurons that act on the appropriate flexors fire in unison. Flexion of a single finger—to the exclusion of others—requires that neurons that normally function together are accessed selectively. This functional separation of certain neurons out of an entire cell assembly is presumably made possible by the direct corticospinal tract that gains access to individual spinal motor neurons—both for their activation and inhibition. Implicit in this assumption is that one and the same motor neuron is both part of a reflex assembly that flexes all fingers and part of a selectively activated circuit that activates flexion in only one finger. The fibers that selectively activate certain cells within the assembly are directly descending fibers from the cortex. From a phylogenetic perspective, the indirect brainstem pathways precede the direct corticospinal connections, but Noback and Scribner (1969) suggested an interrelation. They proposed that, initially, the direct corticospinal tracts are projections from the cortex to the brainstem. Further descent is accomplished by the development of collaterals that extend beyond the brainstem to establish contact with spinal motor neurons. A distinctly two-layered differentiation of the direct corticospinal system is also suggested by myelinization studies that find that the cortex–brainstem portion of the pathway matures much earlier than the further descending portion (Flechsig, 1920). It is very tempting to suggest that the synaptic contacts that the corticospinal tract fibers make at the brainstem levels are with cells that give rise to those brainstem–spinal cord fibers that terminate on spinal motor neurons, the common target of both fiber systems. Figure 8.1 gives a schematic illustration of the proposed relation between the two fiber systems. Tentative support for such a relation between direct and indirect descending fiber systems comes from observations made by Brinkman and Kuypers (1972), who found that both the direct and the indirect descending systems contain elements that project bilaterally to the spinal gray matter and elements that project unilaterally to spinal gray matter. Interestingly, the zones of termination for the bilateral projections are similar for both fiber systems, and this also applies to the unilaterally projecting systems. There is a clear coincidence of target zones for the corresponding components of the direct and indirect fiber systems.

The close anatomical links between the directly and indirectly projecting corticospinal tracts are reflected in normal hand movements. For instance, early in life, grasping movements are accomplished by activation of a spinal cell assembly that activates flexors in all fingers. The precision grasp is superimposed on the flexion of the hand and, even in the adult, it normally occurs in conjunction with the flexion of the other fingers un-

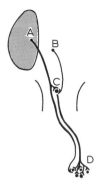

Figure 8.1. Model of how direct corticospinal tract fibers establish contact with spinal motor neurons. (A). Direct corticospinal tract fibers arising from cortical motor neurons. (B). Fibers from various sources, including the indirectly descending corticospinal tracts. (C). Lower brainstem region and neurons therein that project to spinal motor neurons. (D). Assembly of spinal motor neurons that act together in a functionally meaningful movement (i.e., flexion of all fingers). The model suggests that the direct corticospinal tract fibers establish functional connections with the help of earlier maturing, indirectly descending fibers. Neurons in (C) cannot activate individual neurons in assembly (D) selectively.

less a special effort is made to extend the three fingers that are not directly involved in the precision grasp. In skilled use of the hand, integrated movement of the fingers remains the rule rather than the exception, and truly independent control of the fingers matures later and remains more limited than is generally realized.

It is suggested here that, in the execution of skilled movement under voluntary control, much of the guidance of movement rests on indirect tracts descending from the brainstem to the spinal cord, and that control over the activation and termination of movement is acquired by the coactivation of the indirect and direct descending systems. The formation of the movement intent and the initiation of movement are functions that are operative before the advent of the direct corticospinal tracts. They continue to be handled by those parts of the brain that, through phylogenetic history, have dealt with them: the basal ganglia, the cerebellum, and parts of the limbic system. This view is consistent with current thinking:

> Whereas the traditional view held that the cerebral motor cortex was at the highest level of motor integration and that the subcortical structures were at a lower level, that is, closer to the muscle, it now appears that the situation is quite the reverse. The inputs going into the cerebellum and into the basal ganglia may be coded in a more abstract and complex manner than the outputs leaving the motor cortex [Evarts, 1980, p. 244].

Rather than being the substrate of voluntary movement, the direct corticospinal system merely provides greater resolution in terms of allowing more precise movements (Phillips & Porter, 1977), and the basic mechanisms that initiate movement in this system are in all probability those that activate and inactivate the supraspinal inputs to spinal reflex assemblies.

If this is so, then some of the difficulties in linking manifestations of handedness early in life (i.e., reaching response) to handedness in the adult are removed. Any directionally consistent bias that is acting on reflex movement early in life will come to bear on movement mediated by the direct corticospinal tracts as well, because the two systems are linked functionally. It was suggested in the first section of this chapter that a fundamental factor in lateral specialization in movement is the need of a bilaterally arranged organism to act as a single unit. Emphasis was placed on a lateralized initiation of movement. Since the mechanism by which movement is initiated in the direct and indirect descending systems is considered to be the same, the underlying asymmetry is not found in the executing motor systems, but in the system that initiates and terminates movements in these systems.

Although asymmetry is therefore not thought to originate in the structural arrangement of the descending motor systems, we suggest here that structural changes can result from even mild directional biases. Such bias will bring asymmetries in the rate at which muscle types differentiate in the periphery and the rate at which multiple innervation of muscle fibers will be eliminated and will consequently result in asymmetries in the efficiency of feedback. In addition, any lateral bias in activity patterns will likely result in the quicker establishment of functional contacts between direct corticospinal tract fibers and spinal motor neurons.

Much of this is highly speculative, but some of the basic premises of the model that has been developed lead to testable predictions. Since the emphasis is on a supraspinal, subcortical source for asymmetry, some directionally consistent asymmetries should not be observed in infants with extensive midbrain damage. The asymmetrical tonic neck reflex (ATNR) will be used as an example. In the normal neonate, this reflex reveals a right-side bias (Gesell, 1945, pp. 129–130; Turkewitz, 1977). In infants with severe midbrain damage, this reflex may occur in exaggerated form and can therefore be observed quite easily. It may be predicted that in such infants, no consistent directional bias (as a group) should be observed since the underlying sources for asymmetry cannot come to bear on the direction of the reflex.

The proposition that subtle directional biases in supraspinal mechanisms that are concerned with the initiation of movement underlie the development of handedness might be interpreted to conflict with the suggestion by Coryell and Michel (1978) and Michel (1981) as to the genesis of hand preferences. These researchers noted that infants in the supine position show a head-right bias that leads to greater visual experience with the right hand, which in turn is seen to lead to right handed-ness. Their claim can be easily tested by investigating the handedness of congenitally blind children. Should they, as a group, show a trend toward right handedness, there would be no reason to accept selective early visu-al experience with the right hand as the sole factor in the development of right handedness. Also, the finding of a right-foot preference in neonates in the stepping reflex (Peters & Petrie, 1979) would be difficult to interpret in terms of selective visual experience. However, selective visual experi-ence due to a head-right bias could be reinforcing already existing biases and constitute an additional factor in the development of a right-hand preference.

Discussion of the role of reflexes in voluntary behavior has stressed how, during development, reflexive movements become integrated into voluntary movement and how, in the early interaction between reflexive and voluntary movement, lateral specialization is transformed from a functional principle at the subcortical level to one that operates at the cortical level as well. Reflexive movement is, however, not only impli-cated in processes that are involved in the execution of voluntary move-ment, but also in processes that are concerned with the development of motor plans.

REFLEXIVE MOVEMENT AND THE DEVELOPMENT OF MOTOR PLANS

Piaget (1971) has pointed out that the basic unit of movement, the reflex, is also a basic level of knowledge. Piaget defines the act of knowing in terms of the assimilation of the object to be known into an action schema. The reflex is an action schema of the most fundamental sort, and the stimulus is "known" by its assimilation into the response. The reflex is based on preformed structures, and, at this level, knowledge can be considered innate. Accordingly, the stimulus does not instruct the orga-nism to respond, but rather selects those elements capable of responding. The reflex itself is also the source of information for higher-order action schemata. Whenever a reflex runs off, the relation of a particular set of spinal motor neurons to each other is clearly expressed. In addition, the allocation of a particular set of muscle fibers to a spinal motor neuron is defined. The information that results when the spinal events and their sequels in the periphery are represented at cortical levels serves two prin-cipal purposes that are interrelated. First, it serves to establish a func-tional circuit between spinal motor neurons, cortical sensory neurons, and neurons of the corticospinal tract. It is assumed here that reflex ac-tivity plays an important role in the establishment of this functional feed-back circuit; the statement made by Jacobson (1978) with regard to the interaction between functional activity and the development of synaptic contacts in the visual system is held to apply in the motor system too: "Theories of strengthening of synapses between neurons that have corresponding functional activities imply that linkages are extensive initially and become more restricted, functionally and anatomically, as a result of sharpening functional activity [p. 442]." The important role of reflexes as templates that build up functional connections to spinal motor neurons is illustrated by the fact that when individual finger movements are made, much of the effort is devoted to inhibiting the integrated reflex responses of the fingers that are not to respond.

The representation of reflexes at the cortical level, however, serves another purpose as well. This will best be illustrated by an analogy to the visual system. When a single line stimulus is presented, this line stimulus does not instruct the primary visual cortex how to respond. Rather, it selects elements capable of responding to it, and these elements are the functional equivalent of the spinal motor neurons that react to a given stimulus with an integrated response.

However, when a more complex stimulus for which there exists no innate knowledge, such as a chair, is presented, the act of perception depends on the combination of a number of constituent elements into a functional whole. Similarly, information from constituent reflex components is also combined into functional wholes, such as the grasping response. The most significant aspect of this higher-level representation of events that take place at spinal levels is that a motor concept can be developed. In the visual system, higher-order processing abstracts the essential relations between constituent components so that a concept "chair" can be established that is not dependent on specific stimulus features. In the motor system, the concept "grasping," through a similar process of abstraction, becomes independent of particular sets of muscles or limbs. Such independence is, of course, prerequisite to the formulation of general movement plans.

This interpretation suggests that during early motor development the cortical representation of reflex movement serves to establish general motor concepts that, as the process of differentiation proceeds, become more and more refined. The manipulation of motor concepts is equivalent to "thinking," and the two, as Piaget has pointed out repeatedly, cannot be meaningfully separated early in life. Manipulation of motor concepts involves memory, categorization, and the establishment of functional hierarchies as well as syntax since the movement elements cannot be randomly combined. In addition, manipulation of motor concepts involves something that can best be described by analogy to the figure–ground principle in vision. In the perception of the figure–ground relationship, attention is focused on the figure, which is defined by its relation to the background. In movement, the volitional act and the guidance of its progress represent the figure on which attention is focused and the host of supportive movements that complement the volitional act can be considered the ground against which the figure is outlined. The metaphor of a figure–ground relationship applies most clearly to the concurrent activity of the two hands in a skilled bimanual activity; this represents the most complex manifestation of handedness in the adult form. In the following section, the relation between the functional demands of coordinated bimanual movements and lateral specialization will be defined.

BIMANUAL MOVEMENT AND LATERAL SPECIALIZATION

So far, the discussion of differentiation in the motor system has been concerned with the biases that are expressed in unilateral movement. However, neonates do not show, as a rule, strictly unilateral movement. As de Schonen (1977) has pointed out, when an infant reaches with one arm, the other arm performs complementary movements with coordinations inherent in the ATNR. A further reduction of this complementary action leads to simple, reciprocally coordinated locomotory patterns, with extension in one limb and flexion in the other. Movements reminiscent of this locomotory pattern occur in nonspecific agitation in the supinely resting infant, whose arms can be seen to be moving about in an alternating fashion. These simple reciprocal alternations form the basis for the remarkable and unique functional division of movement during skilled bimanual activities in the adult. The earliest indicator of a differentiation that goes beyond spinal coordinations is the functional division of movement when the infant reaches for an object.

Here, an asymmetry emerges quite early. De Schonen (1977) reports a clear functional division in infants ranging from 17 to 40 weeks of age; when reaching for an object with two hands, the right hand will tend to contact the object while the left will land on a support near the object. The precise pattern of this complementary movement will vary with the nature of the object and the way in which it is presented (Bresson, Maury, Pieraut-Le Bonniec, & de Schonen, 1977). Ramsay (1980) observed that, in infants some 11 months old, the right hand will be the one to manipulate an object while the left hand holds and supports it. In both these instances of bimanual coordination, the left hand plays a supportive role while the right hand actually manipulates or acts on the object on which attention is focused. Bimanual coordinated movement in adults follows, in principle, the same pattern. In the use of tools, the left hand tends to support the object that is to be manipulated while the right hand acts on it. For example, in striking flakes off a stone arrowhead, the left hand positions the arrowhead so that the right hand can strike in the appropriate area. In sewing, the left hand holds and positions the material while the right hand guides the needle. These examples, both in the infant and in the adult, suggest that the right hand is more immediately linked to the goal of the movement. This is of some importance. Bernstein (1967), and after him Evarts (1980), suggest that the only part of the entire movement process that can properly be called volitional is the formulation of the goal or objective of the intended movement. Thus, the link between the volitional act and the movement of the right hand is more direct than is the case for the left hand. To the extent that volition implies a focusing of attention, it can be said that attention is focused more directly on the right hand than on the left hand.

An argument can be made that the funneling of attention into one motor system has very old roots indeed. In early basic vertebrates, the limbs or precursors of limbs (fins) largely served a locomotory function. Manipulation of objects was carried out with the mouth and jaws. Thus, the movement intent came to bear on a motor system that, although bilaterally organized, behaved as one single system since its movements were bilaterally symmetrical around the midline axis. In the human neonate, in keeping with its behavior as "basic vertebrate," movement intent is initially directed to the mouth and jaws to which preference is given over the hands in the grasping and exploration of objects. In functional terms, the neonate possesses the neurological machinery necessary to focus attention on a single acting motor system, and it is suggested here that this machinery is also of importance for the way in which the movement intent comes to bear on the activities of the two hands. This interpretation carries the implicit claim that the machinery underlying functional division of labor during bimanually coordinated movement does not rest on the functional integrity of the direct corticospinal tracts since it is operative before these have fully matured. However, the particular role these tracts play in the execution of skilled movement interacts with the focusing of attention into a single motor system to yield a powerful force toward lateral specialization. This interaction will be considered next.

In skilled movement, there is first the formulation of the general movement plan, which is defined in terms of the goals of movement rather than in terms of specific sets of muscles and limbs (Bernstein, 1967). The formulation of the movement plan arises out of an appraisal of the context within which movement is to occur, and it is hard to imagine that each brain half formulates a separate movement plan. Instead, this process requires an integration of the particular contributions that each brain half makes to the appreciation of context. The movement plan, in its initial stages, is a functional whole that does not reside in either brain half or in any specific set of structures. In a way, the formulation of a movement plan is not much different from the way in which the two hemispheres give rise to "thought," where the dialectical interaction of the two separate hemispheric processes gives rise to something that is more than the sum of the contributory processes (TenHouten, 1978).

At this stage of the movement process, lateralization is a concept that has no meaning. However, when the general movement plan is translated into a specific movement program, the physical reality of a "left" and a "right" imposes itself, as the two hands have to perform a coordinated action. But how can a single, unitary process coordinate the movements of two separate motor systems? An answer is found in the structure of skilled bimanual coordinations. During such coordinations, each hand performs movements with a very distinct topography. For instance, in striking flakes off a stone arrowhead, the topography of movement for the left hand consists of a complex positioning movement. The topography of movement for the right hand consists of a strike that proceeds in a certain direction with a certain force. The motor systems that perform these movements are independent not only functionally, but also structurally. It is no accident that there are no direct transcortical connections between the primary motor areas of the cortices; during the performance of concurrent bimanual activities, the guidance of the movement topographies requires independence of the two motor systems. The requirement of independence applies only to the actual execution of the particular movement pattern that defines the movement topography; there is dependence in terms of how the topographies are related to each other in time.

During bimanual coordinations, movement of the left hand derives meaning only if it is performed in a specific temporal context defined by the movement of the right hand and vice versa. Once the independence of the actual movement topographies is accepted, the only way in which the general movement plan can come to bear on the two independent motor systems is in the initiation and termination of the specific movement topographies. This, then, is the only requirement made of whatever processes underlie the translation from a general movement plan into action, that they provide a sequenced pattern of impulses that initiate and terminate movement topographies in the two motor systems that guide the hands. The diagram in Figure 8.2 provides a schematic illustration of how the unitary process interacts with the two motor systems.

In keeping with current views on the role of subcortical structures in the guidance of movement, the two halves of Figure 8.2 are not to be interpreted as hemicortices. At each of the levels portrayed in Figure 8.2, there is an intimate interaction between cortical and subcortical structures. The system that guides the initiation and termination of movement in the two hands is thought to be located in the left hemisphere since a number of researchers feel that the control of praxis proceeds from the left hemisphere (Geschwind, 1975; Liepmann, 1908). Their views, however, have not taken into account the need to differentiate between the initiation and termination of movement in each hand and the actual guidance of movement topography. Nevertheless, the essential aspect of the model is that the initiation and termination of movement proceeds from one hemisphere and feeds into both the right and the left brain halves. The model has a considerable advantage in that it can account for the simultaneous initiation of movement in both the right and left hand. In principle, it is difficult to see how one unitary process can come to bear simul-

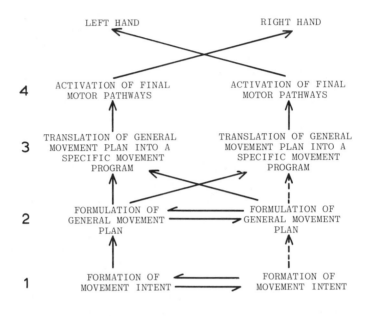

Figure 8.2. *Model of how a general movement plan comes to bear on the mechanisms that guide the movement topographies of the right and left hand. Stippled lines indicate that the right brain half has the capacity to initiate and terminate movement topographies in the right and left hand but does not normally do so in bimanual skilled activities.*

taneously on two separate systems, but the answer is provided by the feature of lateralization. Lateralization implies that the unitary system has more immediate and direct access to the motor system that is on the same side (Peters, 1981). If movement is to proceed simultaneously in both the right and the left hand, this means that impulses that initiate movement in the system that is structurally removed have to be issued before the impulses that reach the motor system that is more directly accessible are issued. Using the arrangement shown in Figure 8.2, this means that if the right and the left hand are to begin movement simultaneously (Kelso, Southard, & Goodman, 1979), impulses are first transmitted to the right brain half and then, after a delay, to the ipsilateral brain half. In this way, a single unitary source can, by simple sequencing of outputs, initiate movement in the two hands at the same time. No attempt is made here to suggest that movements in both hands can be initiated and terminated only from one brain half. Instead, it is proposed that such initiation and termination can be guided by either brain half, but that under normal circumstances one brain half is specialized in providing this function.

The model outlined in Figure 8.2 shows the relation between manual control during bimanual coordination and the control of speech processes in a rather simple way. While the speech musculature (including tongue and jaw movements, larynx and pharynx movements, and the intercostal musculature) is bilaterally organized, the speed of successive movements is such that the two halves cannot be activated in parallel by two interacting control systems. Instead, there must be provision for a single input that can activate the two half-systems simultaneously (Peters, 1976). Both the coordination of bimanual movement and the sequencing of movements during speech require great delicacy of timing, and it is proposed here that the specialization of the lateralized system that terminates and initiates movement lies in the precision of timing that it provides for its subordinate motor systems. Coemergence of the production of more complicated speech sounds and bimanual specialization, as reported by Ramsay (1980), therefore, is not unexpected. Implicit in this model is that directional consistency in the system that initiates and terminates movement (i.e., using the right or the left brain half consistently for this purpose rather than switching from one occasion and task to the next) results in greater efficiency in the acquisition of motor control. If Annett's (1972) model of handedness is correct, it can be predicted that infants who will grow up to be left-handed will, as a group, display different consonant and vowel sounds across syllables (Ramsay, 1980) later than is the case for infants who will grow up to be right-handed. The reason for stressing the manifestation of the developmental delay in left-handers in speech productions rather than bimanual coordination is due to the belief that the delicacy of timing required for sequencing polysyllabic utterances is greater than that required for the integration of bimanual movement (before the direct corticospinal tracts have matured).

Conclusions

This chapter examined some of the factors basic to the development and expression of handedness. The conclusions can be summarized as follows: The most essential elements in the development of handedness are the processes involved in the initiation and termination of movement, the focusing of attention on the goal of movement, and the formulation of general movement plans. These processes interact with structural elements that are involved in the execution of movement to yield directional biases. These biases were said to reinforce each other in a positive feedback manner. Implicit in this view is that the clarity with which lateral specialization is expressed depends both on the nature of the movements performed and on the complexity of the processes that guide the movements. During development, similar movement topographies may be guided by different underlying processes, and the resulting expression of lateral specialization may vary depending on the stage of differentiation of the organism. As a result, consistency in the degree and direction of lateral specialization cannot be taken for granted, particularly in the first few years of life, when differentiation of processes that guide movement proceeds rapidly.

References

Annett, M. (1972). The distribution of manual asymmetry. *British Journal of Psychology 63*, 343–358.
Bernstein, N. (1967). *The co-ordination and regulation of movement.* Oxford: Pergamon.
Bresson, F., Maury, L., Pieraut-Le Bonniec, G., & de Schonen, S. (1977). Organization and lateralization of reaching in infants: An instance of dissymmetric functions in hand collaboration. *Neuropsychologia 15*, 311–320.
Brinkman, J., & Kuypers, H. G. M. (1972). Splitbrain monkeys: Cerebral control of ipsilateral and contralateral arm, hand and finger movements. *Science 176*, 536–539.
Bruner, J. S. (1969). On voluntary action and its hierarchical structure. *International Journal of Psychology 3*, 239–255.
Corballis, M. C., & Beale, I. L. (1976). *The psychology of left and right.* Hillsdale, New Jersey: Erlbaum.
Corballis, M. C., & Morgan, M. J. (1978). On the biological basis of human laterality: 1. Evidence for maturational left–right gradient. *The Behavioral and Brain Sciences 2*, 261–269.
Coryell, J. F., & Michel, G. F. (1978). How supine postural preferences of infant can contribute toward the development of handedness. *Infant Behavior and Development 1*, 245–257.
de Schonen, S. (1977). Functional asymmetries in the development of bimanual coordinations in human infants. *Journal of Human Movement Studies 3*, 144–156.
Easton, T. A. (1972). On the normal use of reflexes. *American Scientist 60*, 591–599.
Evarts, E. V. (1980). Brain mechanisms in voluntary movement. In D. McFadden (Ed.), *Neural mechanisms in behavior.* New York: Springer-Verlag.
Flechsig, P. (1920). *Antomie des menschlichen Gehirns und Rückenmarks auf myelogenetischer Grundlage.* Leipzig: Thieme.
Geschwind, N. (1975). The apraxias: Neural mechanisms of disorders of learned movement. *American Scientist 63*, 188–195.
Gesell, A. (1945). *The embryology of behavior.* New York: Harper.
Glick, S. D., Jerussi, T. P., & Zimmerberg, B. (1977). Behavioral and neuropharmacological correlates of nigrostriatal in rats. In S. Harnad, L. Goldstein, R. W. Doty, J. Jaynes, & G. Krauthamer (Eds.), *Lateralization in the nervous system.* New York: Academic Press.
Gould, S. J. (1977). Ontogeny and phylogeny. Cambridge, Massachusetts: Belknapp.
Guth, L., & Yellin, H. (1971). The dynamic nature of the so-called "fibre types" of mammalian skeletal muscle. *Experimental Neurology 31*, 277–300.
Hildebrand, C., & Skoglund, S. (1971). Caliber spectra of some fibre tracts in the feline central nervous system during postnatal development. *Acta Physiologica Scandinavia (Suppl.) 364*, 5–41.
Jacobson, M. (1978). *Developmental neurobiology.* New York: Plenum.
Jerison, H. J. (1976). *Evolution of the brain and intelligence.* New York: Academic Press.
Kelso, J. A., Southard, D. L., & Goodman, D. (1979). On the coordination of two-handed

movements. *Journal of Experimental Psychology: Human Perception and Performance* 5, 229–238.

Kinsbourne, M. (1974). Lateral interactions in the brain. In M. Kinsbourne & W. L. Smith (Eds.), *Hemispheric disconnection and cerebral function*. Springfield, Illinois: Thomas.

Kots, Y. M. (1977). *The organization of voluntary movement*. New York: Plenum.

Liepmann, N. (1908). *Drei Aufsätze aus dem Apraxiegebiet*. Berlin: Karger.

McDonnell, P. M. (1979). Patterns of eye–hand coordination in the 1st year of life. *Canadian Journal of Psychology 33*, 253–267.

MacLean, P. D. (1964). Man and his animal brains. *Modern Medicine 3*, 95–106.

Michel, F. (1981). Right-handedness: A consequence of infant supine head orientation preference? *Science 212*, 685–687.

Morgan, M. J. (1977). Embryology and the inheritance of asymmetry. In S. Harnad, R. Doty, L. Goldstein, J. Haynes, & G. Krauthamer (Eds.), *Lateralization in the nervous system*. New York: Academic Press.

Noback, C. R., & Scribner, J. E. (1969). Encephalization and the lemniscal systems during phylogeny. *Annals of the New York Academy of Sciences. 167*, 118–128.

Oke, A., Keller, R., Mefford, I., & Adams, R. M. (1978). Lateralization of norepinephrine in human thalamus. *Science 200*, 1411–1413.

Peters, M. (1976). Unilateral control of bilaterally symmetrical movement as factor in the lateralization of speech. *Perceptual and Motor Skills 42*, 841–842.

Peters, M. (1981). Attentional asymmetries during concurrent bimanual performance. *Quarterly Journal of Experimental Psychology 33A*, 95–103.

Peters, M., & Petrie, B. F. (1979). Functional asymmetries in the stepping reflex of human neonates. *Canadian Journal of Psychology 33*, 198–200.

Phillips, C. G., & Porter, R. (1977). *Corticospinal neurons: Their role in movement*. New York: Academic Press.

Piaget, J. (1971). *Biology and knowledge*. Chicago, Illinois: Univ. of Chicago Press.

Ramsay, D. S. (1980). Beginnings of bimanual handedness and speech in infants. *Infant Behavior and Development 3*, 67–78.

TenHouten, W. D. (1978). Hemispheric interaction in the brain and the propositional compositional and dialectical modes of thought. *Journal of Altered States of Consciousness 4*, 129–140.

Trevarthen, C. (1974). Functional relations of disconnected hemispheres with the brain stem, and each other: Monkey and man. In M. Kinsbourne & W. L. Smith (Eds.), *Hemispheric disconnection and cerebral function*. Springfield, Illinois: Thomas.

Turkewitz, G. (1977). The development of lateral differences in the infant. In S. Harnad, R. W. Doty, L. Goldstein, J. Jaynes, & G. Krauthamer (Eds.), *Lateralization in the nervous system*. New York: Academic Press.

Twitchell, T. E. (1965). The anatomy of the grasping response. *Neuropsychologia 3*, 247–259.

Webster, K. E. (1979). Some aspects of the comparative study of the striatum. In I. Divac & R. G. E. Oberg (Eds.), *The neostriatum*. Oxford: Pergamon.

Young, G. (1977). Manual specialization in infancy: Implications for lateralization of brain function. In S. J. Segalowitz & F. A. Gruber (Eds.), *Language development and neurological theory*. New York: Academic Press.

Zelazo, P. R. (1976). From reflexive to instrumental behavior. In L. P. Lipsitt (Ed.), *Developmental psychobiology*. New York: Wiley.

9

Unimanual Hand Preference and Duplicated Syllable Babbling in Infants[1]

DOUGLAS S. RAMSAY

Introduction

Evidence at birth for anatomical asymmetries between the two cerebral hemispheres for areas mediating later language (e.g., Galaburda, LeMay, Kemper, & Geschwind, 1978; Wada, Clarke, & Hamm, 1975; Witelson & Pallie, 1973) has underscored the need for research designed to test for functional asymmetries in infancy. Several studies have reported evidence for hemispheric specialization in newborns (Davis & Wada, 1977; Molfese & Molfese, 1979) and young infants (Entus, 1977; Gardner & Walter, 1977; Glanville, Best, & Levenson, 1977; Molfese, Freeman, & Palermo, 1975) for the perception of linguistic and nonlinguistic stimuli. Nevertheless, hemispheric specialization for infants' vocal abilities has not been investigated. Infants' vocalizations undergo major developmental changes in the first 2 years of life (Kaplan & Kaplan, 1971; McCarthy, 1954; Oller, 1980; Stark, 1980). It is possible that the appearance of different vocal milestones in infancy reflects successive levels or stages in the expression of hemispheric specialization. Thus, although hemispheric specialization for some aspects of infants' receptive abilities may be congenital, hemispheric specialization for their productive abilities may show developmental change.

Historically, research with adults has attempted to link handedness to

[1]This research was supported by National Institute of Mental Health Grant No. MH 34157 and by National Science Foundation Grant No. BNS 79-26702. A preliminary version of this chapter was presented at the International Conference on Infant Studies, April, 1980, New Haven, Connecticut.

MANUAL SPECIALIZATION
AND THE DEVELOPING BRAIN

hemispheric specialization for speech (Lenneberg, 1967; Levy, 1974). Several theorists have argued that the onset of handedness in children indicated the point in development when speech was dependent on hemispheric specialization (e.g., Bay, 1975; Steffen, 1975; Zangwill, 1975). These views disregarded the possibility that lateralized manual behavior might be present in infants before speech onset, and therefore seemed to presuppose that handedness was related to some linguistic (e.g., syntactic) aspect of speech as opposed to some other aspect(s) of vocalizations that emerge prior to speech.

In particular, advances in articulatory control reflect advances in finely tuned sequential motor activity often related to left-hemisphere specialization (e.g., Bradshaw & Nettleton, 1981). Clear evidence exists for the emergence of different types of handedness in infancy, each with a different age of onset during the first 2 years of life (Ramsay, Campos, & Fenson, 1979; Young, 1977). These different types of hand preference might index successive levels of hemispheric specialization for articulatory control. Accordingly, the onset of a particular type of hand preference might be related to the appearance of a specific articulatory change in infants' vocalizations.

Prior research has indicated the presence of one such developmental relation. Ramsay et al. (1979) found that infants began to demonstrate a hand preference in tasks requiring bimanual manipulation by the end of the first year of life, that is, at the point that most infants begin to speak. In this study, infants were required to hold toys in one hand and to manipulate them appropriately with the other hand and were credited with bimanual right or left handedness according to the hand used consistently for this manipulation. Ramsay (1980a) found that the onset of this bimanual hand preference was related to infants' ability to articulate dissimilar syllables in speech (e.g., *doggie, thank you*) as opposed to duplicated syllable (e.g., *baba*) or single syllable (e.g., *da*) utterances. Psycholinguists (e.g., Ferguson, Peizer, & Weeks, 1973; Moskowitz, 1973) have argued that the presence of dissimilar syllables in infants' speech indicates the ability to use linguistic contrasts at a phonemic level. On the surface, the finding by Ramsay (1980a) might suggest that bimanual hand preference was related to a linguistic (i.e., phonological) aspect of speech. Nevertheless, bimanual hand preference might prove to index developmental change in hemispheric specialization for articulatory control, since dissimilar syllables also appear in infants' babbling about this point in development (Oller, 1980; Stark, 1980).

Ramsay (1980b) suggested the possibility of another developmental relation between infants' manual and vocal development, one that more directly links hand preference to articulation. In this study, infants began to demonstrate a hand preference in tasks of unimanual manipulation between 5 and 7 months of age. Nearly all the 7-month-olds, but only a few 5-month-olds, had begun to babble duplicated consonant–vowel syllables (e.g., *dada*). This babbling reflects the first indication of syllabic structure in infants' vocalizations (Ling & Ling, 1974; Nakazima, 1970). Clear evidence for a developmental relation between unimanual hand preference and duplicated syllable babbling would support the view that different types of hand preference index successive levels of hemispheric specialization for the control of different articulatory units (e.g., syllable, phoneme).

A relation between unimanual hand preference and duplicated syllable babbling could be predicted over and above the apparent concordance in the age of onset of these two milestones. Infants' unimanual manipulation often takes the form of banging (i.e., pounding on a toy's surface in a stereotypic and rhythmic manner [cf. Slovin-Ela & Kohen-Raz, 1978]). Banging and duplicated syllable babbling share the same repetitive properties and, therefore, might conceivably be mediated by common mechanisms. Numerous characterizations of hemispheric specialization in adults have emphasized the role of the dominant hemisphere in several abilities, including speech, that require sequential processing (e.g., Bradshaw & Nettleton, 1981; Corballis, 1980; Geschwind, 1970; Levy, 1974; Nebes, 1974; Wolff, Hurwitz, & Moss, 1977). Consequently, evidence for this developmental relation might reflect developmental changes in the role of the dominant hemisphere in the programming of sequential motoric (articulatory or manual) acts.

The present research used longitudinal designs and an age-held-constant design to test for this relation. The age-held-constant design was used to rule out the possibility that the proposed relation simply reflected a general correspondence in time of emergence of the two milestones. Six-month-olds, half of whom had begun to babble duplicated syllables, were tested for unimanual hand preference. It was predicted that the babbling 6-month-olds would demonstrate a unimanual right-hand preference, whereas the nonbabbling 6-month-olds would not show a unimanual hand preference. Two longitudinal studies were then conducted. In Longitudinal Study 1, infants were tested for unimanual hand preferences on three occasions during the 1-month interval following the onset of duplicated syllable babbling to determine whether a unimanual right-hand preference was present with babbling onset. In Longitudinal Study 2, infants were tested at monthly intervals from 4 months of age to determine whether the emergence of a unimanual right-hand preference coincided with the beginning of duplicated syllable babbling.

In each of these studies, the performance of left-handed infants would depress the predicted right-handed trend. In an attempt to overcome this difficulty, the 6-month-olds in the age-held-constant study were retested for unimanual handedness at 9 months of age (i.e., well after the onset of duplicated syllable babbling). The 6-month data were transformed according to infants' preferred hand at 9 months of age to test for the presence of handedness in the babbling as opposed to the nonbabbling group. In addition, infants from all three studies were tested for bimanual hand preference at 13 months of age. The unimanual hand preference data were also transformed according to infant's preferred hand for bimanual manipulation at 13 months of age to test for the presence of unimanual hand preference with duplicated syllable babbling onset. This latter procedure was based on previous findings that unimanual hand preference in young infants (7- and 9-month-olds) did predict their eventual bimanual hand preference at 13 months of age (Ramsay, 1980b).

Method

Subjects

In the age-held-constant study, 32 infants (16 females, 16 males) were tested for unimanual hand preference at an average age of 6.1 months (range: 5, 20–6, 13). There were equal numbers of girls and boys who had or had not begun to babble duplicated syllables. All 32 infants were retested for unimanual hand preference at 9 months of age and for bimanual hand preference at 13 months of age. A total of 38 infants were contacted for this study, but 6 infants (4 babbling females, 2 nonbabbling males) were not included in order to achieve this counterbalancing.[2]

In Longitudinal Study 1, 18 infants (9 females, 9 males) were tested for unimanual hand preference on three occasions during the 1-month interval following the onset of duplicated syllable babbling. The three sessions occurred during the first week (2–5 days), between 2 and 3 weeks, and between 4 and 5 weeks after the beginning of duplicated syllable babbling. At the first session, infants ranged in age from 5, 5 to 7, 9 (median: 6, 14). These 18 infants were tested for bimanual hand preference at 13 months of age. The data from an additional 3 infants who received the unimanual hand preference testing but who could not be tested for bimanual hand preference were not used.

In Longitudinal Study 2, 13 infants (7 females, 6 males) were tested for unimanual hand preference at monthly intervals from 4 months of age.

---

[2]At first glance, these data seemed to suggest that females showed an earlier onset of duplicated syllable babbling than males. Nevertheless, an analysis of variance with group and sex as factors performed on the ages of the subjects used in the age-held-constant study failed to yield any significant effects. The mean ages of the four subgroups ranged from 6.05 to 6.15 months. Moreover, the two longitudinal studies failed to indicate any sex difference in this regard. In the first longitudinal study, the age of infants at the first test session did not differ significantly (by *t* test) between girls and boys (6.5 versus 6.1 months, respectively). In the second longitudinal study, the mean age of duplicated syllable babbling onset did not differ between the two sexes (6.3 months in each case).

Unimanual hand-preference testing continued through 8 months of age or, as necessary, through 2 months after the onset of duplicated syllable babbling. These 13 infants were tested for bimanual hand preference at 13 months of age. The data from an additional 3 infants who received the unimanual hand-preference testing but who could not be tested for bimanual hand preference were not used.

Infants in all three studies were unselected for birth order and familial sinistrality. Of the 63 infants used in this research, 39 were first-born, 16 were second-born, and 8 were later than second-born. For 47 infants, both parents were right-handed; for 15 infants, one parent was left-handed; whereas for 1 infant, both parents were left-handed. Parents and infants were recruited by local newspaper advertisements in the San Diego, California metropolitan area.

Procedure

DUPLICATED SYLLABLES

The presence or absence of duplicated syllable babbling was determined by maternal report. For the age-held-constant study, mothers were asked whether or not their infant had shown this vocal milestone at the 6-month session. In Longitudinal Study 1, mothers were telephoned when their infant turned 5 months of age and were asked to call back to schedule the unimanual hand-preference testing as soon as they heard the first duplicated syllable utterance in their infant's babbling. In Longitudinal Study 2, mothers reported at each monthly session whether they had heard any duplicated syllables in their infant's babbling during the previous 1-month interval. Babbling was considered to have begun at the first session it was reported. In both longitudinal studies, all mothers reported that their infants continued this babbling on succeeding sessions. Interviews in the three studies were conducted by an experimenter who was unaware of the infants' performance with the unimanual hand-preference toys.

UNIMANUAL HAND PREFERENCE

The unimanual hand-preference testing was identical to the procedure previously used (Ramsay, 1980b). Toys were presented individually to infants at their midline for a 60-sec period while they were seated on their mother's lap and supported by her at their hips. The experimenter presenting the toys was positioned to one or the other side of the infants to permit a frontal videotape recording of the infant and toys. Both the side of the experimenter and the side from which the mother observed the testing (i.e., which shoulder of her infant she looked over) were randomized across infants. Prior to each toy presentation, the experimenter, randomly choosing his or her right or left hand, showed the infants how to manipulate the toy. Then the experimenter placed the toy directly in front of the infants, between waist and chest level, and verbally encouraged them to play with it. Each 60-sec period began with the infants' initial toy contact. If, at any point, infants lost interest in a toy, the experimenter attempted to regain their attention by reactivating the toy's mechanism.

For each toy, the number of unimanual right- and left-handed contacts was scored from videotape by scorers who were not aware of the infants' age and babbling history. A unimanual toy contact was defined as an attempt to activate the movable portion of each toy wih one hand while the other hand was not engaged in such an attempt. Typically, the inactive hand remained at the infants' side, was suspended in the air, or rested on the edge of the toy. These data were used to determine the mean frequency of right- and left-handed contacts and the proportion of right-handed contacts across toys for each test session. Statistical analyses of the frequency and proportion measures yielded comparable results in all three studies. Only the results for the proportion measure are reported to simplify the presentation and because proportions avoid the problem of individual differences in total frequency of toy contacts.

Infants in the age-held-constant study received the four toys used previously (Ramsay, 1980b) in different random orders at 6 and 9 months of age: a Playskool "Baby chimes"; a Fisher-Price "Rattle ball"; a Fireball "Kaleidoscope"; and a Tomy "Freddy phone." Infants in the longitudinal studies received an additional four toys in different random orders at each test session: an Ambi-Toys "Rota-rattle"; a Fisher-Price "Pop-up-pal" chime phone; a Galanite sand mill; and a Steven "Wonder wheel" kaleidoscope. Distracting features and asymmetrical parts had been removed from the toys. The comparability of the new and old toys was assessed for one test session in each longitudinal study. For the first session of Longitudinal Study 1, the proportion of right-handed toy contacts was significantly correlated for the two toy sets ($r = .52$, $p < .05$). For the month of duplicated syllable babbling onset in Longitudinal Study 2, the proportion measure was again significantly correlated for the two toy sets ($r = .85$, $p < .001$). These two test sessions were chosen since they reflected comparable points in development for infants in the two studies. The difference in the two correlation coefficients might stem from the fact that the correlation in the first study was obtained on the initial test session, whereas the correlation in the second study was obtained on a later test session.

No attempt was made to determine interscorer reliabilities since the scorers in the present research had scored the data in the previous unimanual hand-preference study and had achieved a satisfactory level of percentage agreement (median: .93; Ramsay, 1980b). Testing was conducted in a psychology laboratory on the campus of San Diego State University, California.

Infants' hand preference for bimanual manipulation (right or left) at 13 months of age was determined according to the procedure used in the cross-sectional study of Ramsay *et al.* (1979). Briefly, nine plastic toys requiring bimanual manipulation were presented individually in different random orders to the infants. Right-handed infants were expected to hold the base of each toy in their left hand while they attempted to manipulate its movable portion with their right hand. Infants received up to four successive trials with each toy. They were credited with consistent use of either the right- or left-handed strategy with a given toy if they used that strategy on the first two trials or on three of the four trials. Infants' bimanual hand-preference scores could range from +9 to −9 for an extreme right- or left-hand preference, respectively. Infants were classified as right- or left-handed according to the dominant trend for using either strategy consistently across the nine toys.[3] The bimanual hand-preference testing was conducted by an experimenter who was unaware of the infants' prior unimanual hand preference.

Results

Age-Held-Constant Study

UNIMANUAL HAND PREFERENCE (SIX MONTHS)

The proportion of right-handed contacts across the four toys is given in Table 9.1 for the babbling and nonbabbling 6-month-olds. In this and the following tables, *t* tests were used to determine whether the proportion of right-handed (or preferred-hand) contacts was significantly greater than the proportion of left-handed (or nonpreferred-hand) contacts. The significance levels reported are one-tailed, since the direction of hand preference had been predicted.

Neither the babbling nor the nonbabbling 6-month-olds showed a significant proportion of right-handed toy contacts. An analysis of variance with group and sex as between-subjects factors yielded a significant interaction, $F(1, 28) = 5.05$, $p < .05$, indicating a greater proportion of right-handed toy contacts for the babbling females than for the other three subgroups. Inspection of the data suggested that the absence of a significant right-handed trend in the babbling group as a whole was due to some babbling males with strong left-handed preferences. The 9-month testing was used to examine this possibility.

---

[3]In previous research, a more strict criterion for bimanual hand preference (a score equal to or more extreme than ± 5) was used. Of the 53 infants in the present research, 42 infants (79%) met this criterion.

Table 9.1
Age-Held-Constant Study: Proportion of Right- or Preferred-Hand Toy Contacts for Six-Month-Olds Who Had or Had Not Begun to Babble Duplicated Syllables

	Proportion right	Proportion preferred based on 9-month unimanual handedness	Proportion preferred based on 13-month bimanual handedness
Babbling 6-month-olds (N = 16)	.61	.72*	.73*
Nonbabbling 6-month-olds (N = 16)	.57	.55	.54

*p < .05, by one-tailed *t* test (*df* = 15).

UNIMANUAL HAND PREFERENCE (NINE MONTHS)

Infants' performance with the unimanual hand-preference toys at 9 months of age was first analyzed to confirm that both groups showed a right-handed preference at this point in development. Both the babbling and nonbabbling groups showed significant right-handed preferences at 9 months of age, .66 and .71, respectively (p < .05 and .005 by one-tailed *t* test). An analysis of variance performed on the 9-month proportion data with group and sex as factors yielded no significant effects, indicating comparable right-handed trends across the four subgroups. As defined by a proportion score greater or less than .50, 25 of the 32 infants (12 females, 13 males) were right-handed, and the remaining 7 infants (4 females, 3 males) were left-handed. There were 12 right-handers in the babbling group and 13 right-handers in the nonbabbling group.

The proportion of unimanual toy contacts at 6 months of age performed by the preferred hand for unimanual manipulation at 9 months of age is also given in Table 9.1. An analysis of variance with group and sex as factors performed on these data yielded a significant main effect of group, $F(1, 28) = 6.01$, p < .05, and no significant effect of sex. As indicated in Table 9.1, the babbling group showed a significant preference for the later-preferred hand, while the nonbabbling group did not show such a preference. The bimanual hand-preference testing was used to confirm this effect.

BIMANUAL HAND PREFERENCE (THIRTEEN MONTHS)

For bimanual manipulation, 26 infants (15 females, 11 males) were credited with a right-hand preference, and the remaining 6 infants (1 female, 5 males) were credited with a left-hand preference. There were 12 right-handers in the babbling group and 14 right-handers in the nonbab-

Table 9.2
Proportion of Right- or Preferred-Hand Toy Contacts for the Three Test Sessions During the One-Month Interval Following Duplicated Syllable Babbling Onset

	Session 1	Session 2	Session 3
Proportion right			
Females (N = 9)	.51	.58	.69***
Males (N = 9)	.63*	.65*	.55
Proportion preferred			
Females (N = 9)	.53	.66**	.62*
Males (N = 9)	.58	.64*	.55

*p < .10
**p < .05
***p < .01, by one-tailed t test (df = 8).

bling group.[4] The proportion of unimanual toy contacts at 6 months performed by the preferred hand for bimanual manipulation at 13 months of age is shown in Table 9.1. An analysis of variance with group and sex as factors performed on these data yielded a significant main effect of group, $F(1, 28) = 6.68$, $p < .05$, and no significant effect of sex. As indicated in Table 9.1, the babbling group showed a significant preference for the later-preferred hand, whereas the nonbabbling group did not show such a preference. Therefore, both the 9-month and 13-month testing indicated that the babbling as opposed to nonbabbling group had begun to demonstrate a unimanual hand preference at 6 months of age.

Longitudinal Study 1

The data from the two longitudinal studies are reported separately for females and males since preliminary analyses indicated an apparent temporary loss in hand preference that appeared at different points relative to duplicated syllable babbling onset for the two sexes. Table 9.2 gives the proportion of right-handed contacts across the eight toys for the three test sessions in the first longitudinal study. As indicated in Table 9.2, girls showed a right-handed preference during the third test session, but not

[4]To assess the stability of hand preference between 9 and 13 months of age, the proportion of unimanual toy contacts at 9 months performed by the preferred hand for bimanual manipulation at 13 months was determined. The proportion of toy contacts at 9 months of age performed by the later-preferred hand was significantly greater than the proportion of later-nonpreferred hand toy contacts for both the babbling and nonbabbling groups (.64 and .68 $p < .05$ and .005, respectively, by one-tailed t test).

during the first two test sessions. In contrast, boys tended to show a right-handed preference on the first two test sessions, but did not show a clear preference during the third test session.

When tested for their hand preference for bimanual manipulation at 13 months of age, 13 of the 18 infants (7 females, 6 males) were credited with a right-hand preference, and the remaining 5 infants (2 females, 3 males) were credited with a left-hand preference. Table 9.2 also indicates infants' performance on the unimanual hand-preference toys for the three sessions according to their later-preferred hand for bimanual manipulation.

The bimanual hand-preference measure showed a similar pattern of results for these infants. As indicated, girls did not show a unimanual hand-preference during the first session, but did so during the second session, with a trend toward significance during the third session. Boys tended to show a unimanual hand preference only during the second session. Contrary to prediction, the results of this longitudinal study failed to indicate that unimanual hand preference was present in infants with duplicated syllable babbling onset.

Longitudinal Study 2

Table 9.3 shows the proportion of right-handed contacts for the eight toys for each sex across sessions relative to the onset of duplicated syllable babbling. As indicated, the only significant right-handed preference was for the boys 2 months after the onset of duplicated syllable babbling. Of the 13 infants, 10 infants (6 females, 4 males) were credited with a right-hand preference for bimanual manipulation at 13 months of age, and the remaining 3 infants (1 female, 2 males) were credited with a bimanual left-hand preference. Table 9.3 also indicates infants' performance on the

Table 9.3

Longitudinal Study 2: Proportion of Right- or Preferred-Hand Toy Contacts for Successive Months Relative to Duplicated Syllable Babbling Onset

	Monthly session relative to babbling onset				
	−2	−1	0	+1	+2
Proportion right					
Females (N = 7)	.45	.57	.49	.59	.47
Males (N = 6)	.38	.43	.65	.60	.68*
Proportion preferred					
Females (N = 7)	.44	.64*	.40	.70*	.52
Males (N = 6)	.47	.54	.77*	.35	.71*

*$p < .05$, by one-tailed t test (df = 5 or 6, as appropriate).

unimanual hand-preference toys according to their later-preferred hand for bimanual manipulation.

Relative to their bimanual hand preference, girls showed a preference for the preferred hand 1 month prior to duplicated syllable babbling onset. Then they showed no clear preference at the month of babbling onset. One month later, girls again showed a preference for the preferred hand. Two months after babbling onset, girls again did not show a clear preference. In contrast, boys did not show any hand preference prior to babbling onset. At the month of babbling onset, boys did show a preference for the preferred hand. One month later, there was a slight preference for the opposite hand, whereas 2 months after the onset of duplicated syllable babbling, boys again showed a preference for the preferred hand. Therefore, these data suggest that unimanual hand preference emerged with duplicated syllable babbling onset in males, but not females, although the preference shown by males was not stable thereafter.

Conclusions

This research tested for the developmental relation between unimanual hand preference and duplicated syllable babbling. An age-held-constant study found that babbling 6-month-olds, in contrast to nonbabbling 6-month-olds, showed a unimanual hand preference relative to their later-preferred hand for unimanual and bimanual manipulation. This result suggests that unimanual hand preference might be associated with the onset of duplicated syllable babbling.

Nevertheless, two longitudinal studies did not clearly show that the emergence of these two milestones coincided in time. The longitudinal data suggested that such a correspondence might be present in males, although the data were not entirely congruent in this respect. Contrary to prediction, evidence for this developmental relation was not found for females in either longitudinal study.

The longitudinal results might reflect a real sex difference in the emergence of unimanual hand preference relative to duplicated syllable babbling onset. Alternatively, these results might be due to the interaction of two factors. One factor is that following unimanual hand-preference onset, infants might show a temporary loss of this preference. The other factor is that, for whatever reasons, mothers of girls might have delayed in reporting their infants as beginning to babble syllables. These two factors together could potentially reconcile the data for the two longitudinal studies. In the second longitudinal study, the unimanual hand-preference data showed comparable developmental trends over sessions for both sexes, that is, a loss in unimanual hand preference approximately 1 month after its appearance. This trend began 1 month earlier in females than in males. The initial emergence of unimanual hand preference in girls might have occurred in conjunction with the failure of some of their mothers to report the onset of duplicated syllable babbling at the proper time.

The results of the first longitudinal study can be accounted for in a similar manner. If mothers of girls delayed in their reporting of duplicated syllable babbling onset, female infants would show a loss in unimanual hand preference on the first test session(s) (i.e., a few weeks or a month after true babbling onset) but would show a recovery in this preference by the third test session. If mothers of boys were accurate in this reporting, most of the male infants would have completed the three test sessions before they showed any loss in hand preference, although some male infants might have started to show this change during the third test session. Examination of these possibilities would require more fine-grained longitudinal testing involving such features as more closely spaced test sessions (e.g., weekly intervals) over a longer period following duplicated syllable babbling onset (e.g., 2–3 months) with a larger group of infants and with better control over the reporting of babbling onset.

Throughout this chapter, developmental relations between infants' hand preference and articulation have been interpreted as reflecting developmental change in hemispheric specialization. Such a conception has at least two potential shortcomings that have important consequences for the study of infant development. First, these developmental relations need not imply underlying change in hemispheric specialization; they could result, instead, from intellectual or other advances that modify a preexisting asymmetry common to the two domains. For example, both unimanual hand preference (especially banging) and duplicated syllable babbling are examples of Stage 3 secondary circular reactions, according to Piaget's theory of sensorimotor intelligence (Piaget, 1952). These behaviors are instances of procedures designed to reinstate prior events initially discovered by accident, here, prolonging an object's action or repeating the same syllable. Similarly, bimanual hand preference and the uttering of dissimilar syllables are reminiscent of Stage 5 tertiary circular reactions. These behaviors reflect trial-and-error experiments designed to identify the unique characteristics of a given object or to vary the sounds of different syllables. Thus, developmental relations between infants' hand preference and articulation could simply reflect the development of sensorimotor intelligence. Nevertheless, evidence for a loss in unimanual hand preference shortly after duplicated syllable babbling onset argues against this possibility. Infants would have no reason to abandon a newly acquired manipulative or articulatory skill just after its emergence if intellectual advances alone were accounting for these developmental relations.

In any case, one crucial feature of Piaget's theory shared by the present line of research is the emphasis on synchronies in development, that is, the identification of stage correspondences across different behavioral domains. Most empirical research within a Piagetian framework has found considerable differences among infants' stages of development across domains (Uzgiris & Hunt, 1975). Such "décalages" have called into question the psychological reality of these stages (Fischer & Bullock, 1981). Research showing developmental relations between infants' handedness and articulation suggests that the development of hemispheric specialization might serve as an organizing principle for both predicting and observing synchronies in development. Alternatively, Piaget's stages may successfully predict synchronies in development to the extent that the behaviors observed depend on hemispheric specialization. Future research should therefore be directed toward determining the relative contributions of hemispheric specialization and sensorimotor intelligence to infants' manual and vocal development.

A second potential shortcoming in the conception proposed for the present line of research is that developmental relations between hand preference and articulation need not reflect developmental changes in hemispheric specializaton per se, but could reflect changes in the asymmetrical organization of brain structures at different subcortical levels. Postural and manual reflexes in the newborn and the young infant (e.g., Gesell, 1938; Turkewitz, 1977) that are related to later hand preferences (e.g., Michel, 1981) are probably mediated by brainstem structures (e.g., Peiper, 1963). It is unclear when later hand preferences reflect *cerebral* dominance for motoric functions. Although it might be reasonable to assume that bimanual hand preference and dissimilar syllables in speech reflect cerebral dominance, it is more problematic to assume that unimanual hand preference and duplicated syllable babbling do so.

Resolution of this ambiguity would clarify one of the major theoretical issues in this area, namely, whether hemispheric specialization develops or remains invariant throughout development. Kinsbourne (1975) has advanced the "invariance hypothesis" on the basis of evidence that indices of specialization do not change in degree of asymmetry shown across different ages (e.g., Hiscock & Kinsbourne, 1980). Most of the evidence in this regard has been obtained from children 3 years of age and older. In view of the evidence for anatomical and functional asymmetries in newborns and young infants, it is tempting to extend the invariance hypothesis to the period of infancy. Nevertheless, the possibility of a temporary loss in unimanual hand preference following the onset of duplicated syllable babbling suggests reorganization in asymmetrical brain function at some cortical and/or subcortical level(s). If the developmental relation between unimanual hand preference and duplicated syllable babbling could be linked to cerebral dominance, this loss in hand preference would be clear evidence against the invariance hypothesis. In any case, if the finding of various developmental relations between infants' hand preference and articulation indicates underlying change in asymmetrical brain organization at different brain levels, this would not be consistent with the spirit of the invariance hypothesis as advanced by Kinsbourne.

A temporary loss of unimanual hand preference might be due to several factors. This loss might indicate a partial disconnection between the two hemispheres, leading to a new level of integration and/or cooperation between the two. Conceivably, the reemergence of unimanual hand preference might be associated with a new level of control by the dominant hemisphere for left-sided motoric function. Infants begin to engage in several bilateral mirror-image activities such as clapping hands at approximately this point in development. Alternatively, this loss might reflect a disruption in part due to the emergence of new skills mediated by the nondominant hemisphere. Many perceptual abilities in adults have been linked to right-hemisphere specialization. Infants' perceptual abilities do, in fact, undergo major changes at approximately this point in development (see Campos & Stenberg, 1981, for a review). This possibility does not readily explain why duplicated syllable babbling is apparently not disrupted during this period, however. In any case, evidence that the loss and reemergence of unimanual hand preference coincides with the emergence of specific motoric and/or perceptual abilities would serve to clarify the significance of this discontinuity in development.

Acknowledgment

The author thanks Larry Fenson of San Diego State University, California, for providing the facilities and support that made this research possible.

References

Bay, E. (1975). Ontogeny of stable speech areas in the human brain. In E. H. Lenneberg & E. Lenneberg (Eds.), *Foundations of language development. A multidisciplinary approach* (Vol. 2). New York: Academic Press.

Bradshaw, J. L., & Nettleton, N. C. (1981). The nature of hemispheric specialization in man. *The Behavioral and Brain Sciences 4*, 51–91.

Campos, J. J., & Stenberg, C. R. (1981). Perception, appraisal and emotion: The onset of social referencing. In M. E. Lamb & L. R. Sherrod (Eds.), *Infant social cognition: Empirical and theoretical considerations*. Hillsdale, New Jersey: Erlbaum.

Corballis, M. C. (1980). Laterality and myth. *American Psychologist 35*, 284–295.

Davis, A. E., & Wada, J. A. (1977). Hemispheric asymmetries in human infants: Spectral analysis of flash and click evoked potentials. *Brain and Language 4*, 23–31.

Entus, A. K. (1977). Hemispheric asymmetry in processing of dichotically presented speech and nonspeech stimuli by infants. In S. J. Segalowitz & F. A. Gruber (Eds.), *Language development and neurological theory*. New York: Academic Press.

Ferguson, C. A., Peizer, D. B., & Weeks, T. E. (1973). Model-and-replica phonological grammar of a child's first words. *Lingua* 31, 35–65.

Fischer, K. W., & Bullock, D. (1981). Patterns of data: Sequence, synchrony, and constraint in cognitive development. In K. W. Fischer (Ed.), *Cognitive development. New Directions in Child Development* 12, 1–20.

Galaburda, A. M., LeMay, M., Kemper, T. L., & Geschwind, N. (1978). Right–left asymmetries in the brain: Structural differences between the hemispheres may underly cerebral dominance. *Science* 199, 852–856.

Gardner, M. F., & Walter, D. O. (1977). Evidence of hemispheric specialization from infant EEG. In S. Harnad, R. W. Doty, L. Goldstein, J. Jaynes, & G. Krauthamer (Eds.), *Lateralization in the nervous system*. New York: Academic Press.

Geschwind, N. (1970). The organization of language and the brain. *Science* 170, 940–944.

Gesell, A. (1938). The tonic neck reflex in the human infant. *Journal of Pediatrics* 13, 455–464.

Glanville, B. B., Best, C. T., & Levenson, R. (1977). A cardiac measure of cerebral asymmetries in infant auditory perception. *Developmental Psychology* 13, 54–59.

Hiscock, M., & Kinsbourne, M. (1980). Asymmetry of verbal–manual time sharing in children: A follow-up study. *Neuropsychologia* 18, 151–162.

Kaplan, E., & Kaplan, G. (1971). The prelinguistic child. In J. Eliot (Ed.), *Human development and cognitive processes*. New York: Holt.

Kinsbourne, M. (1975). The ontogeny of cerebral dominance. *Annals of the New York Academy of Sciences* 263, 244–250.

Lenneberg, E. H. (1967). *Biological foundations of language*. New York: Wiley.

Levy, J. (1974). Psychobiological implications of bilateral asymmetry. In S. J. Dimond & J. G. Beaumont (Eds.), *Hemisphere function in the human brain*. New York: Halsted.

Ling, D., & Ling, A. H. (1974). Communication development in the first three years of life. *Journal of Speech and Hearing Research* 17, 146–159.

McCarthy, D. (1954). Language development in children. In L. Carmichael (Ed.), *Manual of child psychology* (2nd ed.). New York: Wiley.

Michel, G. F. (1981). Right-handedness: A consequence of infant supine head-orientation preference? *Science* 212, 685–687.

Molfese, D. L., Freeman, R. B., Jr., & Palermo, D. S. (1975). The ontogeny of brain lateralization for speech and nonspeech stimuli. *Brain and Language* 2, 356–368.

Molfese, D. L., & Molfese, V. J. (1979). Hemisphere and stimulus differences as reflected in the cortical responses of newborn infants to speech stimuli. *Developmental Psychology* 15, 505–511.

Moskowitz, A. I. (1973). The acquisition of phonology and syntax: A preliminary study. In K. J. J. Hintikka, J. M. E. Moravcsik, & P. Suppes (Eds.), *Approaches to natural language*. Dordrecht: Reidel.

Nakazima, S. (1970). A comparative study of the speech developments of Japanese and American English in childhood (Part 3): The re-organization process of babbling articulation mechanisms. *Studia Phonologica* 5, 20–35.

Nebes, R. D. (1974). Hemispheric specialization in commissurotomized man. *Psychological Bulletin* 81, 1–14.

Oller, D. K. (1980). The emergence of the sounds of speech in infancy. In G. H. Yeni-Komshian, J. F. Kavanagh, & C. A. Ferguson (Eds.), *Child phonology* (Vol. 1): *Production*. New York: Academic Press.

Peiper, A. (1963). *Cerebral function in infancy and childhood* [B. Nagler & H. Nagler, trans.]. New York: Consultants Bureau.

Piaget, J. (1952). *The origins of intelligence in children* [M. Cook, trans.]. New York: International Universities Press.

Ramsay, D. S. (1980a). Beginnings of bimanual handedness and speech in infants. *Infant Behavior and Development* 3, 67–77.

Ramsay, D. S. (1980b). Onset of unimanual handedness in infants. *Infant Behavior and Development 3*, 377–385.

Ramsay, D. S., Campos, J. J., & Fenson, L. (1979). Onset of bimanual handedness in infants. *Infant Behavior and Development 2*, 69–76.

Slovin-Ela, S., & Kohen-Raz, R. (1978). Developmental differences in primary reaching responses of young infants from varying social backgrounds. *Child Development 49*, 132–140.

Stark, R. E. (1980). Stages of speech development in the first year of life. In G. H. Yeni-Komshian, J. F. Kavanagh, & C. A. Ferguson (Eds.), *Child phonology* (Vol. 1): *Production*. New York: Academic Press.

Steffen, H. (1975). Cerebral dominance: The development of handedness and speech. *Acta Paedopsychiatrica 41*, 223–235.

Turkewitz, G. (1977). The development of lateral differences in the human infant. In S. Harnad, R. W. Doty, L. Goldstein, J. Jaynes, & G. Krauthamer (Eds.), *Lateralization in the nervous system*. New York: Academic Press.

Uzgiris, I. C., & Hunt, J. McV. (1975). *Assessment in infancy: Ordinal scales of psychological development*. Urbana: Univ. of Illinois Press.

Wada, J. A., Clarke, R., & Hamm, A. (1975). Cerebral hemispheric asymmetry in humans. *Archives of Neurology 32*, 239–246.

Witelson, S. F., & Pallie, W. (1973). Left hemisphere specialization for language in the newborn: Neuroanatomical evidence of asymmetry. *Brain 96*, 641–646.

Wolff, P. H., Hurwitz, I., & Moss, H. (1977). Serial organization of motor skills in left- and right-handed adults. *Neuropsychologia 15*, 539–546.

Young, G. (1977). Manual specialization in infancy: Implications for lateralization of brain function. In S. J. Segalowitz & F. A. Gruber (Eds.), *Language development and neurological theory*. New York: Academic Press.

Zangwill, O. L. (1975). The ontogeny of cerebral dominance in man. In E. H. Lenneberg & E. Lenneberg (Eds.), *Foundations of language development: A multidisciplinary approach* (Vol. 1). New York: Academic Press.

Laterality of Function in the Infant: Historical and Contemporary Trends in Theory and Research[1]

LAUREN JULIUS HARRIS

Introduction

The last two decades have witnessed a period of research on lateralization of human cerebral function comparable to the great era of discovery initiated by Broca in 1861. Most of this new work has been devoted to the study of cerebral functions in adults, but of late there has been growing interest in infants and young children, especially in the study of hand preference. In these studies, psychologists hope to be able to address certain fundamental questions in neuropsychology and human development. For example, is lateralization of cerebral function present from birth and largely age-invariant, or does lateralization develop only with time? If the former (as recent studies suggest), is cerebral lateralization also expressed in early differences in use of the hands, the most public manifestation of laterality, or do hand differences emerge only gradually? What is the relationship between hand use and hand skill, or manual specialization (handedness in the stricter sense)? Are landmark changes in the expression of differences in hand use also linked to the development of important communicative skills, such as the first uses of gesture

[1]Some of the historical material in this chapter first appeared, in different form, as part of a general review of early theories of handedness (Harris, 1980a). Brief, selected accounts also have been presented at the 1980 NATO Advanced Study Institute on Neuropsychology and Cognition, Augusta, Georgia (Harris, 1982), and at the 1980 52nd Annual Meetings of the Midwestern Psychological Association, Saint Louis, Missouri. Research for this chapter was supported, in part, by the College Scholar Program of the College of Social Science, Michigan State University, and by grants from the Michigan State University Foundation and The Spencer Foundation.

and speech? Does familial handedness influence the timing and form of expression of hand differences? Are some forms of handedness pathological, a result of early unilateral cerebral injury? Are other forms a product of environmental training? Do parents and other caretakers significantly influence hand preference? If so, when and how?

Like the new research on adults, the study of hand preference and laterality in infants represents not just a new but a *renewed* effort. Indeed, the human infant's relevance for theories about handedness and lateral specialization was recognized even before the era launched by Broca. But, unlike the early studies of adults, the story of this work on infants has not been told. This history is worth recounting in its own right, but because the contribution made by the infant in early theories in many ways prefigures its role in current-day thinking, there is additional benefit in providing an historical context for developmental theory and research today. These, then, are my two aims in this chapter. As for the historical periods to be covered, a review could easily embrace the whole of recorded history, so pervasive has our subject proven itself to be. Some of the full sweep of this history will be shown, but my emphasis will be on the work of the nineteenth, and early twentieth centuries.

Theories of Handedness

At least since the Hellenistic Age, nearly all accounts of handedness have recognized right handedness to be the modal state. What was not agreed to was the reason. Many regarded handedness as a native attribute, with social factors playing only a secondary or supporting role. First, possibly, was Aristotle himself, for whom the right side of the body and the Heavens alike was the source of all motion. His teacher, Plato, took a contrary view. Symmetry was the natural state, and any deviation was the result of education and training. Both views would claim many advocates over the centuries, and the infant and child would be enlisted in the cause of each.

Nativist Theories

Central to the nativist view was the assumption that differences in function are the expression of differences in structure. But what to measure? Every sort of possibility seems to have been considered.

MUSCLE AND BONE WEIGHT

As was plain to see, in adults the dominant arm was usually more muscular. Greater muscularity, of course, would grow out of greater use, but it also was suggested that muscularity and use jointly represented the culmination of a predisposition for superior development of one side. If so, examination of the arm muscles of the newborn infant was widely regarded to be the critical test. In the nineteenth century, several such investigations were carried out—with mixed results. In 1869, Pieter Harting, a Dutch physician and natural historian, reported the findings of a medical student who had measured the circumference of the forearms of 12 newborn infants. There was no constant difference between the arms; sometimes the difference (of 1–3 mm) favored the left arm, sometimes the right, and Harting (1869, p. 53) concluded that there are no remarkable asymmetries at this age. The anatomist Jules van Biervliet (1899), however, compared the total *weights* of the muscles of stillborn infants and found a difference of as much of 1.85 gm favoring the right arm (p. 138).

Besides differences in total weight of the muscles, differences were reported in the weight of the forearm bones. Harting (1869) himself examined the skeletons of two stillborn infants and, finding in each case the right forearm bone to be $\frac{1}{4}$ to $\frac{1}{2}$ gm heavier, concluded that the weight of the right arm "surpasses that of the left arm from the time of birth [p. 54]." Three German anatomists—Bischoff (1863), Gaupp (1889), and Theile (1884)—found similar differences. However, a French anatomist, Debierre (1887), could detect no differences in three 6–7-month-old fetuses and eight infants varying in age from birth to 2 years (p. 30). And Gaupp called the difference in his own study "so weak ['si faible'] that it does not exceed the limits of possible error of measurement [quoted in French translation in Biervliet, 1899, p. 132]."

In 1902, the question was taken up again by T. G. Moorhead, Chief Demonstrator of Anatomy in Trinity College, Dublin. Moorhead (1902) reviewed Gaupp's and Bischoff's reports, as well as Biervliet's and Thiele's, and concluded that "no real differences exist, and that when any has been found, it has been due to unavoidable errors in the preparation of the specimens [p. 401]." Moorhead himself had weighed the right and left limbs of eight fetuses and was unable to find any constant differences between them, either for the muscles or the bones, individually or collectively.

SIZE OF THE HANDS

Biervliet (1899, p. 142) also was interested in possible differences in the size of the hands and turned to glove-makers for information. From their records, Biervliet calculated that in men, the right hand was .25 in. (.64 cm) larger in circumference; in women, the difference was smaller (.12 in.), but in the reverse direction. In children, however, no differences were apparent until the fourteenth or fifteenth year.

WEIGHT AND DISTRIBUTION OF VISCERA

Whatever the outcome of their measurements of muscle, bone weight, or hand size, only a few of those who looked for anatomical differences ever considered the behavioral question at issue: Were there differences in the use of the hands and arms in early life? One who did was Andrew Buchanan (1862), a professor of physiology at the University of Glasgow. "All observant persons," he wrote, will admit that infants "exhibit no tendency to use the one hand in preference to the other, as they employ indifferently the nearest hand to clutch at any object within their reach [1862, p. 144]." Following a kind of "maturationist" reasoning, Buchanan proposed that hand preference would appear only gradually, and then from a simple mechanical advantage favoring the right side.

This mechanical advantage also depended on a physical asymmetry, but in the lungs and liver rather than the arm muscles and bones. Buchanan argued as follows: The right lung, being more capacious than the left, receives more air on inspiration, making the right side of the chest bulge out more than the left, carrying with it the lower ribs, which, in turn, carry with them the liver. As the liver swings to the right, the center of gravity shifts in the same direction. The result is "a shift of balance to the left side, leaving the right leg—and right arm—freer for action [1862, p. 152]." Buchanan assumed that this development typically would occur after the first year, or at least after the child had begun to walk, because only by that time would the child have become vigorous enough to put forth the whole strength of its body. "[T]hen a mechanical advantage necessarily accrues to the muscles of the right side, and the child becoming conscious of the superior power of those muscles, soon learns spontaneously to call them into action [p. 144]."

Buchanan himself made no measurements of the weights of the internal organs, but his countryman, John Struthers (1863), did, and the results showed "a clear predominance of at least 15 ounces in favour of the right side [pp. 1103–1104]." Struthers also agreed with Buchanan that hand preference was absent in young infants: "I have again and again verified the fact in my own children, that in early childhood there is no preference for one hand more than the other [quoted in Wilson, 1891, p. 163]."

Struthers (1863) had measured the organs only of adults and 2–3-year-old children. As for the fetus, he supposed that the large size of the left lobe of the liver would equalize the weight of the left side with the right. Moorhead (1902) thought otherwise. Inspired by Struthers' work, he repeated the measurements on "several" fetuses from 5 to 8 months of age and found that, at least from the fifth month on, the center of gravity of the body was to the right of the mesial plane, the viscera on that side amounting to 52.6% of the total weight of the viscera. The excess was due to the right portion of the liver. So, after having rejected the proposition that there are innate lateral differences in the weight of bone or muscle of the arms, Moorhead (1902) concluded from these new measurements that the child "enters upon its extra-uterine existence with a marked right-sided bias [p. 403]."

BLOOD SUPPLY TO ARMS

Some years earlier, in 1828, a young French physician named Joseph Achille Comte (1828*a*, 1828*b*) had come to a conclusion very similar to Moorhead's. For Comte, however, the reason for handedness was not the weight of the viscera but the blood supply to the arms. Here, Comte was following an old tradition. Aristotle (1912) himself had a kind of thermal theory—the blood flowing to the nobler right side was purer and hotter than that flowing to the left (*De Partibus Animalium,* 670b and *passim*). In the mid-fifteenth century, an Italian scientist, Ludovico Ricchieri (cited in Browne, 1646, p. 188), proposed the actual mechanism to be the rightward displacement of the liver, which he believed to be a source of blood. (Though a contemporary of William Harvey, Ricchieri still held to Galen's views.) In the sixteenth century, the anatomist Gabriello Fallopio laid responsibility for right handedness on the rightward location of the Azygos vein (cited in Browne, 1646, p. 188). Finally, by the nineteenth century, reference began to be made to the subclavian arteries, the design of which supposedly perfused the right arm with a greater supply of blood (e.g., Hyrtl, 1860). (The right subclavian arises off the innominata artery and is closer to the heart by about 1 in.; the left subclavian arises later, although directly off the aorta.)

Where Comte broke rank was in proposing that any asymmetry in blood flow to the arms would have been imposed by external forces. While performing his duties in the obstetrics ward of a Paris hospital, Comte noted that among infants born in the vertex position (about 95% of all births in his survey), there were many more "first" presentation than "second" presentation births. In the first presentation, the forehead is toward the mother's right sacroiliac joint. In the second presentation, the orientation is reversed. The ratio, in fact, was 9:1, which Comte remarked was the same as the ratio of right- to left-handers in the population.[2] Comte saw a connection. He argued that the first birth position implies that *in utero,* at least from about the fifth month of gestation on, the infant's left arm would have been against the mother's back, the right against the abdomen. Here is where blood supply was affected. The resistance of the mother's back, in contrast to the yielding quality of her abdomen, would create a continuous compression that would delay the flow of arterial blood, impair the return of venous blood, and thus diminish "the vital energy" of the left side and lead to right handedness. In the

---

[2]The 9:1 ratio of right- to left-handers was not inconsistent with then-contemporary estimates, although it perhaps was slightly on the low side, depending on the measure used. (For handwriting, it perhaps would have been closer to 9:5:1; see Harris, 1980*a*). However, I know of no evidence of a comparable 9:1 ratio of first to second position births. The first position typically is cited only as the more common (e.g., Holmes, 1969).

same way, those fewer infants born in the second position became left-handed. Thus, "at the moment of birth, in the great number of cases, the vital activity of the left arm is less than the right, which makes the left comparatively weaker than the right [Comte, 1828a, p. 32]."

Comte saw the need to establish whether the similarity in ratios between birth positions and adult handedness was more than coincidental, but all we learn from his published work is that for some children (*quelques enfants*) whose birth he witnessed, their mothers' reports of the children's arm movements were consistent with the children's intra-uterine position. Comte did not give these children's ages at the time of observation. Little notice was paid to Comte's work (a handful of citations through 1900), although it won generous praise from one of the leading experimental physiologists of the nineteenth century, François Magendie, and was published in his *Journal de Physiologie* (Comte, 1828b).

Buchanan's dynamic balance theory as well as all of the other blood supply theories did not fare much better. In their case, the problem lay simply in their further implication that any individual for whom the usual internal arrangement of organs, arteries, or veins was the reverse of that normally found would be left- rather than right-handed. But, as many nineteenth-century critics observed (e.g., Pye-Smith, 1871), these so-called situs-inversus individuals were far rarer than was left handedness itself, and even the rare individuals with situs inversus were not invariably left-handed.

BRAIN THEORIES AND GROWTH GRADIENTS

Whatever the strengths or short-comings of visceral balance and other theories, all such lines of argument began to lose force in the 1860s, when the psychiatrist Jean Baptiste Bouillaud (1864–1865) and the neurologist and anthropologist Paul Broca (1865) first enunciated the principle of a linkage between handedness and the hemispheres of the brain. The reasons for handedness thus lay not within the mother's womb or in her child's chest, abdomen, or even the arms themselves; the brain itself held the key to the puzzle. By this view, handedness was widely believed to be a product of the greater weight or specific density of the left cerebral hemisphere (see review in Harris, 1980a, pp. 23–25). Blood supply explanations were adjusted accordingly: Now more blood supposedly would flow to the left than to the right hemisphere because of the presumably more advantageous location of the left carotid artery (i.e., its emergence directly off the aorta). Broca (1877) himself proposed an explanation of this sort.

Handedness having been identified as a product of the brain, the question of the *development* of handedness for the first time could be considered from the standpoint of what was known about the development of the brain. Debate thus began as to whether there were differences in the rates of growth of the cerebral hemispheres. Possibly the first person to have raised this question was Louis Pierre Gratiolet, in his monumental work, *On the comparative anatomy of the nervous system* (Leurat & Gratiolet, 1857).[3] Here, Gratiolet (Leurat & Gratiolet, 1857) wrote that it "appeared" to him (*'Il m'a semblé'*), following a series of "carefully made observations," that the two hemispheres "do not develop in an absolutely symmetrical manner. The development of the frontal convolutions is faster on the left than on the right, while the reverse occurs for the occipital–sphenoidal lobe [pp. 241–242]."[4]

Gratiolet's statement, although made almost in passing, was widely cited (e.g., Broca, 1865; Carrier, 1867, p. 38; Delaunay, 1874, p. 32; Font-Réaulx, 1866, p. 9; J. H. Jackson, 1874, p. 100; Jobert, 1885, p. 26; Wilson, 1891, pp. 154–155). What was generally overlooked was the cautious tone, as well as a later remark indicating that Gratiolet had been speaking of fetal brains and leaving open the question whether the same differences were apparent in the newborn infant: "Moreover, the cerebral convolutions develop so quickly that at birth the system of convolutions is complete and differs from that of an adult by only a few flexuosities and details [Leurat & Gratiolet, 1857, p. 242]."

Understandably, the question of lateral differences in growth rate was taken up in subsequent studies. Possibly the first to do so was the author of a "Note" in the *Bulletins de la Société d'Anthropologie de Paris* (Roques, 1869), who recounted that in a *"grand numbre"* of brains of children and newborns, he had found asymmetries consistent with Gratiolet's report. In particular, in the left frontal lobe, the convolutions were more numerous and, above all, deeper (*plus profounds*) (Roques, 1869, p. 728). Similar findings were reported by Jules Gromier (1874) and by the physiologist Jules Luys (incomplete citations in Ireland, 1880, pp. 209–210; and Jobert, 1885, p. 27; probably Luys, 1865). According to Ireland (1880, p. 210), Luys also found differences in the weight of the hemispheres in the newborn child, the left being a "few grammes" heavier than the right. Ireland (1880) added an account of his own observations, not of the brain directly, but of the conformation of the skull: The

---

[3]This is a two-volume work, the first volume of which was written by François Leurat in 1839, the second by Gratiolet (Leurat & Gratiolet, 1857), after Leurat's death. Both volumes had enormous influence on thinking about localization of function, but especially the second, since in it Gratiolet provided extensive macroscopic descriptions of the cerebral convolutions as well as a nearly complete vocabulary of names for the convolutions and fissures (see discussions in Clarke & Dewhurst, 1972; Meyer, 1971; Schiller, 1979).

[4]The sphenoid bone is in the base of the skull, in front of the temporal bones and the basilar part of the occipital, so the cortical area overlying this region, namely, the basilar temporal, would seem to have been the region to which Gratiolet was referring. Elsewhere, however, Gratiolet (Leurat & Gratiolet, 1857, p. 241) evidently was simply designating posterior regions. J. Hughlings Jackson (1874, p. 100) among others, interpreted the area in question to be the "posterior lobe."

left side was more protuberant than the right in the area "a little above or behind the ear, [indicating] a greater development of the brain on the left side, near the region where physiologists have placed the motor area of the brain [p. 210]." Ireland did not identify the ages of the specimens. However, Jobert (1885, p. 27) reported similar differences from his examination of the heads of 50 children (ages unspecified).

However these various reports are best interpreted, many writers were impressed with what the "finding" about earlier left-brain development implied about the origins of handedness and the timing of first appearance of differences in hand use. For instance, with only Gratiolet's somewhat sketchy account to guide him, Broca (1865) confidently said:

> One therefore understands why, from the first moments of life ['*dès les premiers temps de la vie*'], the young child shows a preference for the limbs having, at that time, the more complete innervation, why, in other words, he becomes right-handed. The superior right limb, being stronger and more skillful than the left from the beginning, for that very reason is called on to work more often; and from that moment it acquires a superiority of strength and skill that only grows with age [p. 383].

Indeed, Broca (1865, p. 393) went on to express a much more general principle: Inasmuch as the two hemispheres were perfectly identical anatomically (as the evidence to date indicated), it was just this earlier *development* of the left hemisphere (by which Broca obviously was referring to the anterior portion only) that predisposed its greater role in the more complex intellectual acts, including the expression of ideas through language and, more particularly, speech.

Although Broca's more general principle seems hardly to have been acknowledged, there was broad agreement with him on the matter of hand preference. For instance, from his own work, Jules Luys concluded that earlier left-brain growth would mean earlier (*plus précoce*) use of the right hand (cited in Jobert, 1885, p. 27). Delaunay (1874, p. 32), one of Broca's own students in anthropology at the University of Paris, evidently was even willing to contemplate the possibility of hand differences *in utero*. According to the Chinese, he said, the fetus, while still in its mother's womb, moves its right hand at 7 months, its left at 8. (Whatever the truth of such a report, its compatibility with Comte's (1828*a*, 1828*b*) intrauterine position theory is certainly tantalizing.)

Ireland (1880) and Jobert (1885), from their reading of Luys' evidence along with their own observations, likewise were ready to assign the primary role in handedness to brain-growth differences. Ireland (1880) said, "If this observation of Luys be correct, the superior weight of the left hemisphere at birth might be held to confirm as well as to account for the habitual preference given to the right limbs [p. 210]." But like Buchanan (1862), and unlike Broca, Luys, and certainly Delaunay, Ireland (1880) held to a kind of maturational view, supposing that some time would be required for hand differences to be expressed: "Certain it is that infants seem at first to use both hands indiscriminately, and the one arm to be at first as well developed as the other, though in process of time the right arm gets more muscular than the left [p. 207]."

The reports of earlier left-brain growth were widely accepted, but not universally so. A French physician, Joseph Parrot (1879), examined the brains of 96 infants from still-born to 7 months of age. In 80% of the cases, the right side of the brain was the more developed; in the remaining cases, the left side, with the most marked differences appearing in the youngest brains. Parrot acknowledged the inconsistency of these anatomical findings with what might have been expected by the fact of dominant right handedness. But like Ireland (1880), Parrot (1879) appealed to a notion of maturation: "[T]he predominance of the right hand, in the same way as speech, makes its appearance only a long time after birth, that is after a long period of improvement [*de perfectionnement*] [p. 517]."

Parrot (1879) gave no evidence for his statement. Nor was he clear about the nature and extent of the anatomical differences between the hemispheres, the ages of the brains in which the differences appeared, or even the number of brains where a left–right comparison was made. Evidently, a comparison was not made in every case. For instance, in one group of ten brains (age 4–39 days), left–right comparisons were made for only two brains. In both brains, however, Parrot reported that the white matter was more accentuated on the right side, and in one brain, the fissure of Rolando (central sulcus) was "very evident" in the right hemisphere but "absolutely lacking" in the left. Nevertheless, Parrot's work— at least through second-hand accounts—was not without influence. Citing a summary by Berillon (1884), Ireland (1886) questioned his prior conclusion (Ireland, 1880) that the left hemisphere develops before the right: "So the question which side is first developed seems still doubtful [1886, p. 293]."

For still other anatomists, the entire question of a maturational difference was doubtful, since they found no such left–right differences in their specimens (Ecker, 1868; also Vogt, cited in Bateman, 1869, p. 383, and in Jackson, 1874, p. 100). Another anatomist reported that asymmetries were present, but only in the brain of the adult, not in the young child (Todd, 1859; incomplete citation in Bateman, 1869, p. 380). The physician Frederic Bateman (1869)—perhaps hearing Milton's words that God reveals himself "as His manner is, first to his Englishmen"—called the entire matter an "extremely interesting and important question about which very few are in a position to give a valid opinion and I regret I can quote no British authority in reference to it [p. 383]." Finally, in 1902, D. J. Cunningham reported different asymmetries on *both* sides in the fetal brain—in the cortical area specifically allotted to the arm, a greater size "almost invariably in favour of the right cerebral hemisphere, [but in the] whole extent of the region of cerebral surface of which [the arm area] forms a part [p. 293]," there was more extensive development on the left side. Cunningham, (1902) was perplexed by the former difference, since it was "exactly the opposite of what I had anticipated [p. 293]," and he was reluctant to speculate whether the latter difference had any association to right handedness or to localization of the speech center in the left hemisphere "because the same condition is also a characteristic of the ape [but] I cannot persuade myself that the ape possesses any superior power in either arm [p. 293]."

BLOOD SUPPLY AND POSTURAL ORIENTATION AFTER BIRTH

In 1880, the "blood to brain," "blood to hand," and postural orientation explanations of handedness all were given a reprise of sorts by the physician and pioneer educator Edouard Sequin.[5] Like Comte (1828a, 1828b), Sequin postulated a connection between blood supply, postural orientation, and handedness. However, unlike Comte, Sequin saw blood supply as primary and as working its effect on the infant's postural position *after* birth. Infants, Sequin (1880) said, "generally lie on their right sides [p. 32]." Hans Ballin (1896), an American writer on education, agreed with Sequin: "We . . . observe as an original inclination that infants prefer to lie on their right side. This is not from mere caprice. These facts have been known for some time [p. 306]."

Sequin (1880) characterized this "reclination" as a "primordial sequence of anatomical structure, [which] soon becomes in its turn, a cause of exaggeration of the structural inequality [p. 32]." The structure in question was the design of the emergences of the cephalic arteries. In man, Sequin noted, there are three, with the right—the largest—bifurcating to form the right subclavian and carotid. Sequin (1880) supposed that this asymmetry was sufficient in its effect on the "hematose" of the two sides to make the infant "one-sided (generally right-handed) in his movements [p. 33]." At the same time, the greater supply of blood to the left hemisphere "incites this hemisphere to more brain-work and the right side of the body to more muscular work [Sequin, 1880, p. 33]."

Sequin's ideas about blood supply were not new and seem to have been ignored (if known at all) in the ongoing debates on the origins of handedness. Nor was Sequin the first to mention postural orientation. As a medical student, Aimé Péré, (1900) pointed out, "*Les auteurs anciens ont disserté avec abondance sur se sujet* [p. 69]," meaning the physicians and

---

[5]The French-American Sequin (1812–1880) was the special United States Commissioner on Education to the Vienna Exposition in 1873. His remarks on handedness appeared as a very brief part of his book-length report on the Exposition, first published in 1875 and revised in 1880.

anatomists of ancient Greece and Rome. Indeed they had. The subject was discussed, for instance, by Aristotle and his followers (Aristotle, *Problemeta*, 1926, p. 169), as well as in more contemporary times, for instance, in an article on sleeping (*Coucher*) by Baron Anthelme Richerand for the 1813 *Dictionnaire des sciences medicales*, and later by several members of Broca's own circle. All agreed that the preference was to lie on the right side, not the left (Delaunay, 1874, p. 28).[6] Judging from Péré's account (1900, p. 69), however, Sequin's blood supply explanation must not have been widely held by his contemporaries; instead, certain other anatomical explanations were proposed (e.g., that lying on the right side would keep the liver from pressing on the stomach, or that food would pass more easily into the pylorus). Nor was there agreement as to the relationship between postural preference and handedness. Some argued that sleeping on the right side *caused* right handedness, the implication presumably being that handedness would have to have been absent initially; others, like Delaunay (1874), argued just the reverse—that "man lies on his right side because he is right handed [p. 81]."

Regrettably, these disputes about the origins of handedness were not better informed, as they might have been, by systematic observations of the actual postural behavior of the young infant. Such observations also might have won some belated and possibly quite deserving attention for Comte's (1828a, 1828b) ideas about intrauterine position.

OCULAR DOMINANCE AND ARM MOVEMENTS IN INFANCY

By the 1880s, investigators *had* begun to take notice of a new behavioral asymmetry, but instead of postural orientation, it was preference in the use of the eyes. Joseph Le Conte, an American geologist and writer on optics, observed that, in pointing at an object with both eyes open, the image of the finger that is ranged with the object is the right-eye image for right-handers, and the left-eye image for left-handers (Le Conte, 1884a, 1884b). In 1908, the psychologist H. C. Stevens proposed a model by which the visual asymmetry (the primary factor) would predispose motor asymmetry (handedness) in the human infant. The mechanism depended on the capacity of the retina to estimate spatial extents, a topic of longstanding interest to the psychophysiologist Gustav Fechner, who carried out experiments on such issues as the applicability of Weber's law to extensive magnitudes and the role of the eye muscles in judgments of extent. Stevens developed a way to test the subjective size of objects in

---

[6]The Greek writers, in fact, supposed that the right position was preferred only for sleeping (sleep was said to come more easily in that position), whereas one would lie on the left side while awake. The suggested explanation reflected the Aristotelian idea that movement arises on the right side ("It is the moving parts which must rest, and the right is the moving side [Aristotle, 1926, p. 169]."

each hemifield of the eyes. In a majority of right-handed adult subjects, a disk appearing in the right hemifield was judged larger than a disk appearing in the left hemifield, and the reverse was found in a majority of left-handers. How could this visual effect lead to differences in use of the hands in infancy? Stevens' (1908) answer was that objects "situated in the right half of vision of a left-hemisphered infant would, by appearing larger, attract its attention. The eyeballs would then turn, reflexly, to receive the attractive object on the fovea. Eye movements would, probably, lead to head movements, and head movements to arm movements. Just the reverse of this would happen with a right-hemisphered infant [p. 273]."

Stevens did not say when the postulated sequence of events would begin or how quickly it would culminate in preferential arm movements. Stevens himself made no test, and the hypothesis does not seem to have had much influence. It certainly did not lead to any studies of the relationship between eye preference and hand movements in infancy, although there was some interest in the more general question of the relationship between eye dominance and handedness. A British psychologist may have been instrumental in damping enthusiasm for Stevens' hypothesis when he reported what he called a "fatal objection"—that among people born blind, a group of whom he himself had studied, the proportion of right- and left-handers was about the same as among sighted persons (Ballard, 1911–1912, p. 305). This would be an unlikely outcome if handedness were merely secondary to visual experience in early life. Nor could Stevens' hypothesis have been helped by later reports that questioned the very existence of a strong relationship between eye preference and handedness (Woo & Pearson, 1927).

Nurture Theories

Despite the many disagreements about mechanism and time of first appearance of hand differences, most of the scientific establishment accepted the idea that handedness was a fundamentally native trait. However, after consideration of much the same kind of anatomical, physiological, and (such as it was) behavioral evidence, some writers concluded that nurture must play the major, even the only, role. Thus, where "maturationists" like Buchanan (1862) and Parrot (1879) saw the supposed absence of differences in hand use in early life as signifying a structural factor not yet active, these "nurturists" saw only symmetry not yet erased by custom and training.

The seventeenth-century English physician Sir Thomas Browne (1646) perhaps was the first to mention the behavior of children in advancing this argument: "And thus have we at large declared that although the right be most commonly used, yet hath it no regular or certaine root in nature: . . . since in children it seemes either indifferent or more favourable in the other, but more reasonable for uniformity in action that men accustome unto one [p. 192]."

Similar reasoning was used by nineteenth-century writers: For example, "[M]y own observations lead me to believe that infants and young children are equally 'handy' with both members [Alcock, 1870, p. 557]"; "there is no asymmetry of body or function in early infancy. The child uses its two arms, legs and hands equally well. If there is any heredity of one-sidedness, it does not appear [Kellogg, 1898, p. 356]."

"MAIMED BY THE FOLLY OF NURSES AND MOTHERS"

How, then, did society enforce right-hand rule? If Aristotle, with his blood temperature theory, was the father of nativist theories of handedness, then Plato may have been first to stress the influence of training. He also pointed the blame. In *Laws*, in the dialogue between the Athenian stranger and Cleinias, a Cretan, the Athenian remarks that in the use of our limbs we are "maimed by the folly of nurses and mothers; for although our several limbs are by nature balanced, we create a difference in them by bad habits [Plato, 1953, *Laws* 7, 795]."

Plato was loud on generalities but quiet on details, never identifying the "folly" or "bad habits" he had in mind. He might have been referring, among other things, to the practice later described by Plutarch in his *Peri Paidon Agoges* (first English translation, *The education or bringinge vp of children*): "[W]e do accustome our chyldren to take meate with the ryght hande, & if they do put forthe the lefte hande, anone [at once] we correct them [Elyot, 1533, Chapter 4, p. 16]." This custom was no less favored in England during the Renaissance. The author of a work on chirology, or study of the hand, says that it is "drawn out of honesty itself, and nature, and hath ever beene in use in those Nations who have addicted themselves to humanity and good manners [F.B., 1644, p. 123]." Likewise, when the child was taught to write, the pen was to be held in the right hand, never the left (e.g., Clement, 1587, p. 55).[7]

By the eighteenth century, not much had changed, as we learn from Benjamin Franklin. Franklin (1779/1904) however, doubtless because of his own left handedness, took a rather dimmer view of these practices. In an essay entitled, "A petition of the left hand" addressed "To those who have the superintendency of education," Franklin let his maligned hand recount how it "was suffered to grow up without the least instruction, while nothing was spared in her [the right hand's] education. She had

[7]There is serious question whether Plutarch was in fact the author of *Peri Paidon Agoges* (e.g., De Lacy, 1967, Vol. 6, p. 360). But whether Plutarch's or not, it proved, through Elyot's (1533) and many subsequent translations, to be immensely influential in European educational theory and Renaissance humanist philosophy. Right-hand training thus received the imprimatur of history.

masters to teach her writing, drawing, music, and other accomplishments; but if by chance I touched a pencil, a pen, or a needle, I was bitterly rebuked; and more than once I have been beaten for being awkward, and wanting a graceful manner [p. 369]."

Franklin's tone was light, but his intention was serious. What is more, he was *taken* seriously, and his petition was occasionally cited in the literature on laterality (e.g., Comte, 1842, p. 142; Marion, 1890, p. 776; Perez, 1901, p. 45). Later writers who subscribed to the nurturist view played variations on Franklin's theme. Thus, any tendency by the infant or young child "to use the left hand in taking food or playthings is instantly corrected by the nurse refusing to give them unless the conventionally proper hand be held out [Alcock, 1870, p. 557]"; "Impregnated with all these traditions, young mothers and nurses check infants, with superstitious horror, in the use of the left hand—which, nota bene, the poor little victims invariably attempt—and do their best to make a pagan tradition an immortal truth, and keep mankind one-handed and right-handed [Reade, 1878, p. 74]"; "Perhaps no mother or conventional nurse ever fails to place an object for the infant to clasp except in its right hand [Kellogg, 1898, p. 356]"; "From seeing young infants grasp objects with either hand indiscriminately and from the frequency with which one hears the admonition 'Not that hand—the other hand,' addressed to children somewhat more advanced in age, one cannot help thinking that right-handedness is not innate and that it is in most cases the result of teaching [Shaw, 1902, p. 1486]."

Without question, direct and deliberate hand training was a common practice, at least in the middle and upper classes. There also was much speculation that hand preference was influenced indirectly by the way the infant was carried in the arms. Comte (1828*b*) was among those who mentioned the practice, although he saw it only as a means of reinforcing the tendency originally induced by intrauterine position:

> I have said that education from the onset tends to maintain this unbalance and this native disproportionate use of the two arms; one will be convinced, as I have been, by the truth of this remark, if one watches how nurses carry their infants: . . . the infant, seated on his nurse's right forearm, has the free use of his right arm, whereas his left arm, caught by his side, is held nearly totally immobile against the nurse's chest. This is nurses' usual practice [p. 45].

The American psychologist G. Stanley Hall and his student E. M. Hartwell (1884) reported the same practice and drew the same conclusion: "Nurses carry children on their own right arm, leaving the child's right arm a freer field of motion [p. 101]." So did a correspondent to the French journal *Révue Scientifique* (Cosmovici, 1889).

Unfortunately for the "mother-holding" theory, as many observers pointed out, the mother's (or nurse's) actual custom was to carry the child on her *left* arm, presumably in order to leave her right arm free. Daniel Wilson (1891, p. 127) pointed this out; so did several correspondents replying immediately to the statement in *Révue Scientifique* (Feré, 1889; H. M., 1889; J. H., 1889); and so did the American psychologist James Mark Baldwin (1894/1900), who found left-arm carrying to be "an invariable tendency with myself and with nurses and mothers whom I have observed [p. 57]." Andrew Buchanan (1862), the dynamic balance theorist, went still further: Carrying burdens was "the special function of the left side [p. 162]" whether the burden was an infant, a heavy trunk, or a basket of eggs. The reason was that the body's equilibrium would be improved, inasmuch as the center of gravity of the body is on the right side (Buchanan, 1862). So if the mother-holding theory were true, then, as Daniel Wilson and others pointed out, all children (of right-handed mothers) ought to be left-handed, meaning that the left-handed nurses and mothers of the next generation would reverse the practice.

Not all those who acknowledged left-side holding dismissed the possible influence on hand preference. One perhaps unlikely observer was Captain John Godfrey (1747), the author of an English treatise on sword-fighting. Handedness being relevant to his subject, Godfrey speculated on its origin:

> The Nurse carries the child in the left Arm; the consequence of that is, it's [sic] right Arm is confined and the left at liberty to play and exercise; and I believe it will be allowed that the child, in its Infancy, is most of the Day in the Nurse's Arms. If accustomed to that Habit, so long as till it can go alone, no wonder of it's [sic] continuing to use the left Arm. . . [p. 17].

As Godfrey saw it, most children so treated would become left-handed if not later broken of the habit by the parents.

Another, later supporter of the idea that side of holding might influence hand preference was a French professor, Henri Marion (1890). Marion, noting the recent disputes in *Révue Scientifique*, recalled that his own children originally had shown "absolute indeterminacy" in the use of their hands, followed by a temporary predominance of one hand or the other, according to the activity or occasion, such as the arm on which the child was carried, or the hand given to him for taking a walk. Finally, there was definitive predominance of one hand over the other as a result of the persistent action of these same causes, that is, imitation and education. Marion (1890) agreed that the question of why a child becomes a right-hander or a left-hander is not "entirely elucidated," but "if it is one part hereditary, it is for a much greater part a matter of habit [p. 776]."

However uncertain we may be as to the exact methods of hand-training used, there seems to have been little question about the outcome and cost. In Europe, remarked the anthropologist Robert Hertz (1909/1973), it was said that "One of the signs which distinguish a well-brought-up child is that its left hand has become incapable of any independent action [p. 5]."

AMBIDEXTRAL CULTURE

Both critics as well as supporters of physiological theories acknowledged the existence of many of the training methods just discussed. Some of these writers, as we have seen, deemed such practices to be right and proper, whereas others, such as Ben Franklin, were rather less enthusiastic. Still others, however, inspired by the revelations of Broca's work, judged these same practices to be nothing less than the first steps on the road to intellectual tragedy, for in the dominance of one hand (and one-half of the brain), they saw man using only half the mental endowments with which nature had provided him. In 1904, these critics, led by one John Jackson, formed a British society for the promotion of ambidexterity. An abundance of educational and health benefits were promised. For instance, left-hand training would produce supplementary speech centers in the right cerebral hemisphere, thereby affording protection against the usual ravages of injury to the speech center of the left hemisphere (Harris, in press). At least for Jackson (1905), all arguments for the inherent superiority of the right hand (and the left hemisphere) were objectionable inasmuch as they threatened the logical as well as the physiological foundations of his views. And the human infant was Ambidextral Culture's shining example of symmetry and either-handedness—at least until, as Charles Reade (1878) had put it, "some grown fool interferes and mutilates it [p. 175]."

Empirical Studies of Hand Preference in Human Infants

We have seen how writers of all theoretical persuasions referred to the infant's hand preference, or lack thereof, either to confirm their own theories or to disconfirm others. The question of evidence was something else. Whereas arguments about the existence of structural asymmetries of brain or body could draw on abundant, if inconclusive, data, disputes about infants' hand preferences were not informed by any hard evidence whatsoever. At best, most of the evidence seems to have been anecdotal, at worst a product of a priori reasoning or sheer introspection, and sometimes it is hard to tell which. For instance, when Broca (1865) stated that hand or limb preference is discernible from the first moments of life, was he referring to actual observations of infants' hand movements or, given his welcome (and seemingly uncritical) acceptance of Gratiolet's account of convolutionary growth and his own hypothesis linking brainedness and handedness, was he merely surmising what he thought must be so?

There is no way to tell. The absence of clear evidence did not go unnoticed. A German physiologist, Karl von Vierordt (1881), wrote, regretfully, that "Reliable data are lacking concerning this question of primary importance—the use of the left and right arms in the first grasping movements of young infants [Vierordt's term was *Saugling*, or 'suckling'; p. 428]."

Even, however, as these largely fruitless arguments about hand preference in infancy were being pursued, a new era was well underway that, before the turn of the century, would shed some real light on the question. The child himself, and not just his blood and bones, had begun to be recognized as a fit subject for scientific study. The roots of this new movement of child study were various: The empiricist philosophy of John Locke (1632–1704) had made the child interesting as a subject of epistemological study; the educational theories of Johann Pestalozzi (1746–1827) and Jean-Jacques Rousseau (1712–1778) made him interesting as a subject of pedagogical study (see Kessen, 1965); and German investigators in the 1850s had hinted at the riches to be won from close observation of early development (e.g., Kussmaul, 1859; Sigismund, 1856). But the single greatest catalyst to the scientific study of the child was the publication, in 1859, of *On the origin of species*, for what Charles Darwin himself envisioned had come swiftly to pass: "Psychology will be based on a new foundation, that of the necessary acquirement of each mental power and capacity by gradation. Light will be thrown on the origin of man and his history [p. 488]."

Infant Handedness and Evolution

With the advent of Darwinism, the question of the existence of functional and anatomical asymmetries in human infants thus came to be seen as relevant not only to extant theories of handedness in man but to fundamental ideas about human evolution as well. Nativists, for their part, welcomed Darwin's theory, for they saw it as providing a suitable framework for their position—handedness not only was innate but now could be seen as a manifestation of a more advanced state in the evolution of the species. As Cunningham (1902) said, "It appears probable that right-handedness assumed form as a characteristic of man at a very early period in his evolution [p. 279]." Nurturists, however, took exception. John Jackson (1905, p. 91), the ambidextral culturist, asked, rhetorically, how dextral superiority, with a corresponding deterioration of the other limb, could possibly be beneficial to (and therefore constitute a more advanced state in) those animals so affected.

Nativists agreed on the evolutionary nature of handedness, but the question of the mechanism of transmission was less clear. Long before Darwin, of course, the scientific world was rife with speculation about evolution, though by other means than natural selection. Comte (1828a, p. 17), for one, had cited (disapprovingly) a proposal by a French nobleman and scientist, the Marquis Henri Dutrochet (probably 1824 or 1826), that the growth of strength and skill produced by exercise of the right side of the body would be transmitted through generations. Darwin himself, contrary to popular belief today, did not totally reject such Lamarckian ideas but admitted use and disuse as an important evolutionary mechanism in addition to natural selection (see Ernst Mayr, "Introduction" to *On the origin of species,* facsimile of first ed., 1859/1964, pp. 24 ff.). This may be why Pieter Harting (1869), Darwin's "most convinced defender" in the Dutch academic world (Bulhof, 1974, p. 280), had invoked Lamarckian principles to account for the differences found in his study of the weight of the arm bones of infants. The differences were "probably the result of hereditary transmission of a characteristic acquired by habit ['à la transmission héréditaire d'une particularité acquise par l'habitude'] [Harting, 1869, p. 54]."

The evolutionary argument also soon became conflated with the biogenetic theory of Ernst Haeckel (1874/1905), a professor of comparative morphology at the University of Jena. Haeckel's theory was that the human child recapitulates in its development the adult stages of phylogeny. As Sir William Gowers (1902) put it, "If 'the child is Father to the man' the child may also exemplify the primitive paternity of the race [p. 1719]." Many embraced this idea in one form or another, pre-eminently, among the psychologists, G. Stanley Hall and James Mark Baldwin.

The implication of the recapitulationist theory for the analysis of handedness were quickly seen, as were new possibilities offered by the study of infants. Cunningham's (1902) proposal was typical. To his remark, quoted earlier, that right handedness appeared early in man's development, he added that the study of infants was of "very especial value [since it could identify] the period in the evolution of man at which right-handedness became a fixed and permanent human characteristic [p. 280]."

To be sure, the recapitulationist principle also was invoked in support of the usual social prejudices. For instance, "from the point of view of evolution, the woman is placed between the child, nearly symmetrical, and the man, who is completely asymmetrical. The newborn infant uses one hand as well as the other, and it is only by a certain time (about two years) that the infant becomes clearly right-handed or left-handed [Jobert, 1885, pp. 12–13; Harris, 1983a]."

Baby Biographies

Darwin not only spurred interest in the scientific study of the child, he gave legitimacy to a particular method of study—the baby biography. First used in 1781 by Dieterich Tiedemann, a professor of philosophy at the German University of Marbury (Soldan, 1890), the baby biography was a diary, typically kept by the parent, concerning the development of an individual child. Darwin's own contribution to the genre appeared in 1877, as an account of the intellectual and emotional development of his firstborn child, William Erasmus. Subsequently, the keeping of these diaries was broadly encouraged: For instance, in 1881, the secretary of the education section of the American Social Science Association published a circular calling for mothers or other interested observers to record such facts as the infant's first attention to stimuli and the development of crawling, walking, and speech. In 1882, G. Stanley Hall, the father of the child-study movement in America, urged the study of the child through observation and questionnaire as the core of a new profession of pedagogy (Ross, 1972, p. 124).

Darwin's account of his son was only a sketch. The work that perhaps best showed the possibilities of the baby biography for achieving a scientific understanding of mental development was much grander in scale. This was *Die Seele des Kindes* ['The mind of the child'] by Wilhelm Preyer (1881/1888), professor of physiology at the University of Jena, and an enthusiatic Darwinist. Preyer's more intensive method typified the style (e.g., "[O]ccupying myself with the child [Preyer's son] at least three times a day . . . and guarding him, as far as possible, against such training as children usually receive, I found nearly every day some fact of mental genesis to record [p. x; from Author's Preface]"). Thus the boy's first 3 years were charted.

As the quotation indicates, Preyer and other biographers were concerned for the most part only to describe the child's spontaneous behavior in natural settings rather than in the kind of experimentally contrived situations where, for purposes of studying hand preference, such factors as object location could be controlled. Consequently, the diarists frequently provided very rich descriptions of motor development, including use of the hands and arms, but often omitted details important for the assessment of hand preference (e.g., identification or exact location of the object reached for or the number of times one hand or the other was used).

TIEDEMANN (1781)

Tiedemann's biography of his child was deficient in all the aforementioned respects.[8] Hand preference, furthermore, was not mentioned. What

---

[8]The version cited here is F. L. Soldan's (1890) English translation of Bernard Perez's commentary in French on Michelan's French translation (1863, *Journal Général de l'Instruction Publique*) of the original German version first recorded, evidently, in 1781. Michelan identified Tiedemann as "Thierry Tiedemann," and Perez apparently agreed, using that name in his commentary ("Thierri Tiedemann et la Science de l'Enfant"; see Perez, 1889, footnote 1, p. 101). The identification of the author as Dietrich Tiedemann was made by Soldan, although no reasons were given (see Soldan, 1890, p. 3 of Preface). Whether the English translation fairly represents the French, or the French the German, I am not prepared to say.

is evident nonetheless, even in this earliest work, is the biographer's appreciation of the significance of the skills of reaching and grasping. Thus, Tiedemann's subject (his son Frederich, according to Soldan, 1890) "began to enjoy it" when, at 3 months and 2 days, he "grasped objects within his reach [Soldan, 1890, p. 18]," and by his fifth month, had "learned to use his hands for grasping and holding things [p. 24]."

SIGISMUND (1856)

Possibly the first biographer to take notice of the child's hand preference, in addition to the usual details about grasping and motor development, was Berthold Sigismund (1856), in his epochal work, *Kind und Welt; die funf ersten Perioden des Kindesalters* ['*The child and the world; the first three stages of childhood*']. Sigismund, according to an account by Voelckel (1913), " 'believes' ['*glaubt*'] that children use both hands in an equal way until the third year [p. 351]."

DARWIN (1877)

Darwin (1877), on the other hand, saw signs of right-hand preference in his son William in early infancy:

> When 77 days old, he took the sucking bottle (with which he was partly fed) in his right hand, whether he was held on the left or right arm of his nurse, and he would not take it with his left hand until a week later although I tried to make him do so; so that the right hand was a week in advance of the left [p. 287].

The right-hand preference was only transient, William later becoming left-handed. Darwin (1877) made nothing of this change, but concluded simply that his son's eventual left handedness was "no doubt inherited— his grandfather, mother, and a brother having been or being left-handed [p. 287]."[9]

PREYER (1881)

Preyer's (1881/1888) baby biography seems to have been the next one to mention hand preference, although the hand used is identified on only three occasions. The first occasion, at 14 months, pertains to his son's

---

[9]Darwin's son was born in late 1839 and, for the first year, Darwin made the observations that were published in the paper in *Mind* (1877) and cited here. Although this paper followed the publication of Broca's major works, there is no indication from the report (or from the major works) that Darwin was following the debates in Western Europe over the question of localization of cortical functions or that he took notice of then-current references to his theory in connection with the handedness of the human infant. (He was, however, familiar with Broca's work in physical anthropology; see Darwin, 1871, pp. 146, 237, 240.) So far as I know, then, the statements quoted here are Darwin's only remarks on the topic of handedness.

"taste" for the news. Whereas before this time, he liked to bite pieces out of a newspaper, which had to be removed from his mouth by an adult, at 14 months "[H]e now of himself took out of his mouth with his right hand every piece he had bitten off, and handed it to me [p. 253]." Similarly, at 9 months, when asked, "Where is the light?", he only turned his head in the correct direction; but at 14 months, "he lifts his right arm besides and points to the light with outspread fingers [p. 321]."

If the child at 14 months preferred his right hand for grasping and pointing, at 19 months he seemed not to have had any hand preference for eating with utensils: "If the spoon is laid on the left side of the plate, then, after a little consideration, he takes it with his left hand, and no difference is noticeable between his use of the left and the right hand in eating [Preyer, 1881/1888, p. 329]." Presumably, Preyer's custom had been to place the spoon on the right side.

SHINN (1894)

As descriptions of the development of handedness, none of the reports thus far were much to go on, but they were a start. In 1894 a much more forthright account, albeit with only marginally more specific data, was provided by Milicent Washburn Shinn, an American psychologist. The subject was her niece, whose development Shinn observed over the first 3 years of life (Shinn, 1894, Vol. 1). For voluntary grasping of objects, Shinn (1894) reported that her niece used both hands together, favoring neither. About the end of the fifth month, after grasping "had become habitual, [the right hand was preferred], and has been consistently so ever since [p. 324]." In the tenth month, the child began to use the tip of her forefinger "for special investigation" and it was always the right finger. So, too, in pointing afterward, and Shinn (1894) concluded that by 10 months, "distinct right-handedness became apparent [p. 324]." Shinn (1894) said that her notes did not make this conclusion clear (for one thing because in many cases she had not recorded the hand used), but added "I am satisfied I should have noted it had it been the left, since the use of the right was after the age of eight or nine months so common and apparently so instinctive with her [p. 324]."

MOORE (1896)

Soon after Shinn's biography appeared, Kathleen C. Moore (1896) published an account of her son's first 2 years. Like Preyer, Moore took care not to interfere with her son's development so as not to distort the developmental record. Therefore, he was "never stimulated to premature action, [and especial] care was taken not to teach him the tricks which are commonly taught to babies; but some he did learn [p. 3]." (Moore did not say which.) With respect to the question of handedness, Moore's study was different from Shinn's in two ways: Moore was somewhat more conscientious in noting differences in hand use, and Moore's son showed evidence of right-hand preference only by the end of the second, rather than the first, year, with, possibly, some periods of left-hand preference intervening. For instance, at 17 weeks, when reaching had become more frequent, he usually reached with both arms; at 34 weeks, when separate use of the hands had become habitual (i.e., in tasks requiring bimanual coordination), he showed no hand preference (Moore, 1896, p. 18). Then, at 38 weeks, when Moore clapped two spoons together, he reached for one spoon with his left hand, and used his left hand again to get the second spoon after passing the first spoon to his right hand (1896, p. 19). At 77 weeks, the left-hand preference was again in evidence, this time for feeding himself (1896, p. 19). During the ninety-third and ninety-fourth weeks, Moore (1896) supplemented her naturalistic observations with special experiments, which showed only "a slight but inconclusive preponderance of actions of a certain class in favor of the right hand [p. 19]." Finally, at 105 weeks, the child "gave evidence of being right-handed [in that he chose to perform] difficult actions with the right hand and arm [1896, p. 19]." Neither the "experiments" nor the "difficult actions" were identified.

HALL (1896–1897)

In the same year as Moore's report was published, there also appeared the first installment of a biography by Mrs. Winfield S. Hall (1896–1897), the wife of a well-known physiologist. Hall observed her son Albert from his birth until nearly his seventeenth month. Again, like Shinn and Moore, handedness was not the focus, and the data provided on hand differences were accordingly no less sketchy. But like Shinn's account, and unlike Moore's, Hall's record suggests the emergence of right-hand preference during the first year, again in the absence of encouragement or training. The first indication—"during the first few months"—was for the behavior of carrying objects to the mouth.

> [This was done] in a peculiar way, the right hand being used for carrying the object, while the left, by making the corresponding motions, was used to balance and direct the right hand. Even when putting the thumb to his mouth he used the left hand in this way, and finally held the left hand under the right one while sucking the right thumb. If the left hand was confined so that he could not use it in this way, it was noticeably harder for him to put the right hand to his mouth, while it always annoyed him, causing him to cry [Hall, 1896–1897, p. 395].

Subsequent accounts of hand preference pertained to reaching. At $3\frac{1}{2}$ months, Hall described motions of both hands toward a vase containing a flower placed before the child. The motions were "illy directed," but

Albert nevertheless succeeded in getting hold of the vase "with the right hand and in maintaining it until he had worked the hand up and procured the flower [1896–1897, p. 396]." This experiment was repeated on 2 successive days with the "same result," although it is not clear that the reference is to the question of the particular hand used.

No other report of hand difference is given until $9\frac{1}{2}$ months, at which time, "finding himself within reaching distance of his baby-carriage, Albert stretched his body and right arm until he had grasped its handle which he then drew near enough to enable him to take hold with both hands [Hall, 1896–1897, p. 308]." At 10 months and 1 week, he used his right hand to reach the window sash, succeeded in gaining a firm hold, and pulled himself high enough to obtain a hold with his left hand also (1896–1897, p. 398).

MAJOR (1906)

After Hall's account, what seems to have been the next baby biography to mention hand preference was a report by David Major (1906), a professor of education at the Ohio State University. Beginning when his son was 3 months old, Major made observations lasting 30 min or longer of the child's hand movements while picking up, reaching, feeling, pulling, and throwing. Unfortunately, Major did not follow this method uniformly and could not provide full details, much less a numerical summary, of the results. The record, in any case, suggests an inconsistent developmental pattern. At 3 months, Major concluded that his son showed no noticeable preference for either hand; in the fourth and fifth months, the right hand "was used more frequently"; from the sixth to the eleventh months, there again was no noticeable hand preference; then, early in the twelfth month, a "slight preference" for the left hand began to appear, and it "increased so rapidly that by the time the child rounded out his first year he was clearly what one would call left-handed. Toys were picked up with the left hand, a ball was thrown or tossed with the left hand, the left hand was used more in reaching. Left hand movements were surer and more graceful as well as more numerous [Major, 1906, pp. 43–44]."

At this point, Major departed radically from the baby biographers' customary practice. For unstated reasons (out of curiosity or because he did not want his son to be left-handed?), he began to interfere with the boy's left-hand preference. When the child reached for articles with his left hand, he was refused, and when toys or other articles were given to him, they were always placed in the right hand. The method was certainly less Draconian than that recalled by Benjamin Franklin, but it may have been as successful: "Either as the result of our training or as the outcome of native tendencies," right-hand preference began to re-emerge by the end of the fifteenth month, until by 24 months, the child was "decidedly right-handed [Major, 1906, pp. 44–45]." He also remained "so strongly right-handed" through his forty-fourth month, the last date given in Major's report (1906, footnote, p. 45).[10]

Major (1906) concluded with more questions than answers. Had he not interfered, would his son "have become as decidedly left handed as he is now right?" Are children "natively either right or left-handed which no amount of training can change," or is it a matter of training? Or is it, instead, that some or all children are "naturally ambidextrous, but will develop right or left-handedness under training? [p. 45]." Clearly, "The whole matter of right and left-handedness should have much wider study than it has so far received [Major, 1906, p. 45]."

DEARBORN (1910)

Four years later, in 1910, Major's call for wider study was answered by George Van Ness Dearborn, a professor of physiology at Tufts Medical College. Dearborn observed his daughter Lucia's hand movements and hand use in numerous situations over the first 3 years of her life. The record convincingly indicates the establishment of right-hand preference by the end of the first year, but it also suggests a change in preference over this same period. Of 16 separate accounts of hand differences for movement, including grasping and reaching, reported between days 82 and 178 (2.7–6 months), the *left* hand was ahead of the right on 11 occasions, the right ahead on three occasions, and no differences on the remaining two occasions. For instance, the left hand, but not the right, grasped "at once" when an object was held within 1 in. of the hand (day 112); the right "is being used in grasping and reaching only after the left has been used" (day 113); while sitting in her carriage, Lucia "noticed the fancy scroll-work on the right side of the vehicle and reached her left hand across in front to take hold of it" (day 125); "uses the left hand voluntarily almost exclusively now" (day 149); "uses her left hand now very much more often than the right" (day 154); "she is very left-handed now" (day 168); "she now uses both hands, but the left rather more readily than the right" (day 178). However, of the remaining 12 different days on which hand differences were mentioned (between days 194 and 820), the *right* hand was named as the leading hand on nine occasions, the left hand on one, and either or both hands on the remaining two occasions. For example, "Today, capriciously, she uses the right hand now as readily as the left for

[10]The writer James Shaw (1902), quoted earlier (page 190), also reported having tried to train infants in hand preference, but for the express purpose of bringing about ambidexterity. In two instances, by putting articles into the left hand, he "taught children, who previously did not grasp with either hand in preference to the other, to use it more and better than the right [p. 1486]." But having given the start to the left hand, Shaw (1902) found it "no easy matter to keep the right hand up to the level of its leader. And that is precisely the difficulty in teaching children to be really ambidextrous [p. 1486]."

most purposes" (day 194); "she uses her left hand apparently now much less than the right" (day 225); "offers her right hand now to take objects much oftener than her left" (day 298); "uses a pencil nowadays always by choice in her right hand" (day 595, in contrast to days 420 and 560); "she uses her right hand for the more difficult acts now" (day 820).

Dearborn (1910) concluded that although Lucia initially was "appreciably more precocious" in use of the left than the right side of her body (especially the face, leg, and arm), . . . "[she] developed right-handed in the average degree [p. 31]."

In summary, we can say that the baby biographies provide quite useful information. In particular, we learn something about the great range of situations in which the infant might express a hand preference, some of these being occasions for which one hand is sufficient (e.g., eating, reaching, and pointing), others being situations calling for the coordinated use of both hands (e.g., Hall's [1896–1897] account of her son's use of his left hand to balance and direct his right while carrying an object to his mouth). There are also hints that "difficult actions" bring out lateralized tendencies more than simple ones do (e.g., Moore, 1896). We also get a strong sense of the sometimes highly ideosyncratic nature of the behavior as well as of the discontinuity—the seemingly "capricious" shifts, as Dearborn put it—in the expression of preference. (We shall have more to say about this matter later.) Finally, several of the biographies give convincing evidence for the existence of hand preference during the first year, in the absence of any obvious encouragement by the environment, although Major's (1906) record also suggests how the preference might be shaped by quite simple measures.

All this said, it must be admitted that even the best biographies provide only fragments of an account of the development of hand preference. Certainly it would be hard to adduce any general principles about the development of handedness from these records.

Experimental and Controlled-Observational Studies

Whatever their methodological and reportorial shortcomings, the descriptions of hand use in the baby biographies were an enormous improvement over the undocumented statements of earlier writers. At the very least, we can be sure that real infants, and not merely a priori opinion, had been consulted. But despite their influence on the field of child study, the biographies do not seem to have significantly affected debate on the question of the origins of handedness, either on the nativist or the nurturist side. For example, none of the ambidextral culturists bothered to challenge any of the reports from Preyer (1881/1888) through Dearborn (1910), assuming that they were aware of them in the first place. But neither did any critic of ambidextral culture, many of whom were quite violent in their objections, even though several of the reports should have been strong ammunition against the ambidextral culturists' strict nurturist views.

What ultimately proved to be influential in the debate on infant handedness was another kind of method altogether. This was the experiment, or controlled observation, conceived for the special purpose of testing specific experimental hypotheses. What seems to have been its first application to the question of infant laterality was reported in 1890, but priority must be shared between two pioneer developmental psychologists on opposite sides of the Atlantic. One was the American, James Mark Baldwin, then just 29 years old and newly named to the Chair of Metaphysics and Logic at the University of Toronto. The other was Alfred Binet, 4 years older than Baldwin and, as Theta Wolf has remarked, "without a professional home [1973, p. 79]."

BINET (1890)

In a single year, at a time when, as Wolf (1973) said, the baby biography and the questionnaire were "waxing brightly," Binet published three articles in *Revue Philosophique* that Wolf has justly called "unmistakably an original contribution to the experimental research on the psychology of children [Wolf, 1973, pp. 79–80]." In two articles Binet (1890b, 1890c) inquired into such questions as the difference between young children's and adults' perceptions of length, quantity, and number. In another article (1890a), he addressed himself to the question of laterality as a small part of a larger study of movements of the limbs.

Binet did not say much about laterality other than to report a substantial change over the first 3 years of life. In the few-weeks-old child, almost all movements were bilateral (including alternate movements, where a broad movement with one arm is followed by a similar movement with the other); by 3 years, however, almost all movements were unilateral. By way of example, Binet (1890a) provided a summary of three 5-min observation periods of a 6-day-old girl; the ratio of bilateral (including alternate) to unilateral movements was more than 4:1. Unfortunately, Binet gave no other details, such as the number of subjects at each age (at least two subjects were his own daughters), the ages of transition from bilaterality to unilaterality, or the nature of the situation or task at different ages. At the youngest ages, Binet noted that he was measuring spontaneous arm movements, and, by 3 years, one supposes that he was recording visually directed reaching, among other behaviors.

Wolf (1973, p. 80) has suggested that Binet failed to recognize the seminal nature of his efforts in his three early papers, for he did not pursue them then. Nor did his contemporaries hail them. With respect to the paper on limb movements, certainly neither Binet's observation on the growth of unilaterality nor his use of a special recording device for other

parts of the study influenced theory or method in subsequent investigations. So far I have found only two citations (Marion, 1890, p. 775; Perez, 1901, pp. 43–44).

BALDWIN (1890, 1894)

Baldwin's results and method proved to be as influential as Binet's were neglected, and not without reason. For one, Baldwin took special interest in the question of handedness; for another, he extensively documented his results. Finally, although Binet's work was no less of a break from the baby biographies and questionnaires than was Baldwin's, Baldwin proclaimed his renunciation of that style in stentorian tones. The biographical method, Baldwin warned (1894/1900), had caught science "in the straight [sic]-jacket of barren observation [p. 35]"; theory was being cast out. Whence Baldwin (1894/1900) issued his famous call:

[G]ive us theories, theories, always theories. Let every man who has a theory pronounce his theory! This is just the difference between the average mother and the good psychologist—she has no theories, he has; he has no interests, she has. She may bring up a family of a dozen and not be able to make a single trustworthy observation; he may be able, from one sound of one yearling, to confirm theories of the neurologist and educator, which are momentous for the future training and welfare of the child [pp. 35–36].

Thus, when Baldwin himself turned his attention to the question of the development of handedness, he tried to marry theory to the experimental method.[12]

To start, Baldwin (1894/1900) saw in the child's hand movements for reaching and grasping a significance transcending the question of the origins of handedness; they were no less than a window to mental development:

The hand reflects the first stimulations, the most stimulations, and, becoming the most mobile and executive organ of volition, attains the most varied and interesting offices of utility. We have spontaneous arm and hand move-

[11]Baldwin's scorn was not, in fact, directed expressly to the biographers cited earlier (those, that is, before 1894), but rather to the rank amateurs—the average mothers (and fathers) and women in reading circles and clubs who, in response to G. Stanley Hall's appeals, were busily publishing anecdotal and usually very naive and sentimental accounts of their children. But even some of the best of the biographies betrayed the ultrapositivistic spirit to which Baldwin had objected.

[12]Baldwin first reported his experiment in a brief communication to Science (1890), and subsequently gave more extensive accounts in an article in Popular Science Monthly (1894) and in the first edition of his book, Mental development in the child and the race (1894/1900) and, without change, in all subsequent editions of this book at least through 1925 (revision of the 1906, third edition), the last edition I was able to examine. The account given here draws from the 1890 and 1894a papers and the first (1894) and second (1900) editions of the book, and also from Baldwin's memoirs (1926, vol. 1).

ments, reflex movements, reaching-out movements, grasping movements, imitative movements, manipulating movements, and voluntary efforts—all these, in order, reflecting the development of the mind [pp. 40–41].

Baldwin further proposed that the intensity of the hand movement would be proportional to the intensity, or "dynamogeny," of a given stimulus, much as the physiologist François Magendie had suggested measuring changes in sensibility by the corresponding changes in blood pressure. Thus by this "dynamogenic" method, a wide range of issues in addition to handedness could be studied, including color perception, color preference, and distance estimation, among others.

For his study of handedness, Baldwin also wanted to test certain extant theories: the mother-holding theory (about which, as I said earlier, Baldwin had serious reservations); Andrew Buchanan's dynamic balance theory; and, finally, a proposal that sounds like a variant of the mother-holding theory—"that infants get to be right-handed by being placed on one side too much for sleep [Baldwin, 1894/1900, p. 57]." Presumably, this would be the *left* side, leaving the right side free. If so, what observations, if any, could have inspired the idea? Had Baldwin interpreted infants' spontaneous position preferences, of the sort mentioned by Sequin (1880) and others, as the result of manner of placement by the mother? But recall that the preference was for lying on the *right* side, not the left.

To preclude all such possible sources of influence on the infant who was his experimental subject, Baldwin (1894/1900) took "certain precautions":

> She was never carried about in arms at all—never walked about when crying or sleepless (a ruinous and needless habit to cultivate in an infant); she was frequently turned over in her sleep; she was not allowed to balance herself on her feet until a later period than that covered by the experiments. Thus the conditions of the rise of the right-handed era were made as simple and uniform as possible [pp. 57–58].

Understandably, not all parents might have consented to such a regimen, so Baldwin volunteered his daughter Helen, his own firstborn child. (One assumes that Baldwin won his wife's cooperation in this venture.)

Baldwin devised a special apparatus for his tests—a chair that kept Helen's posture constant by a band passing around the chest while leaving her arms free to move, and a set of rods attached to the chair on which objects could be displayed, one at a time, at precisely different positions and distances. Various objects were presented, including pieces of newspaper and squares of blotting paper of different colors.

From the beginning of Helen's fifth month to the end of her tenth, Baldwin (1890) administered 2187 "experiments" (i.e., trials) in a total of 96 series. All of these evidently were the 9–10-in. shorter-distance trials, this being "her reaching distance (based on tabulated experiments) [p. 247]." (Baldwin [1894/1900] referred to these trials as "cases of free movement of hands near the body [p. 64]). The number of experiments at each sitting was varied (from 10 to 40), as was the child's position (reversed as to light from windows, position of observation, "etc." after half of each test series).

The results were plain: Across this period of time, Helen used her right hand a total of 577 times, her left hand 568, and both hands 1042. Baldwin (1894/1900) concluded that "no trace of preference for either hand is discernible. . . . [T]he neutrality is an complete as if it had been arranged beforehand, or had followed the throwing of dice [p. 61]."

For a 24-day-long period during the eighth month, Baldwin (1894/1900) began use of a "severer" test—placement of an (unnamed) "neutral stimulus" from 12 to 15 in. from the child. "This resulted in very hard straining on her part, with all the signs of physical effort (explosive breathing-sounds . . . flushing of the face . . . and flow of urine) [p. 61]." Over the first 14 days of this period, 80 such trials were presented. Both hands reached together only once, the right hand 74 times, and the left hand 5 times. Thus, the right hand was overwhelmingly preferred on this more difficult task. When the same cases were distributed according to distance, from 12 to 15 in., all six instances of left- or both-hand reaching occurred at 12 in. Finally, reaches were most frequent at 12 and 13 in. much less so at 14 in. and absent altogether at 15 in.[13]

During the last 10 days, Baldwin (1894/1900) continued the far-distance trials but also began to vary the point of exposure of the object from 2 to 6 in. to the right or left, his purpose being "to attract the hand on one side or the other, and so to determine whether the growth of such a preference was limited to experiences of convenience in reaching to adjacent local objects, etc. [p. 62]." The result was still further enhancement of the right-hand preference. On 35 trials (29 placements to the left and 6 to the right), Helen used her right hand every time. Baldwin (1894/1900) concluded, "This seems to show that dextrality is not derived from the experience of the individual in using either hand predominantly for reaching, grasping, holding, etc., within the easiest range of the hand. The right hand intruded regularly upon the domain of the left [p. 63]."

These latter results, in turn, suggested to Baldwin that the hand preference was influenced by eye preference. On this possibility, Baldwin began observing his daughter's hand movements in the color-perception experiments being carried out at that same time. His idea was that the most dynamogenic color, that offering the strongest inducement to reach,

[13]Presumably, the signs of physical effort mentioned here appeared only on those out-of-reach trials where reaching still occurred (12–14-in. distances), although Baldwin is unclear on this point.

might have the same effect in determining the use of the right hand as increased distance had in the laterality experiments (1894/1900, p. 63). The inquiry was rewarded: In 86 trials at lesser distances than had been required for the "neutral objects" in the laterality experiments, Helen used her right hand 84 times, her left hand only twice.

From all these results, Baldwin felt himself on sure ground: The mother-holding, infant placement, and dynamic balance theories could be dismissed. Nor does habit in reaching determine right-hand use, since Helen's use of her right hand carried over to her left side. So Baldwin cast his lot squarely with the brain physiologists: Hand movements were under the direct control of the motor arm center in the contralateral hemisphere of the brain; handedness was an expression of inherent differences in the functioning of the two hemispheres.

Still to be explained was why the preferential use of the right hand appeared only under the pressure of muscular effort. Baldwin's answer was that right handedness varies directly with the dynamogenic influence of the stimulus, whether that influence is color or distance. Why, then, would increasing distance, which presumably would lessen the drawing-out tendency of a stimulus by lessening its intensity or clearness, tend to do what a bright color at a lesser distance does (i.e., call out increased use of the right hand)? Baldwin (1894/1900) proposed that his daughter had learned by experience or knew already ("inherited an organic experience") that more effort, more dynamogeny (D), is necessary in the case of a more distant stimulus; "and so a central supply goes out to reinforce the influence D of this distant stimulus, and the right-handedness is the evidence of this reinforced D. We would expect, on the other hand, that the colour, being itself a more dynamogenic stimulus, would have the same effect, without the central reinforcement, and also bring out the right hand. And so it does [p. 76]."

Finally, why had Helen not reached when the object distance was 15 in or more? Evidently, she already could accurately estimate distances beyond her reach, "undoubtedly . . . from associations of visual indications of distance with sensations of hand and arm movements [Baldwin, 1894/1900, p. 76]." Baldwin concluded that such associations give rise to a total of three separate determinations: the safe reaching distance, where either or both hands are used; the uncertain reaching distance (use of right hand); and the impossible-to-reach distance (no hand movement, but a turning away of face and body) (1894/1900, pp. 76–77).

Baldwin's experiment was cited in textbooks (e.g., Ladd, 1903, pp. 222–223; Tracy & Stimpfl, 1894, pp. 102–103) as proof that handedness exists in infancy and is not a result of training. Popular magazines also picked up the story: Said one, "Babies of six months are right-handed [Brewster, 1913, p. 170]." The damage inflicted on certain theories of handedness was appreciated as well. For instance, the physician Sir

James Crichton-Browne (1907) used Baldwin's results—as Baldwin himself had—to hammer the last nail into the coffin of Andrew Buchanan's (1862) dynamic balance theory. According to Crichton-Browne (1907), the experiment showed that "unmistakable right-handedness" declares itself about the eighth month, "before the infant can have profited by experience or has assumed the erect posture; and it would be as reasonable to maintain that the emergence of its teeth is due to the use of its jaws as it is to argue that the emergence of its right-handedness is due to the use of the hands." The results thus proved that right handedness "is unquestionably congenital and innate, and not acquired in any way [pp. 639–640]."[14]

D. J. Cunningham (1902) also was impressed with Baldwin's findings, but his anatomist's eye was on the time of appearance of handedness as much as on handedness itself. Baldwin had not addressed this question directly, e.g., he did not suggest that greater effortfulness might or might not have worked as well if required prior to the seventh or eighth month. Cunningham proposed some (unspecified) lower limit, presumably before 7 months. At birth, the still unmyelinated motor paths in the brain and spinal cord would not have attained their full functional capabilities, meaning that impulses originating in the brain would not be adequately transmitted to the lower motor centers in the spinal cord and thence to the limbs. Consequently, an infant's muscular efforts at first would be "more or less purely automatic," and a characteristic such as right handedness would not become manifest "until the paths which connect the higher and lower motor centres are fully established and have been systematically practiced [Cunningham, 1902, pp. 280–281]."

Baldwin's findings also were cited by Stevens (1908), who saw them as supporting his retinal theory of handedness. Stevens noted that the time (7 months) at which a pronounced right handedness developed in Baldwin's daughter was but little later than the time—5 months—at which an object was recognized when its image fell on the periphery of the retina (here Stevens referred to work by "Raehlman" cited in Sharpey-Schaefer, 1898–1900, vol. 2, p. 759). Curiously, Stevens overlooked a different clue provided by Baldwin himself, namely, his comment that his daughter's hand preference was influenced by eye preference.

Finally, Baldwin's findings figured in attacks on the program of the Ambidextral Culture Society. Clearly, the ambidextral culturists were

[14]What both Baldwin and Crichton-Browne had overlooked, however, was that the desideratum in Buchanan's theory was effortfulness, not onset of walking. (Recall that Buchanan supposed that this condition typically would be met after the child had begun to walk because only by that time would the infant have achieved sufficient strength to apply a vigorous effort and thereby become aware of the greater mechanical power of the right hand.) That Baldwin's daughter showed right-hand preference only where effort was required—and, judging from Baldwin's own account, strongly expended—might well have been construed by Buchanan as support for his own theory.

mistaken in contending that handedness was unnatural. As one critic, the American physician George M. Gould (1904), wrote, "[Before the infant] is one year old, dextrality is clearly pronounced. Baldwin [1894] has demonstrated experimentally that it is plainly established as early as the seventh or eighth month [p. 361]."

Baldwin's study had convinced many that handedness, as Crichton-Browne (1907) said, was "congenital and innate, and not acquired in any way [p. 640]," but it did not convince all. One who held back, in a respectful way, was Daniel Wilson, the president of the University of Toronto. Himself the author of a scholarly and influential book on handedness, Wilson (1891) warmly endorsed his young colleague's work, noting that the "initial proclivities" toward hand preference could be identified only by following Baldwin's procedure—prolonged observations "made at the first stage of life, and based on the voluntary and unprompted actions of the child [p. 209]." But if there was a natural bias toward preferential use of one hand, Wilson (1891) believed that, in probably the majority of cases, the bias was "slight" and in itself would not present "an obstacle to conformity to any prevalent usage, or to the influence of education [pp. 209–210]."

Two other writers had stronger misgivings. About Baldwin's (1894/1900) statement that "the influences of infancy have little effect" on handedness (p. 71), a reviewer for *The American Journal of Psychology* remarked, without explanation, "a conclusion which must seem in the end unsatisfactory [Bolton, 1895, p. 143]." A later critic was full of explanation—and not a little scorn. Challenged by Gould's (1904) use of Baldwin's report against the Ambidextral Culture Society, its president, John Jackson, went to the attack. Baldwin's conclusions were "premature" and "in one or two points inaccurate"; furthermore, "no reliable or general deduction, such as Professor Baldwin offers, can logically be drawn from the phenomena of a single case [Jackson, 1905, p. 82]." Still, how to explain this "single case"? Where the moderate Daniel Wilson admitted the existence of a natural but slight bias in the majority of cases, Jackson (1905) declared Baldwin's child an abnormality, a "freak of nature" (p. 97): "Its early, pronounced—and shall we say unconscious?—right-handed preference clearly marks it out as one of the strongly and naturally biased individuals forming the 20 percent of lopsided beings who, *all through life*, and in spite of all pressure, punishment, education, or custom, maintain unimpaired a one-handed pre-eminence [p. 82]." Jackson seems to have pulled the 20% figure out of the air.

Daniel Wilson (1891) had praised Baldwin's method. Nevertheless, a dozen years after Baldwin's report first appeared, no other comparable study seems to have been conducted. The need was not unappreciated, and in 1902 Cunningham wrote, "It is a matter for regret . . . that this ready means of investigation has not been more fully taken advantage of [p. 280]." But a dozen years more, and Cunningham's call had been answered several times. Some of the new studies, however, used Baldwin's controlled-observation method (or some adapted form) not to address the question of handedness, but to further study the infant's color sense (a question, as noted earlier, with which Baldwin also was concerned). In these studies, the matter of hand preference therefore was of only secondary interest. Nor were any of the infants in the new studies subjected to the sort of "precautions" in upbringing to which Baldwin had treated his daughter. (It was hardly to be expected in those studies whose primary goal was the evaluation of color sense.) All these qualifications notwithstanding, most of the new experiments provide sufficiently clear results to contribute meaningfully to the data base.

MARSDEN (1903)

The first new study was by an American psychologist, Rufus Marsden (1903). An apparatus was used in which colored cards could be set level with the child (Marsden's son) and at different distances (11–15 in.) from his eyes. The cards were presented one at a time, following Baldwin's procedure, but were always placed "exactly in front of the child [p. 38]" rather than sometimes to the left or right, as Baldwin began to do in the last part of his experiment.

Starting when his son was just under $7\frac{1}{2}$ months old and ending when he was $10\frac{1}{2}$ months old, Marsden administered 1400 trials (i.e., individual presentations of a color). Baldwin had allowed as many as 40 experiments per day, a figure Marsden feared would kill incentive. Marsden (1903) therefore gave an average of only 14 trials per day, with no more than 28 on the busiest day, so that "At the end of each sitting our child was always left, like Oliver Twist, wishing for more [p. 41]."

Of the 1400 trials, there were 948 reaches, or "acceptances" (i.e., trials on which, according to Marsden, the child accepted the color as being close enough to reach). Most reaches were at the closest distances, with acceptances, by about the half-way mark in the study, nearly 100% at 11 in., nearly 90% at 12 in., approximately 70% at 13 in., and only 30% and 5% at 14 and 15 in., respectively. Marsden calculated the incidence of use of each hand and of both hands together for each 100 of the first 900 acceptances, and then for the last 48, making a total of 10 blocks of trials over the 7.5-month (32-week) to 10.5-month (46-week) period. For the first block, both hands were used together about 85% of the time; for the third block, two-handed acceptances (i.e., reaches) had been nearly eliminated in favor of right-hand reaches. After that, use of the left hand grew until, by the fifth- and sixth-hundred acceptances (between the child's fortieth and forty-third week), it nearly equaled use of the right hand. From then on, however, the left hand lost ground until, ultimately, it was used only 6% of the time. This waxing and waning of the relative dominance of the right hand notwithstanding, the results clearly showed that the child preferred to use his right hand for reaching beginning about when he was 34 weeks old, roughly the same age as Baldwin's daughter.[15]

The effects of object distance also seem to have been consistent with Baldwin's (1894/1900) results. Evidently, 80 and 100% of the occasions when the left hand was used were for the shorter distances (9–13 in.). Only 65% of the occasions when the left hand was used were for the longer distance of 14 in., and only 25% of occasions for left-hand use were for the longest distances of 15 in. Again, as Baldwin had found, for the longest distances, at which the number of reaches (acceptances) was lowest (5–30%), the reaches made were primarily right-handed.

Marsden, being one of those interested primarily in the infant's color sense, said nothing about the implications of his findings for understanding the origins of handedness. Perhaps for the same reason, his report, unlike Baldwin's, did not figure in the debate on this question. One wonders how John Jackson would have reacted. Would he have called Marsden's son yet another "freak of nature," like Baldwin's daughter?

MCDOUGALL (1908) AND MYERS (1908)

In 1908, two more studies using Baldwin's controlled-observation procedure were published back-to-back in the *British Journal of Psychology*. Both authors were already prominent figures in psychology: William McDougall, then the Wilde Reader in Mental Philosophy at Oxford University and the author of many experiments on vision; and Charles S. Myers, then at Cambridge University and subsequently (1913) the first director of its Psychological Laboratory.

Like Marsden (1903), McDougall's and Myers' primary interest was in the infant's color sense, and to this end they made certain changes in Baldwin's method. Baldwin (1894/1900) had placed individual squares of colored paper before his daughter and then determined the ratio of reaches (by each hand) to total number of presentations of each color. McDougall (1908) modified the procedure in different ways, ultimately settling on presentation of two objects (balls of colored wool and pieces of colored paper) at a time, one to his subject's left, one to her right, with the positions transposed on a second presentation. The balls were about 5 in. apart and "at a convenient distance for her to grasp them [McDougall, 1908, p. 340]." A total of 476 trials were given on 29 different days between the subject's twenty-third and twenty-ninth weeks (5.75–7.25

---

[15]In the absence of data from still earlier periods, we cannot conclude that this period marked the very *first* appearance of hand preference for reaching in this child. In fact, Marsden did carry out earlier tests between the one hundred and eighty-ninth and the two hundred and third day (6.5 and 6.8 months) with a somewhat different method (presentation of pairs of colored balls), but the hand used for reaching was not recorded.

months). The subject, McDougall's daughter Lucia, either sat in her mother's lap or was propped up in a basket or cart.

Myers' (1908) method was different still. It consisted of what today would be called *operant discrimination training:* Pairs of wooden cubes of different uniform colors were placed on a table before the infant (Myers' daughter), who was seated on her mother's lap. One cube was placed to the infant's right, one to her left, about 5 in. apart, and "at such a distance from her that she could easily grasp either of them without effort [Myers, 1908, p. 354]." Choice of one color was reinforced with a taste of honey or syrup. The left–right position of the cubes was varied over trials, although it is not clear that a true counterbalanced design was ever used.

Testing began when the child was 24 weeks (6 months) of age, with approximately 60 trials distributed equally across 5 testing days. Testing then was interrupted because the infant seemed "quite unable to connect grasp and reward [Myers, 1908, p. 354]," then was resumed when she was 35 weeks old (8.75 months) and continued through her fifty-eighth week (13½ months).

Of the two investigators, McDougall (1908) was the less interested in handedness even secondarily, and was, accordingly, the stingier with details. But, judging from what he did say, Lucia showed no obvious hand preference: "In most cases she grasped the object with one hand only, generally but not always with the hand of the same side as the object grasped. She grasped with both hands in turn, usually with free alternation, the use of the right hand predominating a little [p. 343]."

Myers provided more details about quite different findings. During the first, aborted testing period (at 24 weeks), his daughter "unquestionably preferred her left hand to her right; the frequency being in the proportion of about five to one [Myers, 1908, p. 357]." But when testing resumed, the right hand was predominant and grew in frequency of use, while both-hand and left-hand reaches diminished. Between the thirty-seventh and fifty-fourth weeks, of a total of 211 reaches, 95 (45%) were with the right hand; 43 (20%) with the left, and 73 (35%) with both hands. Ninety-six more reaches were elicited between the fifty-fourth and fifty-eighth weeks, of which 72 (75%) were with the right hand, 21 (22%) with the left, and 3 (3%) with both hands.

Despite the authors' prominance, neither McDougall's nor Myers' reports made any impression on the literature on laterality. Again, the probable reason is that each report, like Marsden's (1903), was concerned more with the question of color preference than with hand preference.

WOOLLEY (1910)

The next investigation to use Baldwin's controlled-observation procedure proved to be far more influential. The author was an American,

Helen Thompson Woolley (1910), a child psychologist already well known for her work on sex differences (Thompson, 1903). Woolley (1909), too, had begun by using Baldwin's reaching method to study color sense, but then was the first, after Baldwin himself, to apply the same method in a separate study of hand preference. Her subject was her infant daughter. Woolley (1910) presented two discs of different colors "laid side by side directly in front of the infant [and] within easy reaching distance [p. 38]." Presumably, this meant 7 in. or less, since Woolley also gave similar tests with squares and circles where the distances named were 3, 5, 7, 8, and 10 in. On these tests, 7 in. was the distance just requiring reaching, and 10 in. "required so much effort that the child was loath to make it [Woolley, 1910, p. 38]."

The color tests (disks) were begun at the start of the seventh month, the other tests at the middle of that month, and all testing was completed by the end of the month. Where the location of the disks remained constant and within easy reach, the right hand was used 206 times, the left hand 194 times, and both hands 68 times.

For the varying distance tests at 3 and 5 in., the right hand was used a total of 11 times, the left hand 21 times; at 7 in. ("just requiring reaching"), right hand 13 times, left hand 7; and at 8 and 10 in., right hand 16 times, left hand 0 times. Thus, except for the two closest distances on the varying distance trials, where the left-hand scores exceeded the right-hand scores, the results supported Baldwin's (i.e., no hand differences at close distances [on the color series] and a right-hand preference where effort was required, increasing in reliability as effort [distance] increased).

A provocative aspect of Woolley's findings is their implication that the child was attracted to the right-hand *position* regardless of the hand used. On the color tests, during which the right hand was used 206 times, the left 194, the right position was selected 285 times, the left position only 183. On the 70 form tests, in which the right hand was used 40 times, the right position was selected 56 times.

Woolley's study was widely cited in the handedness literature. In addition, Stevens and Ducasse (1912) seized upon the evidence of a right-position preference as providing further support for Stevens' (1908) retinal theory of handedness. Woolley herself was at a loss to explain this preference. She dismissed the possibility that it was related to her daughter's posture or to her relation to the light in the room, since, again following Baldwin's method, these factors had been varied from day to day. Possibly, the preference "might be conditioned [by her daughter's eyes, although they seemed] not only normal, but unusually good [Woolley, 1910, p. 40]." So, having raised the question, Woolley dismissed it, calling it "scarcely worth making so long as the observation is an isolated one [p. 41]." Stevens and Ducasse (1912), however, found it "difficult to imagine stronger corroborative evidence [p. 28]" that the development of right-handedness depends on vision, although they acknowledged that Woolley's results had not yet shown the necessary connection between preference for the right position and differences in spatial sensitivity of the peripheries of the retinas.

DIX (1911), STIER (1911), AND GUTZMANN (1911)

In Germany, the question of laterality in infancy had long been of interest to anatomists, as we saw in Bischoff's (1863) and others' studies of bone weight. Subsequently, German scientists turned to behavioral measures. In one year, 1911, three such reports appeared (cited in Voelckel, 1913, pp. 351–352), two of which agreed with the studies from England and America. Dix (1911) reported that his son failed to show any hand preference during the first 6 months but preferred his right hand for "drawing" by the end of the first year. Stier (1911) came to a similar conclusion, but for a reaching task. Gutzmann (1911), however, reported a much earlier difference for still another measure. He laid his finger alternately into each of his child's hands and noted from the twelfth day a stronger grasping reflex in the right hand.

VALENTINE (1914)

Gutzmann's (1911) findings on strength of grip in very early infancy were soon corroborated by a British child psychologist, C. W. Valentine (1914). Valentine (1914) reported that during the early months of his son "W.'s" life, "his right-hand reflex grasp was stronger than his left; and when voluntary grasping began the right hand learned to grasp much more readily than the left [p. 384]."[16]

Valentine's observations were made more in the fashion of the baby biographies than through controlled testing. Later, when W. was 7 months old, Valentine began a more formal assessment of the child's hand preference by means of Baldwin's "grasping method." W. sat on his mother's knee before a screen behind which different-colored wool balls were positioned, one ball opposite each shoulder and just out of reach. The screen then was removed and W. was brought forward, within reaching distance. On the next trial, the left–right position of the balls was reversed, and so

---

[16]Valentine (1942/1950) published a detailed day-by-day record of the observations made during the first 3 months as part of an extensive Appendix on handedness in his book, *The psychology of early childhood*. (I am grateful to Douglas Carlson for bringing this book to my attention.) These records clearly support Valentine's brief characterization of the results in the 1914 paper, and perhaps even warrant the sentiment expressed to Valentine by his British colleague, Cyril Burt: " 'The data you give are, I think, most valuable. I fancy most of us had assumed that a difference in handedness did not appear until between the ages of 6 and 12 months, i.e., when the child was beginning to grasp things. . . . Your evidence on thumb-sucking and the like seems definitely to show that the bias may exist from the very start [cited in Valentine, 1942/1950, p. 505]."

on through 10 presentations each day, with the color pairs changing each day. By this means, 36 separate experiments, totaling 360 choices (or reaches), were conducted, with experiments being performed "practically every day" until W. was 8½ months old.

The results were striking. Over the first 13 experiments (130 reaches), 105 reaches (81%) were with the right hand, 24 (18%) with the left, and only 1 (.01%) with both hands. W.'s hand preference obviously was stronger than his color preference, so at this point (presumably about 7 months, 2 weeks), Valentine tried Myers' (1908) tactic of placing the wools in the median plane, one being about 4 in. nearer the child than the other. The ploy was abandoned when W. invariably chose the nearer color. (Valentine did not name the hand used.) Valentine then placed one wool 3 in. to the right, and the other 3 in. to the left of a point immediately in front of W.'s right shoulder, so that each wool was about equally well placed for grasping with the right (preferred) hand. This tactic worked, and for the 20 trials of Experiments 14 and 15, W. made 19 reaches, 16 with his right hand, only 2 with the left, and 1 with both hands. In the sixteenth session, however, he suddenly changed. Despite the unfavorable position of the wools for the left hand, he now used his left hand 7 times, his right only 3, thus evidently crossing over midline. Valentine, ever the flexible experimenter, immediately reverted to his original method of placing one wool immediately opposite each shoulder, but the left-hand preference remained, and through the last 20 experiments (Experiments 17–36), W. made 199 reaches: 29 with the right hand (15%), 141 with the left (71%), and 29 with both hands (15%).

Following these experiments, when W. was 8½ months old, Valentine began a series of new experiments using Myers' (1908) "grasp and reward" method. W. seemed to make the association between color and reward (a taste of honey) only fleetingly, strong on some sittings, absent on others, and not, in any case, persisting from day to day. What did persist was his left-hand preference. Of 120 grasps made during these experiments, 105 (82%) were with the left hand, only 15 with the right (12%).

VOELCKEL (1913)

Thus far, as we have seen, all of the data on infant hand preference came from studies of individual children, whether in the baby biographies or the controlled-observation and experimental studies. In 1913, a German physician, Ernst Voelckel, noting this limitation and remarking on the "surprising" absence of "systematic surveys" (p. 351), set out to right the situation, which he did most impressively. He arranged to test 52 infants ranging in age from 3½ to 17 months. All were patients at the Children's Hospital of the Royal University in Munich, and were mostly either malnourished or convalescing from illness. Seriously ill children (including children with nervous-system disorders) were excluded.

The infants were tested while supine. An object (a small toy, usually a rattle) was held at a "reachable" distance at the child's midline at an equal distance from both hands, and the hand with which the child reached for the toy was noted. Each infant was tested on several days in succession until 50 trials had been administered. The result was that among the 17 infants from $3\frac{1}{2}$ to $6\frac{1}{2}$ months old, 16 infants used their hands approximately equally for reaching ($\bar{X}_{\text{Number of right hand (RH) reaches}} = 22$; $\bar{X}_{\text{LH}} = 23.2$). The seventeenth infant, one of three $6\frac{1}{2}$-month-olds in the sample, showed a strong right-hand preference, using that hand 45 times, the left hand only 5 times.

For the 35 infants 7 months of age or older, the results changed appreciably, with the right hand increasing in frequency of use from month to month. Among the 11 7–$8\frac{1}{2}$-month-olds, all showed a right-hand preference ($\bar{X}_{\text{RH}} = 35$; $\bar{X}_{\text{LH}} = 9.4$). Among the remaining 24 9–17-month-olds, 22 preferred the right hand ($\bar{X}_{\text{RH}} = 42.3$; $\bar{X}_{\text{LH}} = 5.1$), and 2 showed an equally strong left-hand preference ($\bar{X}_{\text{LH}} = 44$; $\bar{X}_{\text{RH}} = 5.5$). These 2 infants "most certainly are left-handed," 1/26, or 4–5% being the usual ratio of left- to right-handers in the general population (Voelckel, 1913, p. 354).[17]

Voelckel (1913) concluded that functional differentiation of both cerebral hemispheres is first recognizable in the seventh month and increases constantly thereafter, whereas before 7 months, both hemispheres function equally. Thus, he cast his lot with Baldwin (1890) and "modern opinion"—right-handedness is a reflection of the inherent superiority of the left cerebral hemisphere.

J. B. WATSON AND THE RISE OF RADICAL BEHAVIORISM

From Baldwin's study in 1890 through Voelckel's and Valentine's reports in 1913 and 1914, a consensus had emerged that hand preference, as measured by reaching, first appears within the first year, usually between the seventh and ninth months; that it appears in the absence of any obvious training; and that the reasons for handedness therefore must lie more fundamentally in the anatomy and physiology of the nervous system than in the practices and prejudices of society. Nativism seemed to have won the day. Then, in 1917, John B. Watson first cast his eye on the question.

In 1913, Watson had published his epochal paper on the new science of behaviorism and had advanced the position that apart from certain life-

---

[17]Because of social customs during this period in Germany, (e.g., all schoolchildren were instructed to use the right hand in writing), Voelckel's estimate of the incidence of left handedness was close to the mark.

sustaining, unconditional reflexes, all human behaviors could be accounted for as the products of conditioning and learning. Which human behaviors were instinctive, which learned or conditioned? At Johns Hopkins University late in 1916, Watson began work to find out, and with the assistance (starting in 1919) of his student Rosalie Raynor (later to be his wife), he conceived a remarkable program of research (Watson, 1919, 1924b; Watson & Morgan, 1917; Watson & Watson, 1921). The subjects were a group of 40 infants who were brought on weekly visits to the Phipps Clinic at Johns Hopkins and whom Watson tested between birth and 1 year of age. A great variety of tests were made, including tests of motor reflexes (see Blanton, 1917) and, of course, the famous tests of emotional responses. The question of handedness was of interest too, and Watson addressed it in several ways. First, on some 20 infants between 1 and 21 days of age (the number of infants varies in different accounts of these studies), Watson and Raynor recorded how long the infant could hang suspended with each hand. The tests were carried out over a 10-day period, starting at birth. No hand differences were found (Watson & Watson, 1921).

A second measure used (on the same 20 infants) was the total number of hand movements. Watson made two kinds of recordings. One was to attach each hand, by means of a thread, to two pivoted writing levers mounted in nearly frictionless bearings, so that each hand movement was translated on a smoked drum. Another method (the "work adder") was to attach a cord at one end to the infant's wrist and at the other to an escapement device, which, when operated, turned a wheel connected to a drum to which a lead weight was fastened. Wrist movement thus caused the weight to be wound higher and higher from the ground. Simultaneous measurements of hand movements by these methods disclosed hand differences on individual days, "but an infant markedly right-handed today is just as likely to be left-handed tomorrow [Watson & Watson, 1921, p. 501]." The result was that averaged scores over the 10-day period disclosed no overall hand differences.

"[O]ne other step [was taken in] the attempt to settle the problem of handedness [Watson & Watson, 1921, p. 501]." Between 15 and 20 infants were tested once a week from about the fifth to the twelfth month to find out which hand was used first in reaching for objects. The test object generally was a candle or a piece of candy placed just in front of the infant (presumably at midline) and then "brought slowly toward" the infant's face (Watson & Watson, 1921, p. 501). Each week, 10–20 trials were given. According to Watson and Watson's (1921) summary of the results, the infants showed no uniformity in the hand used; sometimes the right hand was extended, sometimes the left, and "if both hands were extended, as was often the case [p. 501]," one touched the object first just as often as the other did.

Watson judged these negative results to be confirmed by anatomical measurements made (according to the 1921 report) on 100 infants. These measurements included the length of the forearm to the tip of the middle finger, the breadth of the wrist, and the width of the palm at the knuckles. There were "almost no differences between right and left measurements [Watson & Watson, 1921, p. 501]."

In light of the negative results of the behavioral and anthropometric tests, Watson and Watson (1921) concluded "albeit tentatively, that there is yet no evidence for assuming a hereditary basis for handedness [p. 501]." Later, Watson (1924a) laid the reasons for handedness squarely on social training:

> Our whole group of results in handedness leads us to believe that there is no fixed differentiation of response in either hand until social usage begins to establish handedness. Society soon thereafter steps in and says, "Thou shalt use thy right hand." Pressure promptly begins. "Shake hands with your right hand, Willy." We hold the infant so that it will wave "bye-bye" with the right hand. We *force it to eat with the right hand. This in itself is a potent enough conditioning factor to account for handedness* [p. 101; emphasis in original].

Charles Reade, John Jackson, and other advocates of ambidextral culture could not have said it better.

In the psychological literature of the 1920s, 1930s, and thereafter, every account of Watson's studies of reaching either accepted or at least did not question Watson's own characterization of the results (e.g., Lederer, 1939, p. 19). However, despite his conclusion that handedness is conditioned, Watson certainly had not brought forth any supporting evidence, although in his conditioning paradigm for studying the origins of fear, one could say that he had the means for carrying out such an analysis. Nor is it clear that the results had utterly failed to support the genetic model, as Watson believed. It is not only that the method used (on the reaching tests) and the time period covered were sufficiently similar to Voelckel's (1913) and others' studies that similarly positive results might have been expected. It is also that the apparent reliance on grouped data rather than on an individual-subject analysis might have masked existing hand differences in at least some of the infants. Indeed, Watson elsewhere (1919/1924b) reported what seems to be a reasonably clear case of right-hand preference for reaching in one of the infant subjects of the group tests. The infant ("L.") was tested on 12 different occasions from her eightieth to her one hundred and seventy-first day. On 7 of those occasions, Watson succeeded in eliciting reaching, on 6 of which occasions hand differences were mentioned. Each time, the right hand was preferred. Watson himself commented on the preference (e.g., at 171 days, "On the whole L used the right hand much more frequently than the left

[Watson, 1919/1924*b*, p. 299]"). He also reported that at 2½ years of age, she was "completely right-handed [p. 299]."[18]

In summary, from Preyer's 1881/1888 study to Watson's work in 1917–1919, we can count six biographies and twelve experimental or controlled-observation studies, with most of the reports providing evidence for the appearance of hand preference for different measures sometime in the first 18 months, usually (in the case of the controlled-observational studies of reaching) before 7–9 months. The fact of early hand preference thus seems well-enough established by this research, and, as I have said, even certain negative reports such as Watson's may perhaps be subject to re-evaluation.

Nondominant-Hand Preference Preceding the Establishment of Dominant Handedness

Although many of the biographical and experimental studies convincingly document the existence of early and largely right-hand preference, many, as we have seen, also suggest that this development is highly discontinuous. In other words, contrary to what Broca (1865) supposed, the behavior protocols do not consistently show the smooth emergence of hand preference "that only grows with age." Instead, there frequently were periods of preference for one hand or the other, and for some tasks more than others, mixed with periods of apparent absence of preference for either hand, with the shifts sometimes occurring with dramatic swiftness. Among the baby biographies, Dearborn's (1910) report has already been mentioned in this connection. Among the experimental studies, Valentine's (1914) results can be cited.

To some extent, what seems discontinuous may be only the haphazard changes in a still undeveloped system. But, in several of the reports, the changes look quite orderly; in particular, prior to the appearance of a reliable dominant-hand preference, there appears to be a transient period of preference for the other hand.

For the left-hander, the earlier preference would be for the right hand, as Charles Darwin (1877) had mentioned about his son. Another instance

[18]Perhaps I am giving this one case too much emphasis, but there also are other aspects of Watson's work that puzzle. Why did he ignore earlier empirical studies, in particular, that of Mark Baldwin, his one-time colleague at Johns Hopkins? And why had he failed to even consider the neurological evidence linking handedness and cerebral lateralization? A full answer to these questions is beyond the scope of this chapter but will be the subject of a separate report (Harris, 1983*b*). For now, suffice it to say that at least three factors probably were significant in Watson's thinking: his colleague S. I. Franz's (1913) failure to find a modal hand preference in monkeys; the demonstration by Karl Lashley (1917), Watson's former student, that this preference could be established through training; and finally, Franz's (1912) criticism of the extremeness of the cortical localization-of-function position as it had developed by Watson's time.

is Major's (1906) son, who showed a right-hand preference prior to becoming left-handed by the end of the first year. (This, of course, is an uncertain example, given the child's subsequent history.) Likewise, McDougall (1908, p. 343) mentioned that his daughter was "by nature left-handed," although her right hand had predominated "a little" at 23–29 weeks.

For the right-hander, the earlier preference would, of course, be for the left hand. Even long before the era of empirical research, Sir Thomas Browne (1646) alluded to this change as his way of challenging the nativist doctrine. Recall his remark that although the right hand "be most commonly used [in adults], in children it seems either indifferent or more favourable in the other [i.e., the *left* hand] [Browne, 1646, p. 192]." Elsewhere, Browne (1646) was explicit: "That there is also in man a naturall prepotency in the right we cannot with constancy affirme, if we make observation in children, who permitted the freedom of both do oftimes confine unto the left, and are not without great difficulty restrained from it [p. 186]." By the late nineteenth century, the same notion that there was an early period of left-hand preference seems to have been routine. Wilson (1891) wrote, "it is . . . no uncommon remark that all children are at first left-handed [p. 127]."

Of the studies reporting a shift from the left hand to the right, Baldwin's (1890) results provide a clear example, and perhaps something more. Recall that on the 2187 reaching trials at short distances for the fifth- to eighth-month testing period, Baldwin's daughter failed to show any hand differences overall. However, there was "a preliminary period of left-handedness" during this time (Baldwin, 1894/1900, footnote, p. 74). In the fifth and sixth months, Helen's right- and left-hand scores were nearly equal (right, 173, 134; left, 166, 141). In the seventh month, the right-hand score was 64% higher than the left (213 to 130), and in the eighth month, the left-hand score was 130% higher (131 to 57).[19] Recall, now, that on the 115 *far*-reaching trials presented during the eighth month (80 midline + 35 lateral placements), Helen had used her *right* hand 109 times. This suggests something other than a simple shifting of preference over time. Rather, during the eighth month, Helen was using her right hand for far distances at the same time as she was using her left hand for short distances.

Something more like simple shifting was mentioned by G. Stanley Hall. In 1884, Hall and his student, E. M. Hartwell, reported the results of a test

[19]Although Baldwin (1894/1900) characterized these scores only as indicating "a preliminary period of left-handedness [p. 74]," we can see that there actually was a preliminary period of right-hand preference preceding the period of left-hand preference. Presumably, Baldwin gave more weight to the greater strength of left-hand preference during the last month of the testing period.

of a 9-month-old infant, probably one of Hall's own two children. The infant's hands were held symmetrically to its sides and freed at the same instant. The result was that it grasped a "desired object" placed on the table directly in front of it 15 times out of 20 with the right hand, and "often even when the object was placed somewhat to the left [Hall & Hartwell, 1884, p. 97]." Subsequently, however, Hall (1891) recalled that in both his children there were "several months of decided left-handedness, when with a tempting object on the table exactly in front and both hands released at the same instant, the left would nearly always grasp the object, and yet distinct right-handedness was developed later in both [p. 131]." Since one of these infants presumably was the 9-month-old described in the Hall and Hartwell (1884) paper, the "several months of decided left-handedness" would have been before 9 months.

Shinn (1894) likewise noted that before the time in her niece's life when grasping "had become habitual" and the right hand had begun to be consistently preferred, there was a brief period ("the first few weeks of [voluntary] grasping [p. 324]") during which the left hand was used more often than the right. Shinn added that she was satisfied with this conclusion even though she could not establish it from her records.

The same is suggested in most of the later studies. Marsden (1903, p. 46) compared "[t]his coming in and going out of the left hand" (between the fortieth and forty-third weeks) to what Baldwin had found in his daughter's case, although we recall that at no time did Marsden's son actually use his left hand *more* frequently than his right. Dearborn (1910) was more certain, concluding that the left side of his daughter's body was "appreciably more precocious" than the right side. We also saw a gradual but very clear shift in Myers' (1908) daughter, who showed a 5:1 left-hand preference at 24 weeks (6 months), no preference between the thirty-seventh and fifty-fourth weeks, and a 3.5:1 right-hand preference between the fifty-fourth and fifty-eighth weeks.

As for Woolley's (1910) daughter, although a hand difference was absent on the shorter-distance trials (3, 5, and 7 in.), Woolley (1910) thought it "interesting to note" that during the first week of the seventh month, the left hand was used more frequently than the right, after which "the right predominated steadily [p. 37]."

A little after the middle of the eighth month, however, Woolley's daughter showed yet another period of left-hand preference. This time, it was not for reaching but for waving "bye-bye," which she had learned to do in connection with starting for a ride. Woolley's (1910) description of this development is most interesting in the way it accords with Marion's (1890) as well as Godfrey's (1747) remarks on the mother-holding theory (i.e., how the method of holding the infant could at least temporarily influence hand preference for a certain action [see pages 190–191]).

In taking her out to her cab, the nurse always carried her on the left arm, leaving the child's left hand free, and as a result, she learned to wave "Bye-Bye" with the left hand. A few days later we noticed that if her left hand was held, she refused to wave, but did so joyfully as soon as the hand was released. Early in the ninth month, she would wave "Bye-Bye" with the right hand if the left were held, but still used the left hand if it were free. . . . Somewhat later she passed through a stage in which she used either the left hand or both hands in waving, but never the right hand alone. Then gradually she began using the right hand occasionally, and by fifteen months, she had ceased using the left hand, and waved habitually with the right [p. 39].

The left-hand preference, furthermore, seems to have been restricted to this one activity, since "long before her right-handedness had conquered habit in the matter of waving 'Bye-Bye,' it was perfectly evident in other activities, such as throwing a ball [Woolley, 1910, p. 39]."

The most confident statement as to the existence of early left-hand preference was made by the American experimental psychologist Max Meyer. Meyer (1911) flatly declared that the left hand is the "preferred member in the activities of the first few months after birth [and that a normal human] is at first left-handed and then changes into being right-handed [p. 179]." This assertion was unadorned by any reference to empirical evidence, which may be why it was so strong, but it was not radically out of line with what Baldwin and others had reported. Later, however, Meyer (1913) certainly threw all caution to the wind in saying that in infancy there would be "general left-handedness [p. 53]."

The last example of a shift is from Valentine's (1914) son, W., who changed in mere days from what, over the previous 2-weeks' time ($7-7\frac{1}{2}$ months), had been strong right-hand preference for reaching (81%) to an equally strong and long-sustained left-hand preference (through $8\frac{1}{2}$ months). This case, however, is different from the rest because Valentine, referring to his earlier tests of reflexive and then voluntary grasping, called his son "naturally right-handed [p. 384]." Valentine also pointed out that the "specialization" of the left hand for wool-grasping was not accompanied by a left-hand preference in other activities, particularly when W. dealt with heavy objects, such as books, or when he played the piano:

In the sixth month he was often seated on my knee by the open piano, and had learned to hit the notes, greatly enjoying the sounds, or his own production of them. This performance, which was done at first with right or left hand indifferently, was soon relegated largely to the *right* hand, and during the eighth month (in which the specialization of the *left* hand for wool grasping was observed) the right hand was used almost exclusively by W. when thumping the piano [p. 384].

In this case, then, a limited kind of left-hand preference, rather than preceding the establishment of right-handedness, seems to have temporarily overlain the right handedness that existed all along.[20]

EXPLANATIONS OF EARLY LEFT-HAND PREFERENCE

From their limited observations of what seemed to be transient, early left-hand preference, neither G. S. Hall (1981), Marsden (1903), nor Shinn (1894) drew any lessons for understanding the origins of handedness. (Marsden, as already noted, drew no conclusions about the origins of handedness from any of his findings.) As for Helen Woolley (1910), her comments about her daughter's waving bye-bye with the left hand indicate that she considered this behavior to have been merely an anomaly induced by a particular set of circumstances (being taught to wave bye-bye while being held on the nurse's left arm) but ultimately swept aside by the greater biological force for right handedness.

In contrast to the others, Baldwin (1894/1900), Dearborn (1910), Meyer (1911, 1913), and Valentine (1914) all saw important, but different, implications in the phenomenon of early left-hand preference. Meyer (1913) dismissed Woolley's explanation that fortuitous circumstances had forced left-hand use: "If our ancestral inheritance could be so easily modified as Mrs. Woolley supposed, what an incentive this would be to enthusiastic educators! [p. 53]."

Dearborn (1910) probably would have agreed, for he seems to have been sure that his own daughter's change from left- to right-hand preference had not been determined by such external agents as doors, implements, or persons: "[A]t this early period their influence must have been small and it is, perhaps, not unreasonable to say, nil [p. 31]." What is more, the right handedness developed despite "sporadic efforts . . . at times to make [Lucia] left-handed and so practically more or less ambidextrous later on [p. 31]." Dearborn (1910) gave no details on this point but did speak disparagingly of Major's (1906) efforts to discourage his own child's increasing left handedness, calling it "a striking illustration of the unfortunate prejudice against what is practically ambidexterity [p. 31]."

The reasons for early use of the left hand therefore must be deeper and more fundamental—nothing less than the workings of a general maturational principle. There is a hint of this sort in Dearborn's (1910) conclusion that the left side was more "precocious" than the right, but that as "volition evolved, the use of the right side gradually became more habitual [p. 31]." Meyer (1911) elaborated this idea into a specific neurological

[20]It is noteworthy that Valentine saw these results as being consistent with McDougall's (1908) account of his daughter, Lucia. Whereas I had supposed that McDougall's calling Lucia "by nature left-handed" was a reference to her eventual handedness manifested beyond the period of the grasping tests (for which she showed a slight right-hand preference), Valentine's reading was that Lucia's natural left handedness was manifested during the testing period.

model. Since the human brain was not fully developed until years after birth, in contrast to the simpler brains of other animals, Meyer proposed that a similar rule might govern the development of the left and right hemispheres. Thus, the left temporal cortex, "with its highly complex speech functions," is not fully developed until years after birth; then "by analogy we conclude that the symmetrically corresponding part of the right hemisphere, with its simpler functions, matures much earlier. If so, then during the first months of life, hand movements would be predominantly controlled by the earlier maturing and functionally simpler right hemisphere [Meyer, 1911, p. 179]."

Meyer did not attempt to support this interpretation with anatomical data, but if he had, he unquestionably would have taken Parrot's (1879) side in the debate about the nature and direction of cortical maturation. Recall that against Gratiolet's (Leurat & Gratiolet, 1857) and others' statements that the left hemisphere matures earlier, and Ecker's (1868) and Vogt's (in Bateman, 1869) reports of no differences, Parrot (1879) and also Cunningham (1902) (for the "arm area") had reported an asymmetry favoring the earlier development of the right side of the brain (see pages 182–186). Meyer also surely would have been pleased with the way Parrot (1879) had linked the anatomical findings to the appearance of right handedness and speech "a long time after birth [p. 517]."

Baldwin's (1894/1900) analysis was not so different from Meyer's, but he saw the matter of early left-hand preference from the more radical perspective of the recapitulationist theorist. Here, though, Baldwin faced a difficulty with which neither of the other writers who had invoked recapitulationist principles had to contend (e.g., Gowers, 1902, and Jobert, 1885). In their analyses, the phylogenetic principle to be recapitulated in ontogeny was the initial absence of handedness followed by the emergence of right handedness. Confronted with different (one might say inconvenient) evidence—an earlier and transient period of *left*-hand preference preceding the establishment of right handedness—Baldwin (1894/1900) could invoke the recapitulationist principle only by being able to demonstrate the existence of left handedness in "lower animals," that is, in creatures whose developmental stage presumably was being recapitulated by the human infant. Baldwin acknowledged knowing of very few published observations of animal laterality but said that at least those few with which he was familiar supported his analysis.[21]

[21]Baldwin (1894/1900) mentioned an assertion by Vierordt (1881, pp. 427–428) that parrots grasp and hold food with the left claw and that lions strike with the left paw; Vierordt's quotation from explorer David Livingstone that "All animals are left-handed"; and a personal communication from W. Ogle that a chimpanzee that had recently died in the Zoological Garden in London was left-handed. Baldwin also acknowledged the need for further data and even inquired from officials in zoological institutions. In a subsequent edition of his book, Baldwin (1915) gives no account of their replies, if any, although he did

Valentine's (1914) explanation, like his findings, was different from all the rest. He concluded that, even at the early age of 7–8 months, there appears to be right-hand specialization for one action and left-hand specialization for another. The levels of functioning, however, are not equal. Rather, for a right-handed child (his own son, W.), "the left hand may tend to specialise in actions which are very simple, thus setting free the right hand for more serious work [Valentine, 1914, p. 384]."

> Perhaps, then, one may explain the change observed in W. from the predominant use of the right hand to the use of the left somewhat as follows. At first, the coloured wools, by their strong attractiveness drew out the right hand of W., naturally right-handed. As, with practice, grasping the colours became easier, and as with familiarity the wools became somewhat less attractive, the right hand was called forth less, and the easy task of grasping relegated largely to the left hand [p. 384].

Valentine (1914, p. 384) also suggested that a similar principle had operated in Baldwin's (1890) finding of right-hand reaching at more distant objects and either-hand reaching at short distances. (Valentine overlooked a point in Baldwin's data that would have strengthened his argument— the eighth-month period when the *left* hand was preferred at short distances.) Still, if his surmise was correct, Valentine admitted that "something of a mystery" remained. Why had his son started to change from right hand to left "just during those experiments in which the wools were most favourably placed for the *right* hand [Valentine, 1914, p. 384]"?

Finally, Watson (1924a) made an interesting observation on how *experiential* factors could lead to temporary shifts from dominant- to non-dominant-hand preference: "[S]ometimes for months the infant reaching the standing stage holds on with one or the other hand—possibly indeed with the better trained, stronger hand! During this period the other hand is left free. It may overtake or even surpass the hand slowed up from non-use [p. 102, footnote 1]."

Handedness and Speech Development

Before the writings of Bouillaud (1864–1865) and Broca (1865), the question of the development of handedness could be asked only in the limited context of the theories of laterality of the day. With the establishment of the principle of cortical localization of speech and the proposed

---

note that he had confirmed Vierordt's report that birds are left-handed: "My birds stand on the right and hold the food with the left claw [p. 74]." Even so, it seems remarkable that Baldwin gave credence to such offhand reports, particularly since Baldwin used the recapitulationist principle in a cautious and qualified way in contrast to G. Stanley Hull's "crude maturationist interpretation," according to which ontogeny was biologically determined by phylogeny (Broughton, 1981, p. 400; see also Sewny, 1945).

relationship to handedness, new possibilities began to take shape. Now, not only could the development of handedness be linked to the hypothesized ascension in functioning of one side of the brain, so could the development of speech through the closeness of its cortical substrate. In other words, both the growth of handedness and speech could be conceptualized as part of a common cortical system. Thus Baldwin (1890) wrote of the "fundamental connection between the rise of speech and the rise of right handedness [p. 65]" and, following Broca, identified both as representing a class of functions coordinated in one hemisphere only, that is, "functions which are crippled only if one selected hemisphere is damaged [p. 66]." Max Meyer (1911) certainly could not have proposed his explanation of early left handedness in the absence of these theoretical developments.

GESTURE AND SPEECH

The fact of cortical proximity provoked the question of commonality of function. What psychological roles did speech and dominant-hand movement share? A French writer, Fortuné Mazel (1892), gave an insightful answer:

> The infant does not speak in the true sense of the word. But even before he can use his tool of phonation, he knows how to express his ideas. During these long months [from the age of about 7 months to the beginning of speech], his gesture, that is to say, of his right arm, will speak with all the petulant eloquence of this age. Later, when phonetic articulation begins to develop but is still imperfect, perhaps he will gesture even more *in order to extend the range of his expression* ['*pour étendre sa surface d'expression*']. And for several years, the gesture will prevail over the voice, without doubt losing its importance gradually and by degrees only as phonation is perfected, but always remaining the voice's obligatory and occasionally exuberant companion [p. 113].

For his reference to the time of first appearance of right-hand gestures, Mazel was, in fact, referring to the results of the far-distance (effortful) reaching trials in Baldwin's 1890 experiment.[22]

Baldwin's (1894/1900, p. 66) analysis was similar. Speech is "*par excellence* the function of expression," all movements "are in a sense expressive," and "details of expression and its relative fullness are matters of co-ordination" that has attained "its ripest and most complex form, apart from speech, in movements of the hand." Right handedness thus is a form of "expressive differentiation of movement [p. 66]."

---

[22]Mazel evidently was equating reaching movements with gestures. He also attributed the findings to Daniel Wilson (1891), who, on his part, was only recounting Baldwin's (1890) experiment. Mazel also was mistaken on the margin of hand difference. He stated (Mazel, 1892, p. 113) that the right hand was preferred 93 times out of 100, a statistic that does not appear in either Wilson's or Baldwin's reports.

TIME OF FIRST APPEARANCE OF HAND PREFERENCE AND SPEECH

If there was agreement about the cortical proximity and common psychological roles of handedness and speech, the question of their temporal coordination in development was less certain. Broca (1865) perhaps implied a close connection from the outset when he declared that both the functions of the left hemisphere for guiding fine movements and for speech are habits carried from earliest infancy [*des notre premiere enfance*] (pp. 384–385). Baldwin (1890), however, noted that his infant daughter "had not yet learned to speak or to utter articulate sounds with much distinctness" when her right-hand preference for reaching first appeared; consequently, "right- or left-handedness may develop while the motor speech centre is not yet functioning [p. 247]"[23]

Woolley (1910) seemed to agree with Broca (or my reading of Broca). She remarked that her daughter first showed a preponderating use of the right hand in picking up the colored disks (middle of seventh month) at just the time when she began to babble syllables. "Before that, the variety of sounds she made had been small [p. 41]." Furthermore, at 10 months, by which time the child showed decided right handedness, she also had said her first word. Woolley (1910) nevertheless concluded on the same note as had Baldwin: Her daughter's early development of right handedness was not accompanied by an early acquisition of speech, since she acquired new words very slowly and at 18 months had but 15 or 20 words, "many of them very indistinctly pronounced [p. 41]." Finally, we recall Cunningham's (1902) remark, about Baldwin's experiment, that the appearance of handedness must await the full myelination of the motor tracts. Cunningham went on to note that the portion of cortex devoted to speech is fully developed much later still (the end of the first postnatal year). Thus, on purely anatomical grounds, Cunningham presumably would have predicted different time schedules for handedness and speech development.

Baldwin and Woolley were describing the acts of reaching and grasping a desired object. Preyer (1888) had taken care to distinguish these from what he saw as the different expressive acts of pointing and gesturing ("when . . . he lifts the right arm . . . and points to the light with outspread fingers, then he has executed the gesture of *pointing*, absolutely distinct from desiring [p. 321]");and, in speaking of his son (and another child), Preyer emphasized that pointing was employed "with perfect correctness before the first attempts at expression in words [p. 321]." What is not evident is that Preyer saw any importance in the fact that it was his son's right hand that had been used.

[23]In his memoirs published some years later, Baldwin (1926) seems to have changed his mind: "[P]referential use of either hand develops along with the faculty of speech, *and only then*; that is, toward the end of the first years [vol. 1, pp. 43–44; emphasis added]."

By contrast, Max Meyer (1911) was explicit about the hand used. However, like Woolley (1910), and unlike the others, he reported *coincident* development of hand preference with a particular aspect of language development. According to Meyer (1911), "The reflex of pointing with the index finger at a thing which impresses the eye [begins to appear] at about the same time when the first articulated sounds (usually gutteral and dental—ga and da) are instinctively produced by the baby [p. 176]." The pointing "is done far more frequently with the right than with the left hand, whereas previous to this time the right hand is by no means favored in action [p. 177]." Meyer also explained the direction of causation. Given the dependence of the growth of speech during the second year of life on the development of the left temporal lobe, and given the close connection between this part of the brain and the hands, but more with the right than the left, speech functions would be expected to bring about use of the right hand. This explains why "certain movements of the baby's speech organs are accompanied by pointing movements of the right hand, and why grown people, too, so frequently accompany their talk by gestures of the right hand [Meyer, 1911, p. 178]."

Meyer's remarkable statements, alas, were completely undocumented (like his statements about early left handedness), and the accounts by Baldwin, Woolley, and the others have the obvious limitations of sample size and method of report. What was needed was a true empirical analysis of the relationship between the development of handedness and speech. A reasonable first approximation was provided in 1918 by Margaret M. Nice.

Nice's work grew out of a different set of concerns from those that motivated her predecessors. By 1918, several reports had appeared, describing either delayed or disturbed speech in left-handed children and adults. Some of these reports went on to suggest that the disturbance was a result of interference with the child's developing left handedness (e.g., Ballard, 1911–1912; Jones, 1915; Lueddekins, 1900; Stier, 1911; Whipple, 1911). Nice (1918) herself saw evidence for speech delay following interference with left handedness in Major's (1906) report of his infant son. These were samples of sentences, spoken by the child at the end of the third year, that Nice (1918) judged to be "markedly imperfect [p. 146]" in articulation and in use of pronouns.

To obtain more information, Nice asked 12 of her acquaintances with infants and young children about their child's handedness and speech development. Ten children, ranging in age from 12 to 30 months, were identified by their parents as being right-handed; a 13-month-old boy was described as "right-handed, yet uses left somewhat"; and a 16-month-old boy was called ambidextrous. By their parents' account, the latter two children also were the least advanced in speech. However, among the other "right-handed" infants, those recalled by their parents as becoming

right-handed "early" were not obviously more advanced in speech than
the others.

Encouraged by these results, Nice made a more detailed analysis of
seven more children, all of whom showed significant speech retardation
that could not be explained by such things as ill health or hearing loss. All
seven children showed "more or less marked ambidextrous tendency,"
that is, "a prolonged state of uncertainty as to which hand should lead
[Nice, 1918, pp. 160–161]." Nice also believed that she had found evidence for a close temporal relationship between the two skills. Her own
daughter, by 27 months, had become entirely right-handed in her use of a
pencil, and, by 28 months, in the use of a spoon. During her twenty-eighth
month, she also had made more progress in talking than she had shown in
any of the preceding months. Nice (1918) suggested that as long as the
dominant-hand center was "not definitely settled the speech center could
not be located [p. 161]," but she added that it was impossible to know the
exact relationship of these two factors—both could be the results of some
other cause. Finally, Nice mentioned other cases in which the coincidence of ambidexterity and delay in talking did not occur. Obviously,
what was needed was more research:

> We have an almost untouched field in this subject of the relationship be-
> tween speech development and the use of the hands. We need a large num-
> ber of studies on children and particularly on those who are more or less
> slow in talking and who have hitherto been almost wholly neglected by
> observers, before we can hope to find the underlying causes of the dif-
> ferences in speech development in different children [Nice, 1918, p. 161].

Retrospect—and Prospect

It is now more than 300 years since Thomas Browne wrote, "although
the right be most commonly used, yet hath it no regular or certain root in
nature . . . since in children it seemes either indifferent or more favourable in the other"; more than a century since Broca declared to the contrary—that the right limb from the outset was the stronger and more skillful; nearly as long since Baldwin traced the emergence of hand preference
for reaching during the first months of life; and over three generations
since Watson's studies seemed to have brought us full circle back to
Thomas Browne.

From the examination of the work of these early periods, has our understanding of the development of handedness and laterality of function
been advanced in any significant ways, or can the early ideas and research
be safely put aside as historical curiosities? I think the answer is clear.
First, several of the early studies provide data on the development of hand
preference that deserve to be incorporated into the body of empirical

evidence on this question. Second, certain models or ideas currently attracting attention are fundamentally similar, even identical, to those of earlier periods. Finally, the early literature may contain some novel clues about the development of hand preference that might significantly aid our thinking today. In closing this chapter, let us note some examples of these points.

Effortfulness and Hand Differences in Reaching

Although recent investigations support the conclusion in Baldwin's (1890), Marsden's (1903) Voelckel's (1913), and other early studies that right-hand preference for reaching emerges sometime around the middle of the first year, the question about the role of degree of effort—Baldwin's principle of "dynamogeny"—seems not to have left a mark. This question is worth pursuing, especially if we think of the high-effort reaching task as one not only calling on a greater measure of skill or motor control but as predisposing a one-handed response. That is, the target being farther away—just beyond reach—mere swiping will not be so likely to capture it, and being just beyond reach when the infant is directly facing it (Baldwin's method), the infant can reach it only by turning his body so as to favor one side. The reported relationship between target distance and lateralized responding (i.e., either-hand or left-hand use for close targets, right-hand use for far targets; Baldwin, 1890; Marsden, 1903; Woolley, 1910) also deserves further study in light of recent ideas on the distinction between proximal and distal motor control of the arm and hand (Brinkman & Kuypers, 1972; Van der Staak, 1975).

Crossing Body Midline

We saw how Baldwin's daughter not only reached preferentially with one hand, but frequently did so by crossing the body midline. As Baldwin (1894/1900) said, Helen's right hand "intruded regularly upon the domain of the left [p. 63]" (also see Valentine, 1914). The recent notion that at this age there is a strict "midline barrier" (Bruner, 1969, p. 231) thus seems to be thrown into doubt not only by new research but by the old work too (see discussion in Hawn and Harris, Chapter 17, this volume).

Other Behavioral Asymmetries

To some extent, the controversies in the early as well as current literature as to the existence of lateral preference in the first year may be resolvable if we try to take into consideration the infant's level of cognitive and motor competence at the time of testing. For instance, although the newborn infant cannot reach, it can grasp, and psychologists have now confirmed Gutzmann's (1911) and Valentine's (1914) observation that the grasping reflex is stronger in the right hand (Petrie & Peters, 1981). The newborn also shows asymmetries in posture, and what the early writers observed—that infants generally lie on their right sides—has been confirmed many times over in more recent years (e.g., Gesell & Ames, 1947; Turkewitz, 1971, 1977; Harris & Fitzgerald, Chapter 14, this volume). At 2 months of age, when the infant still shows no hand preference for "reaching" (or what at that age might better be called "arm movement and extension in response to a target"), it does show reliably longer right-hand grasping of a rattle or wood barbell (Caplan & Kinsbourne, 1976; Petrie & Peters, 1981; Hawn & Harris, Chapter 17, this volume).

Handedness and Language

The question so prominent in early writings—that of the relationship between the development of handedness and language—is also starting to be re-addressed. For instance, there is much interest today in the analysis of pointing as one of the infant's first communicative acts (e.g., Bates, 1976; Murphy, 1978). In other words, like Preyer (1888), psychologists today appreciate the distinction between the acts of reaching and grasping a desired object and the different expressive acts of pointing and gesturing. In agreement with Preyer's (1888) account but contrary to Meyer's (1911, 1913), the new research finds that when pointing first emerges (9 months), it is not yet integrated or synchronized with vocal activity; that comes 5 months later (Murphy, 1978). But if Meyer was wrong on the timing of the synchronization of pointing and vocalizing, what of hand preference? Is the pointing hand the dominant hand, as Meyer declared? And by 7 months to the beginning of speech, does the right hand "speak [i.e., gesture] with all the petulant eloquence of this age," as Mazel (1892) declared? We do not know the answer to this question either. Some recent research, however, suggests that a coincidence or synchrony, possibly of the sort meant by Meyer, may exist for certain other measures of hand preference and speech development. Ramsay (1980; Ramsay, Campos, & Fenson, 1979) has found that the infant's first use (as determined by mother's report) of two-syllable utterances with dissimilar conso-nant–vowels across syllables is significantly correlated in time with the first appearance of bimanual hand coordination in the infant's manipulation of a toy such as a plastic nut-and-bolt. That is, each hand assumed a qualitatively different function for the use or manipulation of the toy, with the left hand holding the nut while the right hand turns ("operates") the bolt.

The new work on pointing and bimanual manipulation is a good beginning. Still, Margaret Nice's call in 1918 for a "large number" of studies of the relationship between speech development and use of the hands remains today unanswered.

Nondominant Preference Preceding the Establishment of Dominant Handedness

Another old question now making a reappearance is whether a transient period of preference for the nondominant hand precedes the establishment of dominant-handedness. Both Gesell and Ames (1947) and Seth (1973) reported trends of this sort for reaching and manipulation. In Gesell and Ames' study, there was a slight preference for the left hand between 16 and 20 weeks, followed by a period of right-hand preference, with periodic reversals through at least 40 weeks. Seth (1973) reported a left-hand preference among the younger of a group of 20–52-week-old infants, with the 28–32-week period appearing to be the critical transition period to right-hand preference.

In both studies, the possibility has been raised that the early left-hand phase was only an artifact of scoring. Young (1977) performed binomial tests on one set of data in each study that accounted for individual differences and found that all the supposed left-hand preferring trends washed out (on Gesell and Ames, see also Annett, 1978, p. 279). Some of the earlier reports likewise might be suspect, although several accounts seem very convincing, especially Baldwin (1890), Myers (1908), Dearborn (1910), and Valentine (1914). What is more, an early, transient period of left-hand preference or greater activity has been reported in several contemporary studies, including Coryell and Michel (1978; see McDonnell, 1979, p. 259), DiFranco, Muir, and Dodwell (1978), and Anderson and McDonnell (1979; cited in McDonnell, 1979). Familial handedness and sex also may be important contributing variables to the appearance of early left-hand usage as well as to the development of handedness generally. Carlson and Harris (1983) tested familial right-handed (FRH) and familial left-handed (FLH) infant boys and girls on a visually directed reaching task at 3-week intervals between 18 and 39 weeks of age. All groups showed comparable decreases in the frequency of bimanual reaches over this period. However, only the girls (both FRH and FLH) showed an increase in the frequency of right-hand over left-hand reaches, whereas the FRH boys showed a marked preference for left-hand reaches (64% versus 22% across ages). The FLH boys, by contrast, showed no hand preference.

However the empirical question of early left-hand preference is finally resolved, a critical point of some of the early work should not be overlooked, namely, that periods of right- and left-hand preference also may coexist, but for different acts. Recall Valentine's (1914) observation that the left hand (in the case of a right-handed child) "may tend to specialize in actions which are very simple, thus setting free the right hand for more serious work [p. 384]." This view sounds compatible with our contemporary understanding of the respective specializations of the right and left hands for fine motor control and localization function (cf. Bresson, Maury, Pieraut-Le Bonniec, & de Schonen, 1977; Harris, 1975, 1980b). Here, work by Hampson and Kimura (1982) may be relevant. When right-handed adults were asked to arrange blocks to solve a verbal task (e.g., complete a crossword puzzle), most task-directed movements were by the right hand; when the task was nonverbal (e.g., creation of a design), there was a leftward shift. Might an infant's hand preference also wax and wane in strength, or even shift, not only as the infant grows older and becomes more verbal, but also at any given age, according to task demands?

Structural Asymmetries

Like our nativist predecessors, we continue to believe that differences in function must be underlaid by differences in structure. The contemporary literature on this question is far too extensive to review here, but suffice it to say that the evidence, at best, is still mixed. On the one hand, gross asymmetries favoring the left side have now been clearly demonstrated in the anatomy of the posterior Sylvian region coinciding with Wernicke's area (secondary auditory cortex). These differences (in the size of the planum temporale) have been found in adult brains (Geschwind & Levitsky, 1968; Wada, Clarke, & Hamm, 1975) as well as in term fetuses and abortuses as young as 5 months postconception (Chi, Dooling, & Gilles, 1977; Wada et al., 1975; Witelson & Pallie, 1973). Together with behavioral evidence of early lateral specialization, these findings have been widely seen as evidence for a prewired neurological substrate of language. However, for every asymmetry favoring the left side, there seems to be another favoring the right, as several of the earlier investigators had also observed. For instance, when Chi et al.'s (1977) study is cited, typically only the results for planum size (longer on left side) are mentioned. But in the same specimens, Chi et al. also found that the transverse temporal (Heschl) gyri were larger and more numerous on the right side. Moreover, in about two-thirds of the cases, these gyri also could be recognized 1–2 weeks earlier on the right side.

In contrast to the perirolandic region of the temporal lobes, no comparable gross anatomical differences favoring the left side have been found in the classical motor-speech areas of the frontal lobes (pars triangularis and pars opercularis) in either adult or in infant brains (Wada et al., 1975). At most, there is a slight difference in the frontal operculum favoring the right. This difference obviously is inconsistent with known functional differences. The investigators, however, have pointed out that the gyri contained within the left frontal operculum appeared to be "more tightly packed" than those of the right, and that the total cortical surface area of the operculum therefore might be larger on the left in most brains (Wada *et al.*, 1975, p. 265).

With respect to the question of handedness, as distinct from language, the anatomical evidence also remains unclear. The absence of gross lateral differences in the motor-speech area obviously precludes assessment of a relationship to handedness, and in the temporal cortex, where left–right differences do appear, the estimated relationship to handedness is still uncertain (Wada *et al.*, 1975; see review in Witelson, 1982). Another possibility is that handedness is related to morphological asymmetries in the nervous system below the level of the forebrain, in particular, in the level of and pattern of decussation and in the size of the pyramidal tracts at the level of the medulla and spinal cord. In both fetal and adult brains, there is a clear right-sided torque in this motor system, with the right side receiving the greater amount of motor fiber innervation in about 80% of the cases. However, the relationship to handedness is uncertain at best, although restrictions in the sample size for sinistrals have precluded a fair test (Kertesz & Geschwind, 1971; Yakovlev & Rakic, 1966; see discussion in Witelson, 1980).

While neuroanatomists and neuropsychologists continue to look for asymmetries in the brain, much anatomical work continues to be directed to the limbs themselves. The results, in large part, corroborate those early studies that found positive results, such as Harting's (1869) and Biervliet's (1899). For such measures as bone length and muscle weight of the arms, the right side shows significantly more development than the left, not only in adults (Chhibber & Singh, 1972; Garn, Mayor, & Shaw, 1976; Jolicoeur, 1963; Latimer & Lowrance, 1965; Plato, Wood, & Norris, 1980) but also in human fetuses (Pande & Singh, 1971; Schultz, 1926). For the legs, however, the asymmetries more frequently favor the left side but by a smaller margin (Chhibber & Singh, 1970; Schultz, 1937). The relationship of any of these asymmetries to handedness remains problematic (e.g., Garn *et al.*, 1976).

Brain-Growth Gradients

The discovery of lateral anatomical differences in the brains and bones of fetuses as well as adults, together with the new evidence of early functional asymmetries, has brought about the resurrection of yet another early explanation of laterality: the maturational growth gradient. The passing years, however, have not brought agreement as to its direction. Like Broca (1865), some writers today are proposing that the gradient favors earlier development and expression on the left side of the brain (e.g., Corballis & Morgan, 1978). By this view, the existence of various asymmetries early in life, including left-hemisphere language specialization, the larger left planum, the head-to-right posture, and right-hand preference itself, are thereby accounted for. Other writers, following the same reasoning as Parrot (1879), see the evidence as more consistent with a gradient working in precisely the reverse direction (e.g., Ettlinger, 1978; Whitaker, 1978). Thus, against the weight of evidence posed by cortical expanse (the larger left planum), they counterpose the evidence of gyrus and fissure development (earlier on the right); and against the evidence of early left-hemisphere specialization for language, they counter with accounts of the precocious nature of the infant's presumptive right-hemisphere skills, such as its ability to recognize faces and nonverbal sounds. (Gratiolet himself presumably could have accepted both alternatives, since, as we recall, what he reported was earlier development on the left side anteriorly, on the right side posteriorly.) Other writers take issue with both these alternative views and suggest that the growth change is, in fact, cyclic, first favoring one side, then the other, and then the first side again (e.g., Mittwoch, 1978, the reference here being to a growth-gradient governing embryological development of the entire body); still others argue that no single growth or maturational gradient can reasonably account for the known complexities of development (e.g., Kraft, 1980).

What is fascinating about this contemporary debate is the role once again being played by the question of early left-hand preference. Like Max Meyer in his own day (1911, 1913), some writers today see contemporary reports of early left-hand preference as possibly reflecting earlier maturation of the right hemisphere (e.g., Anderson & McDonnell, 1979; McDonnell, 1979; Whitaker, 1978). The same reports for advocates of the gradient-to-the-left model pose an obvious problem. The solution proposed by Corballis and Morgan (1978, p. 262) is to conceptualize the left-to-right shift as corresponding to a shift from *peripheral* to cerebral influences, with both favoring the left. Thus, the left hand may be favored initially because of earlier development of the motor system on the left side of the body. Then, assuming that the influence of cerebral maturation on motor functions occurs somewhat later, right-hand preference would arise with the emergence of contralateral left-cerebral control.

As Steklis (1978) has pointed out, however, Corballis and Morgan had failed to consider the anatomical findings reported by Chi *et al.* (1977). Since pyramidal motoneurons originate in the perirolandic region (whose convolutions, according to Chi *et al.*, appear earlier on the right side), Steklis suggests that their projections, composing the pyramidal tracts, may actually develop earlier on the right, and hence provide earlier dexterity to the left hand. The subsequent specialization of the left hemisphere for sequential motor activity in right-handed individuals would then favor the right hand in such activities (Steklis, 1978, p. 317). By this reasoning, according to Steklis, it would be unnecessary to assume a shift from peripheral to a central left–right growth gradient in the control of the upper limb.

These are all interesting possibilities, and the idea that functional asymmetries, including handedness, might be explained as the product of a maturational growth gradient (or gradients) continues to look worth pursuing. The finding of sex-related effects on the development of hand preference (Carlson & Harris, 1983) also suggests that any maturation gradient may work at different times and perhaps in different ways for males and females. But for the time being and until further work is done, William Ireland's (1886) judgment may suit our day as well as it did his: "So the question which side is first developed seems still doubtful [p. 293]."

In utero *Position*

Although the emphasis in contemporary theories of the development of handedness is on neuroanatomical and neurophysiological factors, as it was in Broca's time, certain other possibilities continue to attract interest. For instance, although Joseph Comte was soon forgotten, in the more than 150 years since he published his intrauterine position theory, the same or similar idea was proposed at least four or five more times (see Harris, 1980a, pp. 34–35). There may be something to it. Radiological studies show that, at least prior to delivery, the fetus tends to lie with its back toward the mother's left side nearly twice as often as toward her right side (Dunn, 1969; cited in Dunn, 1976, p. 74). This asymmetry may represent an accommodation to uterine asymmetry (torsion usually to right, causing displacement of bladder to right, leaving more room on left side for left occiput position of fetus' head when it is anterior or transverse; Taylor, 1976; this also was Comte's [1828a, 1828b] opinion). Whatever the reason, in this position, the fetus' left arm would lie posteriorly, the right arm anteriorly, and the result presumably would be to allow the right arm freer movement. Perhaps, as the Chinese said, the fetus does move its right arm before its left! What is not yet known is whether position prior to delivery represents the modal position during the last trimester, or how accurately intrauterine position prior to delivery predicts birth presentation position.

Is there, then, a link between birth presentation and infant hand preference? Grapin and Perpère (1968) have reported supporting evidence, although the link may be less direct than Comte supposed. Michel and Goodwin (1979) have found that birth position predicts newborn *head* position preference while the infant lies supine. That is, infants born in the first vertex position tend to lie with their head turned to the right, whereas infants born in the second position tend to lie with their head turned to the left. Coryell and Michel (1978) also found that in the head-right position, the right hand is more likely to be in the infant's field of view, and they went on to show that the more frequently regarded hand, whether left or right, was the more likely to be used in a visually elicited reaching task when the infant was 3 months old. So Coryell and Michel (1978) concluded that handedness may arise from asymmetrical postural preference during early infancy, which "biases visual experience of the hands, giving one hand an advantage in eye–hand coordination tasks [p. 245]" (see also Goodwin & Michel, 1981). We can perhaps recognize in this idea some continuity with Stevens's (1908) proposal about the effects of eye movements on head and arm movements in "left-" and "right-hemisphered" infants. Coryell and Michel's interpretation, however, may put undue stress on visual experience alone, insofar as it seems to imply different proportions of right- and left-handedness in the congenitally blind than in the sighted. Recall that Ballard (1911–1912) reported no differences in proportions between these groups. Of course, adult handed-ness implies much more than merely the preferential use of the "domi-nant" hand. So, at least with respect to visually elicited reaching in infan-cy, one of the *proximate* conditions leading to hand preference might well be frequency of visual hand regard.

How Infants Are Held

Still another old puzzle now attracting interest is, why do babies tend to be held on the parent's left side? The preference *is* real, as several studies have shown, and apparently only for babies, not, as Buchanan (1862) believed, for all burdens (see Burt, 1937, p. 299; Finger, 1975; Richards & Finger, 1975). This preference is not merely a result of the handedness of the person holding the infant. Salk (1973) observed 255 right-handed mothers during the first 4 days after they had given birth and found that 83% held their baby on the left side of their chest or on the left shoulder and 17% held the baby on the right side. The percentages for 32 left-handed mothers were 78% and 22%—in the same direction. Salk proposed that the preference is related to the left-sided heartbeat of the mother, and that both baby and mother profit from this arrangement, the baby being soothed by the heartbeat, the mother having the sensation of her own heartbeat being reflected back from the baby. Perhaps, but the infant also could be making a different and more direct kind of contribu-tion.

One sort of contribution might be visual. For right-handers, faces are better recognized when briefly projected in the observer's left- than right-visual half-field, which is consistent with the known specialization of the right cerebral hemisphere for perception of faces and other nonverbal and emotional stimuli (Bradshaw & Nettleton, 1981). If we assume that there is also a preference for inspecting a face in the left visual field during free observation, then left-sided cradling of an infant would be preferred by most right-handers. In left-handers, the preference should still be for the left side but by a smaller margin, since roughly only 60% of left-handers follow the modal right-handed pattern of cortical organization (see reports in Herron, 1980).

Another of the infant's contribution might be postural-motoric. Ginsburg, Fling, Hope, Musgrove, and Andrews (1979) found that new-born infants who exhibited the modal head-to-right position after birth were typically held over the mother's left shoulder when tested 2–3 weeks later, whereas infants exhibiting an initial head-to-left preference were typically held over the right shoulder (see also Bundy, 1979.) Thus neonatal head turning, as Ginsburg et al. (1979) say, "may dictate an interesting mode of mother–infant interaction [p. 281]."

In this connection, recall Baldwin's (1894/1900) reference to the proposal that infants get to be right-handed "by being placed on one side too much for sleep [page 204]." I had supposed Baldwin to mean the left side (in keeping with the reasoning applied in the case of the related mother-holding theory). But perhaps Baldwin meant the right side after all. Perhaps he had accurately noted a maternal (or nursing) practice for placing the infant in this supine position (the more likely position if the mother had been holding the infant in the modal in-arms position, i.e., on her left side, so that the infant's head was to the right, toward the mother), and that, with the infant in this supine position, Baldwin had taken note of the greater proximity of its right hand to its line of sight.

Training of Hand Preference

Despite the increasingly strong consensus that the fundamental variables underlying the development of handedness are structural, the old idea that hand preference also can be shaped by training and experience has never entirely slipped from consideration. For instance, in Coryell and Michel's (1978) work, we see a model of how, in the normal course of development, structural factors might predispose the practice of eye–hand coordination preferentially on one side so as to influence the hand used for reaching. Other kinds of inadvertent training might well be able to influence hand preference for certain other actions. Woolley's (1910) description of the circumstances apparently causing her daughter to use her left hand for waving bye-bye exemplifies both the power and specificity of these experiences. Shaw's (1902) account (see footnote 10, page 200) of his unsuccessful attempt to encourage equal hand use shows how even the mildest of means can dramatically tip the balance in an infant not yet showing hand preference, although presumably the effect was not sustained (also see Lederer, 1939, pp. 93–94).

Where left handedness is concerned, the influence of training on the development of hand preference for certain actions can hardly be doubted. For instance, in Taiwan, where, following Chinese custom, the use of the left hand for writing and eating is deliberately proscribed, only 0.7% of elementary school and college students use the left hand for writing (Teng, Lee, Yang, & Chang, 1976) compared with 6.5% of Oriental school children in the United States (Hardyck, Goldman & Petrinovich, 1975). The difference, presumably, is a reflection of the extent to which natural left-hand preference can be suppressed under certain circumstances. But of precisely *how* and *when* in life the left-hand preference begins to be discouraged in favor of the right hand in these societies, we are still largely in the dark. For instance, does it happen as it happened to Benjamin Franklin, or is Major's (1906) gentler treatment of his son the commoner style? And whatever the training may be, do some children change hand preference more readily than others? (Who are the 0.7% of the individuals in Teng *et al.*'s [1976] study who persisted in their use of the left hand?) As we recall, Major (1906) drew no strong conclusions from his demonstration as to the preeminence of nature or training; for example, "some or all children [might be] naturally ambidextrous, but will develop right- or left-handedness under training [p. 45]." Major may have been right about "some" children. According to Annett's (1972) genetic model, most people inherit a disposition to be right-handed, whereas others inherit no disposition at all, in which case handedness arises from the play of random factors. This raises the question of whether lateral preferences are weaker or more variable in infants with than without familial sinistrality. If they are, we might expect the hand preferences of infants with familial sinistrality to be more sensitive to environmental influence.

Here, then, are the major themes linking the work of today with that of the past. For all the theoretical and empirical progress of recent years, some readers nevertheless may be alarmed at the extent to which we still seem to be plowing the same old ground. So it would appear, but what seems equally clear is how fortunate we have been in our scientific heritage. Much of that same old ground continues to look fertile with possibilities.

Acknowledgments

Any work of this sort would be impossible without original source material. The staff members of the Reference, Science, and Special Collections Libraries and the Inter-library Loan Office of Michigan State University have been constantly supportive, and I thank them all. I also am grateful for the help of several other institutions, in particular, the A. Alfred Taubman Medical Library and the Harlan Hatcher Graduate Library of The University of Michigan (Ann Arbor), the Houghton Library of Harvard University, the Francis A. Countway Library of Medicine (Boston), the Newberry Library (Chicago), the Library of Congress

(Washington, D.C.), and the National Library of Medicine (Bethesda, Maryland). I also thank Martin Doettling, department of German and Russian, Michigan State University, for help with German translation. Finally, I owe special thanks to Margaret Hall for typing the numerous drafts of the manuscript.

References

Alcock, J. (1870). Left-handedness. *Lancet 2*, 557.

Anderson, V. E. S., & McDonnell, P. M. (1979). *The sinister infant: Unexpected laterality at three to eight weeks.* Paper presented at the meetings of the Canadian Psychological Association, Quebec City, June.

Annett, M. (1972). The distribution of manual asymmetry. *British Journal of Psychology 63*, 343–358.

Annett, M. (1978). Throwing loaded and unloaded dice. *Behavioral and Brain Sciences 2*, 278–279.

Aristotle. (1912). De Partibus Animalium [The parts of animals, W. Ogle, trans.] *The works of Aristotle* (vol. 5). Oxford, England: Clarendon Press.

Aristotle. (1926). *Problemeta*. [W. S. Hett, trans.] London: Heinemann.

Baldwin, J. M. (1890). Origin of right or left handedness. *Science 16*, 247–248.

Baldwin, J. M. (1894). The origin of right-handedness. *Popular Science Monthly 44*, 606–615.

Baldwin, J. M. (1900) *Mental development in the child and the race.* (2nd ed.). New York: Macmillan. (Originally published, 1894.)

Baldwin, J. M. (1915). *Mental development in the child and the race.* 3rd ed., Rev.). New York: Macmillan.

Baldwin, J. M. (1926). *Between two wars, 1861–1921, being memories, opinions and letters received.* (2 vols.). Boston, Massachusetts: Stratford.

Ballard, P. B. (1911–1912). Sinistrality and speech. *Journal of Experimental Pedagogy and Training College Record (London) 1*, 298–310.

Ballin, H. (1896). Symmetry in education. *The child-study monthly 2*, 306–309.

Bateman, F. (1869). On aphasia, or loss of speech in cerebral disease. *Journal of Mental Science 15*, 367–392; 489–504.

Bates, E. (1976). *Language and context: The acquisition of pragmatics.* New York: Academic Press.

Bérillon, E. (1884). *Hypnotisme expérimental. La dualité cérébrale et l'indépendance fonctionnelle des deux hemispheres cérébraux.* Paris: A. Delahaye et E. Lecrosnier.

Biervliet, J. J. van. (1899). L'homme droit et l'homme gauche. *Revue Philosophique de la France et de l'Étranger 47*, 113–143; 276–296; 371–389.

Binet, A. (1890a). La perception des longueurs et des nombres chez quelques petits enfants. *Revue Philosophique de la France et de l'Étranger 30*, 68–81.

Binet, A. (1890b). Perceptions d'enfants. *Revue Philosophique de la France et de l'Étranger 30*, 582–611.

Binet, A. (1890c). Recherches sur les mouvements chez jeunes enfants. *Revue Philosophique de la France et de l'Étranger 29*, 297–309.

Bischoff, E. (1863). Einige Gewichts- und Trocken-bestimmungen der Organe des Menschlichen Korpers. In J. Henle & C. Pfeufer (Eds.), *Zeitschrift für rationelle Medicin.* Leipzig and Heidelburg.

Blanton, M. G. (1917). The behavior of the human infant during the first thirty days of life. *Psychological Review 24*, 456–483.

Bolton, T. L. (1895). Review of J. M. Baldwin, "Mental development in the child and the race." *The American Journal of Psychology 7*, 142–145.

Boring, E. G. (1957). A history of experimental psychology. New York: Appleton.

Bouillaud, J. (1864–1865). Discussion sur la faculté du langage articulé. Bulletin de l'Academie Imperiale de Médecin 30, 724–781.

Bradshaw, J. L. & Nettleton, N. C. (1981). The nature of hemispheric specialization in man. The Behavioral and Brain Sciences 4, 51–92.

Bresson, F., Maury, L., Pieraut-Le Bonniec, G., & de Schonen, S. (1977). Organization and lateralization of reaching in infants: An instance of asymmetric functions in hands collaboration. Neuropsychologia 15, 311–320.

Brewster, E. T. (1913). The ways of the left hand. McClure's Magazine (June), 168–183.

Brinkman, J., & Kuypers, H. (1972). Cerebral control of contralateral and ipsilateral arm, hand, and finger movements in the splitbrain rhesus monkey. Brain 96, 653–674.

Broca, P. (1861). Remarques sur le siège de la faculté du langage articulé, suivies d'une observation d'aphémie (perte de la parole). Bulletins de la Société Anatomique 6, 330–357.

Broca, P. (1865). Sur le siège de la faculté de langage articulé. Bulletins de la Société d'Anthropologie de Paris 6, 377–393.

Broca, P. (1875). Sur le poids relatifs du deux hémisphéres cérebraux et de leur lobes frontaux. Bulletins de al Société d'Anthropologie de Paris 10, 534–535.

Broca, P. (1877). Recherches sur la circulation cérébrale. Bulletin de l'Academie de Medecine (2e serie) 6, 508–539.

Broughton, J. M. (1981). The genetic psychology of James Mark Baldwin. American Psychologist 36, 396–407.

Browne, T. (1646). Pseudodoxia epidemica, or, Enquiries into very many received tenents, and commonly presumed truths. London: Edward Dod.

Bruner, J. S. (1969). Eye, hand, and mind. In D. Elkind & J. H. Flavell (Eds.), Studies in cognitive development: Essays in honor of Jean Piaget. London and New York: Oxford Univ. Press.

Buchanan, A. (1862). Mechanical theory of the predominance of the right hand over the left, or, more generally, of the limbs of the right side over those of the left side of the body. Proceedings of the Philosophical Society of Glasgow 5, 142–167.

Bulhof, I. N. (1974). The Netherlands. In T. F. Glick (Ed.), The comparative reception of Darwinism. Austin: Univ. of Texas Press.

Bundy, R. S. (1979). Effects of infant head position on sides preference in adult handling. Infant Behavior and Development 2, 355–358.

Burt, C. (1937). The backward child. New York: Appleton-Century.

Carlson, D. F., & Harris, L. J. (1983). The development of hand preference for visually-directed reaching: A longitudinal study of infants between 18 and 39 weeks of age. Paper presented at Seventh Biennial Meetings of the International Society for the Study of Behavioural Development, University of Munich, W. Germany, 31 July–4 August.

Carrier, A. (1867). Étude sur la localisation dans le cerveau de la faculté du langage articulé. Paris: Giermer Bailliere.

Chhibber, S. R., & Singh, I. (1970). Asymmetry in muscle weight and one-sided dominance in the human lower limbs. Journal of Anatomy 106, 553–556.

Chhibber, S. R., & Singh, I. (1972). Asymmetry in muscle weight in the human upper limbs. Acta Anatomica 81, 462–465.

Chi, J. G., Dooling, E. C., & Gilles, F. H. (1977). Left–right asymmetries of the temporal speech areas of the human fetus. Archives of Neurology 34, 346–348.

Clarke, E., & Dewhurst, K. (1972). An illustrated history of brain function. Oxford: Sandford.

Clement, F. (1587). The petie schole with an English orthographie. London: Thomas Vautrollier. (Facsimile in R. D. Pepper [Ed.], Four Tudor books on education. Gainesville, Florida: Scholars' Facsimiles & Reprints, 1966.)

Comte, J. A. (1828a). Recherches anatomico-physiologiques, relatives à la prédominance de bras droit sur le bras gauche. Paris, Chez l'auteur. No. 7 in a volume of pamphlets with binder's title: *Mémoires. Physiologie. Système nerveux. Mémoire lu à l'Academie des sciences le 25 février.*)

Comte, J. A. (1828b). Recherches anatomico-physiologiques, relatives à la prédominance du bras droit sur le bras gauche. *Journal de Physiologie Expérimentale et Pathologie 8*, 41–80.

Comte, J. A. (1842). *Organisation et physiologie de l'homme* (4th ed.). Paris: Ches Les Principaux Libraires Scientifiques, et Chez L'auteur, Rue Belle Chasse, 34.

Corballis, M. C., & Morgan, M. J. (1978). On the biological basis of human laterality: I. Evidence for a maturational left–right gradient. *The Behavioral and Brain Sciences 2*, 261–269.

Coryell, J. F., & Michel, G. F. (1978). How supine postural preferences of infants can contribute towards the development of handedness. *Infant Behavior and Development 1*, 245–257.

Cosmovici (1889). Comment on deviant gaucher. *Revue Scientifique 44,572.*

Crichton-Browne, J. (1907). Dexterity and the bend sinister. *Proceedings of the Royal Institution of Great Britain 18*, 623–652.

Cunningham, D. J. (1902). Right-handedness and left-brainedness. The Huxley lecture for 1902. *Journal of the Royal Anthropological Institute of Great Britain and Ireland 32*, 273–296.

Darwin, C. (1859). *On the origin of species.* London: John Murray. (Facsimile. Cambridge, Massachusetts: Harvard Univ. Press, 1964.)

Darwin, C. (1871). *The descent of man, and selection in relation to sex.* London: John Murray. (Photoreproduction. Princeton, New Jersey: Princeton Univ. Press, 1981.)

Darwin, C. (1877). A biographical sketch of an infant. *Mind 2*, 285–294.

Dearborn, G. V. N. (1910). *Motor-sensory development.* Baltimore, Maryland: Warwick and York.

Debierre (1887). Le developpement des membres du cote droit l'emporte-t-il originairement sur celui des membres du cote gauche? *Comptes Rendus Hebdomadaires des Seances et Mémoires de la Société de Biologie 4*, 28–31.

De Lacy, P. H. (1967). Plutarch of Chaeronea. In P. Edwards (Ed.), *The encyclopedia of philosophy* (vol. 6). New York: Macmillan and The Free Press.

Delaunay, C.-G. (1874). *Biologie comparée du coté droit et du coté gauche chez l'homme et chez les etres vivants.* Paris: N. Blanpain.

DiFranco, D., Muir, D., & Dodwell, P. (1978). Reaching in very young infants. *Perception 7*, 385–392.

Dix, K. W. (1911). *Körperliche und geistige Entwicklung eines Kindes.* (Vol. 1) Leipzig: E. Wunderlich.

Dunn, P. M. (1969). *The influence of the intrauterine environment in the causation of congenital postural deformities, with special reference to congenital dislocation of the hip.* Unpublished thesis, University of Cambridge, Cambridge, England.

Dunn, P. M. (1976). Congenital postural deformities. *British Medical Bulletin 32*, 71–72.

Dutrochet, H. Marquis. (1824). *Recherches anatomiques et physiologiques sur la structure intime des animaux et des végétaux, et sur leur motilité.* Paris: J. B. Ballière.

Dutrochet, H. Marquis. (1826). *L'agent immédiat du mouvement vital dévoilé dans sa nature et dans son mode d'action, chez les végétaux et chez les animaux.* Paris: J. B. Baillière.

Ecker, A. (1868). Zur Entwicklungsgeschichte der Furchen und Windungen der Grosshirn-Hemispharen im Foetus des Menschen. *Archiv für Anthropologie 3*, 212–223.

Elyot, T. (1533). *The education or bringinge vp of children/translated oute of Plutarche* (Thomas Elyot, trans.). London: Thomas Berthelet. (University Microfilms No. 20057)

Ettlinger, G. (1978). Have we forgotten the infant? *The Behavioral and Brain Sciences 2*, 294–295.

F. B. (1644). *Chirology: Or the natural language of the hand. Composed of the speaking motions, and discoursing gestures thereof . . . Whereupon is added Chironomia: Or the art of manuall rhetoricke . . .* London: T. Harper.

Feré, C. (1889). La gaucherie acquise. *Revue Scientifique 44,* 605–606.

Finger, S. (1975). Child-holding patterns in Western art. *Child Development 46,* 267–271.

Font-Réaulx, J. de. (1866). *Localisation de la faculté spéciale du langage articulé.* Paris: Adrien Delahaye.

Franklin, B. (1904). A petition of the left hand. In J. Bigelow (Ed.), *The works of Benjamin Franklin* (vol. 7). New York and London: G. P. Putnam's Sons. (Originally published, 1779.)

Franz, S. I. (1912). New phrenology. *Science 35,* 321–328.

Franz, S. I. (1913). Observations on the preferential use of the right and left hands by monkeys. *Journal of Animal Behavior 3,* 140–144.

Garn, S., Mayor, G. H., & Shaw, H. A. (1976). Paradoxical bilateral asymmetry in bone size and bone mass in the hand. *American Journal of Physical Anthropology 45,* 209–210.

Gaupp, E. (1889). Ueber die Maass und Gewichts-Differenzen Zwischen den Knochen der rechten und der linken Extremitäten des Menschen. *Inaug. Dissert.,* Breslau.

Geschwind, N., & Levitsky, W. (1968). Left/right asymmetries in temporal speech region. *Science 161,* 186–187.

Gesell, A., & Ames, L. B. (1947). The development of handedness. *Journal of Genetic Psychology 70,* 155–175.

Ginsburg, H. J., Fling, S., Hope, M. L., Musgrove, D., & Andrews, C. (1979). Maternal holding preferences: A consequence of newborn head-turning response. *Child Development 50,* 280–281.

Godfrey, J. (1747). *A treatise upon the useful science of defence, connecting the small and back-sword, and shewing the affinity between them.* London: T. Gardner.

Goodwin, R. S., & Michel, G. F. (1981). Head orientation position during birth and in infant neonatal period, and hand preference at nineteen weeks. *Child Development 52,* 819–826.

Gould, G. M. (1904). Dextrality and sinistrality. *Popular Science Monthly 65,* 360–369.

Gowers, W. R. (1902). Right-handedness and left-brainedness, *Lancet 2,* 1719–1720.

Grapin, P., & Perpère, C. (1968). Symétrie et latéralisation du nourrisson. In R. Kourilsky & P. Grapin (Eds.), *Main droite et main gauche.* Paris: Presses Universitaires de France.

Gromier, J. (1874). Étude sur le circonvolutions cérébrales chez l'homme et chez les singes. Paris: A. Parent.

Gutzmann, H. (1911). *Beobachtungen der ersten sprachlichen und stimmlichen Entwicklung eines Kindes. Monatsschrift für die gesamte Sprachheilkunde.*

Haeckel, E. (1905). *The evolution of man* (2 vols., J. McCabe, trans.). London: Watts. (Originally published, 1874.)

Hall, G. S. (1891). Notes on the study of infants. *Pedagogical Seminary 1,* 128–138.

Hall, G. S., & Hartwell, E. M. (1884). Research and discussion, bilateral asymmetry of function. *Mind 9,* 93–109.

Hall, Mrs. W. S. (1896–1897). The first five hundred days of a child's life. *The Child Study Monthly,* 1896, *2,* 330–342; 394–407; 1897, *2,* 458–473; 522–537.

Hampson, E., & Kimura, D. (1982). Hand movement asymmetries during verbal and nonverbal tasks. (Research Bulletin #567). London, Canada: University of Western Ontario, Department of Psychology. (Mimeo)

Hardyck, C., Goldman, R., & Petrinovich, L. (1975). Handedness and sex, race, and age. *Human Biology 47,* 369–375.

Harris, L. J. (1975). Neurophysiological factors in the development of spatial skills. In J. Eliot & N. J. Salkind (Eds.), *Children's spatial development.* Springfield, Illinois: Thomas.

Harris, L. J. (1978). Sex differences in spatial ability: Possible environmental, genetic, and neurological factors. In M. Kinsbourne (Ed.), *Asymmetrical function of the brain*. London and New York: Cambridge Univ. Press.

Harris, L. J. (1980a). Left-handedness: Early theories, facts, and fancies. In J. Herron (Ed.), *Neuropsychology of left-handedness*. New York: Academic Press.

Harris, L. J. (1980b). Which hand is the "eye" of the blind?—A new look at an old question. In J. Herron, (Ed.), *Neuropsychology of left-handedness*. New York: Academic Press.

Harris, L. J. (1982). The human infant as focus in theories of handedness: Some lessons from the past. In R. N. Malatesha & L. C. Hartlage (Eds.), *Neuropsychology and cognition* (vol. 2). The Hague: Nijhoff.

Harris, L. J. (1983a). *"Delicacy of fibres in the brain": Some early neurological explanations of sex differences in cognition.* Paper presented at the meetings of the Society for the Study of Human Biology—First Symposium on Sexual Dimorphism, Leuven, Belgium, April.

Harris, L. J. (1983b) *John B. Watson's studies of laterality in infants:* A re-examination. Paper presented at Annual Meetings of the Midwestern Psychological Association, May 5–7. Chicago, Illinois.

Harris, L. J. (in press). Teaching the right brain: Historical perspective on a contemporary educational fad. In C. T. Best, (Ed.), *Developmental neuropsychology and education*. New York: Academic Press.

Harting, P. (1869). Sur une asymétrie du squelette humain se transmettant hereditairment. *Archives Néerlandaises des Sciences Exactes et Naturelles 4*, 44–54.

Herron, J. (Ed.). (1980). *Neuropsychology of left-handedness*. New York: Academic Press.

Hertz, R. (1973). [The pre-eminence of the right hand: a study in religious polarity.] In R. Needham (Ed. and trans.), *Right and left: Essays on dual symbolic classification*. Chicago: Univ. of Chicago Press. (Originally published, 1909.)

H. M. (1889). Sur la gaucherie. *Revue Scientifique 44*, 764.

Holmes, J. B. (1969). *Concise medical textbooks, obstetrics*. London: Bailliere & Cassell.

Hyrtl, J. (1860). *Handbuch der topographischen Anatomie*. (4th ed.). Vienna: Braumüller.

Ireland, W. W. (1880). Notes on left-handedness. *Brain 3*, 207–214.

Ireland, W. W. (1886). *The blot upon the brain: Studies in history and psychology*. New York: G. P. Putnam's Sons.

Jackson, J. (1905). *Ambidexterity or two-handedness and two-brainedness*. London: Kegan Paul, Trench, Trubner & Co.

Jackson, J. H. (1874). On the nature of the duality of the brain. *Medical Press and Circular 1*, 96–103.

J. H. (1889). La gaucherie acquise. *Revue Scientifique 44*, 701.

Jobert, L. (1885). *Les gauchers comparés aux droitiers aux points de vue anthropologique et médico-legal*, Lyon, France (Pamphlet No. 5076, National Library of Medicine, Medical History Department).

Jolicoeur, P. (1963). Bilateral symmetry and asymmetry in limb bones of *Martes Americana* and man. *Review of Canadian Biology 22*, 409–432.

Jones, W. F. (1915). The problem of handedness in education. *Journal of Proceedings and Addresses of the National Educational Association 53*, 959–963.

Kellogg, G. M. (1898). The physiology of right- and left-handedness. *Journal of the American Medical Association 30*, 356–358.

Kertesz, A., & Geschwind, N. (1971). Patterns of pyramidal decussation and their relationship to handedness. *Archives of Neurology 24*, 326–332.

Kessen, W. (1965). *The child*. New York: Wiley.

Kraft, A. von. (1980). On the problem of the origin of asymmetric organs and human laterality. *The Behavioral and Brain Sciences 3*, 478–479.

Kussmaul, A. (1859). *Untersuchungen uber das seelenben des neugeborenen menschen. . . .* Program zum eintritt in den Königlichen akademischen senat der Friedrich-Alexanders-universität zu Erlangen. Leipzig, Winter.

Ladd, G. T. (1903). *Psychology: Descriptive and explanatory.* (4th ed.). New York: Charles Scribner's Sons.

Lashley, K. S. (1917). Modifiability of the preferential use of the hands in the rhesus monkey. *Journal of Animal Behavior 7,* 178–186.

Latimer, H. B., & Lowrance, E. W. (1965). Bilateral asymmetry in weight and in length of human bones. *Anatomical Record 152,* 217–224.

Le Conte, J. (1884a). Right-sidedness. *Nature 29,* 452.

Le Conte, J. (1884b). Right-sidedness. *Nature 30,* 76–77.

Lederer, R. K. (1939). An exploratory investigation of handed status in the first two years of life. (Iowa Studies in Child Welfare). *Studies in Infant Behavior* 16(2), 9–103.

Leurat, F. (1839). *Anatomie comparée du système nerveux, consideré dans ses rapports avec l'intelligence* (vol. 1). Paris: J. B. Ballière et Fils.

Leurat, F., & Gratiolet, P. (1857). (written by P. Gratiolet). *Anatomie comparée du système nerveux, consideré dans ses rapports avec l'intelligence (vol. 2).* Paris: J. B. Baillière et Fils.

Lueddekens, F. K. A. (1900). Rechts-und Linkshandigkeit. Leipsig: W. Engelmann.

Luys, J. (1865). *Recherches sur l'anatomie, la physiologie et la pathologie du système nerveux.* Paris: J. B. Ballière.

McDonnell, P. M. (1979). Patterns of eye–hand coordination in the first year of life. *Canadian Journal of Psychology 33,* 253–267.

McDougall, W. (1908). An investigation of the colour sense of two infants. *British Journal of Psychology 2,* 338–352.

Major, D. R. (1906). *First steps in mental growth.* New York: Macmillan.

Marion, H. (1890). Les mouvements de l'enfant au premier age; premiers progres de la volunte. *Revue Scientifique 65,* 769–777.

Marsden, R. E. (1903). A study of the early color sense. *Psychological Review 10,* 37–47.

Mazel, F. (1892). Pourquoi l'on est droitier. *Revue Scientifique 49,* 112–114.

Meyer, A. (1971). *Historical aspects of cerebral anatomy.* London and New York: Oxford Univ. Press.

Meyer, M. (1911). *Fundamental laws of human behavior: Lectures on the foundations of any mental or social science.* Boston, Massachusetts: R. G. Badger.

Meyer, M. (1913). Left-handedness and right-handedness in infancy. *Psychological Bulletin 10,* 52–53.

Michel, G. F., & Goodwin, R. (1979). Intrauterine position predicts newborn supine head position preferences. *Infant Behavior and Development 2,* 29–38.

Mittwoch, U. (1978). Changes in the direction of the lateral growth gradient in human development—left to right and right to left. *The Behavioral and Brain Sciences 2,* 306–307.

Moore, K. C. (1896). *Mental development of a child.* New York: Macmillan.

Moorhead, T. G. (1902). The relative weights of the right and left sides of the body in the foetus. *Journal of Anatomy and Physiology 36,* 400–404.

Murphy, C. M. (1978). Pointing in the context of a shared activity. *Child Development 49,* 371–380.

Myers, C. S. (1908). Some observations on the development of the colour sense. *British Journal of Psychology 2,* 353–363.

Nice, M. M. (1918). Ambidexterity and delayed speech development. *Pedagogical Seminary 25,* 141–162.

Pande, B. S., & Singh, I. (1971). One-sided dominance in the upper limbs of human fetuses as evidenced by asymmetry in muscle and bone weight. *Journal of Anatomy 109,* 457–459.

Parrot, M. J. (1879). Sur le developpement du cerveau chez les enfants du premier age. *Archives de Physiologie Normale et Pathologique* (2nd series) 6, 505–521.

Péré, A. (1900). *Les courbures latérales normales du rachis humain.* Toulouse: Marques & Co.

Perez, B. (1889). [The first three years of childhood] (A. M. Christie, trans.). Syracuse, New York: C. W. Bardeen.

Perez, B. (1901). L'education intellectuelle des le berceau (Rev. 2nd ed.). Paris: Ancienne Librairie Germer Bailliere.

Petrie, B. F. & Peters, M. (1981). Handedness: Left/right differences in intensity of grasp response and duration of rattle holding in infants. Infant Behavior and Development 3, 215–221.

Plato. (1953). [The dialogues of Plato] (vol. 4, 4th ed., B. Jowett, trans.). London and New York: Oxford Univ. Press.

Plato, C. C., Wood, J. L., & Norris, A. H. (1980). Bilateral asymmetry in bone measurements of the hand and lateral hand dominance. American Journal of Physical Anthropology 52, 27–31.

Preyer, W. (1888). [The mind of the child. Part I: The senses and the will.] (2nd ed., H. W. Brown, trans.) New York: D. Appleton and Co. (Originally published, 1881.)

Pye-Smith, P. H. (1871). Left-handedness. Guy's Hospital Reports (3rd series) 16, 141–146.

Ramsay, D. S. (1980). Beginnings of bimanual handedness and speech in infants. Infant Behavior and Development 3, 67–77.

Ramsay, D. S., Campos, J. J., & Fenson, L. (1979). Onset of bimanual handedness in infants. Infant Behavior and Development 2, 71–76.

Reade, C. (1878). "The coming man." Letters to the Editor of Harper's Weekly, January 19, pp. 50–51; January 26, p. 74; February 2, pp. 94–95; March 2, pp. 174–175; March 23, pp. 234–235; May 18, pp. 394–395.

Richards, J. L., & Finger, S. (1975). Mother–child holding patterns: A cross-cultural photographic survey. Child Development 46, 1001–1004.

Richerand, A. B. (1813). Coucher. Dictionnaire des sciences médicales. Par une société de médecins et de chirurgiens: Adelon, Alard, Alibert, Barbier, etc. (60 vols.). Paris: Crapart & Panckoucke.

Roques, F. (1869). Sur un cas d'asymetrie de l'encephale, de la moelle, du sternum et des ovaires. Bulletins de la Société d'Anthropologie de Paris 4 (2nd series), 727–732.

Ross, D. (1972). G. Stanley Hall: The psychologist as prophet. Chicago, Illinois: Univ. of Chicago Press.

Salk, L. (1973). The role of the heartbeat in the relations between mother and infant. Scientific American 228, 24–29.

Schiller, F. (1979). Paul Broca, founder of French anthropology, explorer of the brain. Berkeley: Univ. of California Press.

Schultz, A. H. (1926). Fetal growth of man and other primates. Quarterly Review of Biology 1, 465–521.

Schultz, A. H. (1937). Proportions, variability, and asymmetries of the long bones of the limbs and the clavicles in man and apes. Human Biology 9, 281–328.

Sequin, E. (1880). Report on education. (2nd ed.). Milwaukee, Wisconsin: Doerflinger Book & Publishing Co. (Photoreproduction. Delmar, New York: Scholars' Facsimiles & Reprints, 1976.) (Originally published, 1875.)

Seth, G. (1973). Eye–hand coordination and "handedness": A developmental study of visuomotor behaviour in infancy. British Journal of Educational Psychology 43, 35–49.

Sewny, V. D. (1945). The social theory of James Mark Baldwin. New York: Kings Crown Press.

Sharpey-Schaefer, E. A. (1898–1900). Textbook of physiology (2 vols.). Edinburgh and London: Pentland.

Shaw, J. (1902). Right-handedness and left-brainedness. Lancet 2, 1486.

Shinn, M. W. (1894). Notes on the development of a child. Berkeley: Univ. of California Press.

Sigismund, B. (1856). Kind und Welt; die fünf ersten Perioden des Kindesalters. Braunschweig: Vieweg und sohn.

Soldan, F. L. (1890). School-room classics. XIII. Tiedemann's Record of Infant-Life. An

English version of the French translation by Michelan and commentary by Bernard Perez (with Notes by F. Louis Soldan). Syracuse, New York: C. W. Bardeen.

Steklis, H. D. (1978). Of gonads and ganglia. *Behavioral and Brain Sciences 2*, 317–318.

Stevens, H. C. (1908). Right-handedness and peripheral vision. *Science 27*, 272–273.

Stevens, H. C., & Ducasse, C. J. (1912). The retina and righthandedness. *Psychological Review 19*, 1–31.

Stier, E. (1911). *Untersuchungen uber Linkshandigkeit und die Funktionellen Differenzen der Hirnhalfen; nebst einem Anhang: "Uber Linkshandigkeit in der deutschen Armee"*. Jena: G. Fischer.

Struthers, J. (1863). On the relative weight of the viscera on the two sides of the body; and on the consequent position of the centre of gravity to the right side. *Edinburgh Medical Journal 8*, 1086–1104.

Taylor, D. C. (1978). The biases of sex and maturation in lateralisation: "isomeric" and compensatory left-handedness. *The Behavioral and Brain Sciences 2*, 318–320.

Taylor, E. S. (1976). *Beck's obstetrical practice and fetal medicine*. (10th ed.). Baltimore, Maryland: William & Wilkins.

Teng, E. L., Lee, P. H., Yang, K. S., & Chang, P. C. (1976). Handedness in a Chinese population: Biological, social, and pathological factors. *Science 193*, 1148–1150.

Theile, F. W. (1884). Gewichtesbestimmungen zur Entwicklung des Muskel-systems und des Skelets beim Menschen. *Nova Acta der kaiserlichen Leopoldina-Carolinae deutsche academie der naturforscher* (Band 46, No. 3). Halle: Blochmann.

Thompson, H. B. (1903). *The mental traits of sex*. Chicago, Illinois: Univ. of Chicago Press.

Todd, R. B. (Ed.) (1859). *The cyclopedia of anatomy and physiology*. London: Longman, Brown, Green, Longmans, & Roberts.

Tracy, F., & Stimpfl, J. (1894). *The psychology of childhood*. Boston, Massachusetts: D. C. Heath & Co.

Valentine, C. W. (1914). The colour perception and colour preferences of an infant during its fourth and eighth months. *British Journal of Psychology 6*, 363–387.

Valentine, C. W. (1950). *The psychology of early childhood: A study of mental development in the first years of life* (4th ed.). London: Methuen & Co. (Originally published, 1942.)

Van Der Staak, C. (1975). Intra- and interhemispheric visual–motor control of human arm movements. *Neuropsychologia 13*, 439–448.

Vierordt, K. von (1881). *Physiologie des Kindesalters*. Tubingen: Druck von Heinrich Laupp.

Voelckel, E. (1913). Untersuchungen uber die Rechtshandigkeit beim Saugling. *Zeitschrift fur Kinderheilk 8*, 351–358.

Wada, J. A., Clarke, R., & Hamm, A. (1975). Asymmetry of temporal and frontal speech zones in 100 adult and 100 infant brains. *Archives of Neurology 32*, 239–246.

Watson, J. B. (1913). Psychology as the behaviorist views it. *The Psychological Review 20*, 158–177.

Watson, J. B. (1924a). *Behaviorism*. New York: The People's Institute Publishing Co.

Watson, J. B. (1924b) *Psychology from the standpoint of a behaviorist*. (2nd ed.). Philadelphia, Pennsylvania: Lippincott. (Originally published, 1919.)

Watson, J. B., & Morgan, J. J. B. (1917). Emotional reactions and psychological experimentation. *The American Journal of Psychology 28*, 163–174.

Watson, J. B., & Watson, R. R. (1921). Studies in infant psychology. *Scientific Monthly 13*, 493–515.

Whipple, G. M. (1911). The left-handed child. *Journal of Educational Psychology 2*, 574–575.

Whitaker, H. A. (1978). Is the right leftover? *The Behavioral and Brain Sciences 2*, 323–324.

Wilson, D. (1891). *The right hand: Left-handedness*. New York: Macmillan.

Witelson, S. F. (1980). Neuroanatomical asymmetry in Left-handers: A review and implications for functional asymmetry. In J. Herron (Ed.), *Neuropsychology of left-handedness*. New York: Academic Press.

Witelson, S. F. (1982). The bumps on the brain: Right–left asymmetry in brain anatomy and function. In S. Segalowitz (Ed.), *Language functions and brain organization.* New York: Academic Press.

Witelson, S. F., & Pallie, W. (1973). Left hemisphere specialization for language in the newborn: Neuroanatomical evidence of asymmetry. *Brain 96,* 641–646.

Wolf, T. H. (1973). *Alfred Binet.* Chicago, Illinois: Univ. of Chicago Press.

Woo, T. L., & Pearson, K. (1927). Dextrality and sinistrality of hand and eye. *Biometrika 19,* 165–199.

Woolley, H. T. (1909). Some experiments on the color perceptions of an infant and their interpretation. *Psychological Review 16,* 363–376.

Woolley, H. T. (1910). The development of right-handedness in a normal infant. *Psychological Review 17,* 37–41.

Yakovlev, P. I., & Rakic, P. (1966). Patterns of decussation of bulbar pyramids and distribution of pyramidal tracts on two sides of the spinal cord. *Transactions of the American Neurological Association 91,* 366–367.

Young, G. (1977). Manual specialization in infancy: Implications for lateralization of brain function. In S. J. Segalowitz & F. A. Gruber (Eds.), *Language development and neurological theory.* New York: Academic Press.

11

Developmental Models of Hemispheric Specialization: Insights Past and Present

CARL M. CORTER

Discussion of the Chapters

Young, Bowman, Methot, Finlayson, Quintal, and Boissonneault (Chapter 7, this volume) make an important point that seems obvious once it is made but has been relatively neglected in discussions of the development of hemispheric specialization. The point is that if the left hemisphere of the brain may be described as possessing specialized skills for executive and sequential control of actions, then it must be adept not only at initiating actions, but at *inhibiting* them as well. For example, sequencing of behavior may require inhibition of one ongoing action at the point in the sequence where another action begins.

Young *et al.*'s (Chapter 7) model of hemispheric specialization is based on elaboration of the basic point that inhibition must be a specialized function of the left hemisphere. In particular, they propose that it is specialized in "at least two kinds of inhibition: (a) coordination with activation to produce smooth, sequential, goal-appropriate behavior; and (b) control of gross, secondary, irrelevant, associated behavior distinct in nature from the appropriate behavior and fined-tuned, interfering, parallel behavior similar in nature to the appropriate behavior [page 122, this volume]."

In a further elaboration, they propose that early social interaction may contribute to the development of the left hemisphere's specialized functions because of its sequential nature and the role of parents in modulating (inhibiting) the infant's behavior.

Young *et al.* (Chapter 7) report two studies of young infants derived

249

MANUAL SPECIALIZATION
AND THE DEVELOPING BRAIN

from their model. The data are consistent with some of their claims and clearly demonstrate the heuristic value of their emphasis on inhibition. This emphasis suggests that indices beyond reaching, such as the non-directed activity of the nonreaching hand, should be studied. In fact, interesting differences between the activity of the infant's right and left hands are shown in such measures. The contention that social interaction contributes to the development of lateralization is supported by some correlations between parental social behavior and right-lateralized directed-arm activity. Nevertheless, Young *et al.* (Chapter 7) are careful to point out that there are other interpretations of the correlations, so the causal role of social interaction in hemispheric specialization remains plausible but far from proven.

Peters's (Chapter 8) speculative review provides the most complete model of developmental relations between the nervous system and lateral biases in motor behavior. He begins by posing the persistent problem in developmental psychology: the changing meaning of behavior, in this case lateral biases in motor behavior, across age. In order to define the meaning of asymmetries in infancy and to elucidate the transforming processes that lead to mature forms such as adult handedness, he carries out a phylogenetic analysis that points to a supraspinal, subcortical source for structural asymmetries at other levels in the nervous system and in behavior.

Peters (Chapter 8) shows how this source fits into a network of interrelated processes and connections. Although the source is germinal, it is amplified by various processes in the network to produce more robust, mature forms of asymmetry. In fact, Peters' (Chapter 8) model would still work even if the "source" were elsewhere in the network he describes. In any case, the subcortical source is presumed to operate during the newborn period by formulating movement intentions that are transmitted via indirect pathways to cell assemblies in the spinal cord that control reflexive movement. Amplification of lateral bias may occur as asymmetrical central nervous system functioning builds asymmetries in the motor periphery, for example, by affecting differentiation of muscle fibers.

This subcortical network is gradually overlaid and intertwined with hemispheric connections. Because the hemispheric connections build on an asymmetrical, subcortical base, the functions of the hemispheres evolve asymmetrically. This cortical involvement allows the development of motor concepts that are abstractions of movement and that can be mediated by cognitive processes, including memory and attention. Such motor "thought" reaches the highest level of complexity in movement plans underlying skilled bimanual movement. The movement plan is formulated by the interaction of both hemispheres, but the left normally assumes the executive role in channeling movement intention and attention through the asymmetrical pathways established earlier in ontogeny. The left hemisphere also issues a sequenced pattern of impulses to both brain halves; these impulses control the initiation and termination of movements, although the particular topography of the right- and left-hand movements are controlled by the motor cortex in the contralateral hemisphere.

Although Peters (Chapter 8) postulates a germinal source for asymmetry, his model is most impressive in suggesting a network of developing processes and neurological links that amplify and overlay the initial source as development proceeds. Both asymmetrical exercise of function and environmental input are given roles as potential amplifiers. The model shows how skilled bimanual actions may evolve out of reflexes as subcortical asymmetries are intertwined with the developing functions of the hemispheres. Not all features of Peters's (Chapter 8) model are firmly anchored in data, but the ideas are provocative and provide a sophisticated account of the ontogenetic interweaving of neural and motor asymmetries.

Ramsay (Chapter 9) proposes a relatively simple, testable model and reports three studies bearing on it. Basically, he argues that motor milestones in articulation and manual manipulation are correlated during development. This concurrence may reflect successive levels of hemispheric specialization underlying motor behavior in both the articulatory and manual realms. His earlier research demonstrated that the onset of bimanual handedness (consistent use of one hand to manipulate an object while the other hand holds it) comes toward the end of the first year, together with the onset of articulation of dissimilar syllables in single utterances. In this case, however, it was not clear to Ramsay whether the articulation milestone is more of a motor than a linguistic accomplishment. The research reported in Chapter 9 explores another potential correspondence in articulatory and manual motor milestones, specifically, the convergence of unimanual handedness (consistent manipulation by one hand without involvement of the other hand) and duplicated (repetitive) syllables in the infant's babbling around the middle of the first year of life.

The data Ramsay (Chapter 9) reports do not provide compelling evidence for the model he proposes. In particular, a different order of emergence for the manual and articulatory milestones for males and females would seem to preclude the argument that the emergence of these milestones is mediated directly by emerging levels of hemispheric specialization. However, it could be argued that a certain level of hemispheric specialization is necessary for both milestones, and that other maturational factors that differ between the sexes are sufficient to produce different patterns of emergence in females and males. If this is the case, the task of providing evidence for the model becomes more complicated. Another, less complex, possibility is Ramsay's (Chapter 9) suggestion that mothers may report milestones differently for males and females, in some systematically biased way.

Harris's (Chapter 10) historical review is convincing on the point that there are questions and answers worth bringing forward from the past. In most cases, the answers are more suggestive than certain, but such uncertainty is not confined to research from previous generations. As an example of an old answer worth comtemporary consideration, Harris cites Ballard's study in the early 1900s showing a normal proportion of right-handers among the congenitally blind. This finding poses a problem for Coryell and Michel's (1978; see Michel, Chapter 3, this volume) suggestion that the infant's early head-right postural bias contributes to right handedness by channeling visual experience toward the right hand. On the other hand, before the contemporary suggestion is discarded, we need to know more about the historical finding. For example, was right-hand use a social convention in which the blind were trained in Ballard's time?

In general, Harris (Chapter 10) shows that the historical research is provocative but often limited by various factors such as omission of details, small sample size, unsystematic design, and questionable statistical conclusions. Despite these limitations, it is interesting that a number of current research questions mirror those suggested by the historical data. Harris (Chapter 10) cites examples such as whether there is a period of left-hand bias and the related issue of whether there are specialized functions for both hands during infancy. In many cases, current questions seem to have developed independently of any particular knowledge of the historical literature. However, given the limitations of previous research, current work is not neccessarily pointless repetition. Furthermore, some of the older work may deserve extension as well as replication. In this regard, Harris (Chapter 10) points to Baldwin's findings concerning the effects of object distance and perceptual salience on lateral bias in the infant's reaching; his principle of "dynamogeny," or effortfulness, suggests that motivational factors may explain why right lateralization is seen in some conditions but not in others.

Perhaps even more enduring are the questions that arose well before there were scientific tools to test and generate ideas. Thus, we still ask about the structural basis for lateralization although the basis has been moved from the blood supply—Aristotle's suggestion—to the brain. Furthermore, the nature–nurture issue survives in the sense that any structural basis for asymmetry will probably have a strong genetic basis. On the other hand, current thinking often specifies an interactive role for the environment in amplifying initial biases.

Conclusions

The chapters in Part II illustrate the proposition that the issues in the study of early lateralization have not changed dramatically in the past century, yet they also show that progress has been made in the conceptualization of these issues. Some of the old issues seen in these chapters concern the structural basis of asymmetry, the relation between language and manual behavior, and the contributions of nature and nurture. However, conceptualization of these issues is broader than before; the models embrace several levels of analysis, including structure, function, and a number of potential mediating processes. Stress is also placed on interaction between the various levels in these models. Thus both Peters (Chapter 8) and Young et al. (Chapter 7) suggest ways in which structural development affects lateralized behavior and how exercise of behavioral function, in turn, affects structural development. At the same time, both chapters postulate important roles for psychological processes ranging from attention to inhibition in the development of lateralization. This sort of multileveled view seems to show that the search for a single cause—whether it be nature, nurture, or one particular point of structural asymmetry—has given way to more complex analysis. This increasing sophistication is also seen in the way variables are defined at each level. For example, at the structural level, Peters (Chapter 8) considers lateralized concentrations of neurotransmitters as well as anatomical lateralization. At the behavioral level, the chapters by Young et al. (Chapter 7), Peters (Chapter 8), and Ramsay (Chapter 9) go beyond an anthropomorphic search for infant precursors of adult handedness in their concern with various features of early manual movement. Ramsay (Chapter 9) refines the old issue of the relation between manual and language development by examining stages in the motor production of prelanguage utterances and relating them to stages of hand use.

Although some levels of analysis in these models have empirical anchor points, some aspects of the models are highly speculative. Clear examples of speculation in the absence of evidence are the ideas about the evolutionary basis for asymmetry. On the one hand, Peters (Chapter 8) sees asymmetry as characteristic of the basic vertebrate brain and emphasizes the subcortical level, whereas Young et al. (Chapter 7) suggest the importance of face-to-face communication as an evolutionary force behind asymmetrical functioning and emphasize the cortical level. Here is a case in which speculation has led Young et al. (Chapter 7) and Peters (Chapter 8) to somewhat differing, but perhaps complementary, conclusions. This is a healthy sign; ideas have not given way to "barren" observation, and the two actually come together at some points.

Reference

Coryell, J. F., & Michel, G. F. (1978). How supine postural preferences of infants can contribute toward the development of handedness. *Infant Behavior and Development 1*, 245–257.

Neonatal Research

12

Neonatal Reflexes:
A Search for
Lateral Asymmetries[1]

SANDRA E. TREHUB
CARL M. CORTER
NANCY SHOSENBERG

Introduction

Numerous asymmetric motor responses have been noted in the early weeks of life. These include spontaneous head turning (Turkewitz, Gordon, & Birch, 1965), turning from aversive tactile or gustatory stimulation (Liederman & Kinsbourne, 1980a), tongue movement in response to somesthetic stimulation (Weiffenbach, 1972), eye movement in response to visual or auditory stimulation (Harris & MacFarlane, 1974; Turkewitz, Moreau, & Birch, 1966), rooting (Turkewitz et al., 1965), stepping (Peters & Petrie, 1979), arm movement (Stubbs & Irwin, 1933), grasp strength (Petrie & Peters, 1980), and grasp duration (Caplan & Kinsbourne, 1976; Petrie & Peters, 1980). Asymmetries in spontaneous postural preference have also been noted. Newborn infants in the supine position tend to spend most of their time with their heads oriented rightward (Casaer, 1979; Coryell & Michel, 1978; Gesell & Amatruda, 1945; Gesell & Ames, 1947; Gesell & Halverson, 1942; Michel & Goodwin, 1979; Turkewitz & Creighton, 1974; Turkewitz et al., 1965). This initial postural preference has been related to intrauterine birth position (Goodwin & Michel, 1981; Michel & Goodwin, 1979) and to later hand use (Coryell & Michel, 1978; Gesell & Ames, 1947; Goodwin & Michel, 1981).

Turkewitz and his associates (Hammer & Turkewitz, 1974; Turkewitz, 1980; Turkewitz et al., 1966; Turkewitz, Moreau, Birch, & Crystal, 1967;

[1]The preparation of this chapter and the research reported herein was assisted by grants from the March of Dimes Birth Defects Foundation and the Medical Research Council of Canada.

Turkewitz, Moreau, Davis, & Birch, 1969) have argued for the influence of asymmetric sensory input from the environment on lateral differences in responsiveness and posture. In contrast, Liederman and Kinsbourne (1980a, 1980b) have suggested that the left side of the brain predominates from birth in governing motoric behavior, resulting in a rightward motor bias.

In the psychological literature, these early asymmetries in movement, responsiveness, and posture are seen as a reflection of neurobehavioral organization (Liederman & Kinsbourne, 1980b; Petrie & Peters, 1980; Turkewitz & Birch, 1971). For example, Liederman and Kinsbourne (1980b) found lateral differences in neonatal head turning to be related to parental handedness. Accordingly, they claim that such lateral preferences, mediated by a dominant left hemisphere, are transmitted genetically. Moreover, they suggest that this neural organization may be a precursor of cerebral dominance for language (Liederman & Kinsbourne, 1980b, p. 582). From a somewhat different perspective, Turkewitz, Moreau, & Birch (1968) have argued that the *absence* of such asymmetries may signal neurobehavioral dysfunction. Indeed, they found early malfunctioning, as reflected in low (1–6) 1-min Apgar (Apgar & James, 1962) scores to be related to symmetrical rooting. In contrast, infants with higher initial Apgar scores rooted more to right than to left stimulation.

If asymmetric responses signal neurobehavioral integrity, then such responses should be observable in a wide range of motor behavior in normal neonates. Moreover, asymmetric responses should be more readily apparent in healthy term neonates than in prematurely born infants, who have a higher incidence of subsequent disorders that are presumed to be related to neurobehavioral dysfunction (e.g., language and reading: Caputo & Mandell, 1970; De Hirsch, Jansky, & Langford, 1964, 1966; Drillien, 1964; Eames, 1945; Ehrlich, Shapiro, Kimball, & Huttner, 1973; Kawi & Pasamanick, 1958; Rabinovitch, Bibace, & Caplan, 1961; Rubin, Rosenblatt, & Balow, 1973; Wiener, Rider, Oppel, & Harper, 1968). Current data, however limited, are consistent with this interpretation. Although premature infants show rightward postural preferences (Gardner, Lewkowicz, & Turkewitz, 1977), they do not show clear right head-turn preferences following release from a midline position (Gardner et al., 1977), nor do they show asymmetric rooting (Lewkowicz, Gardner, & Turkewitz, 1979). As late as the school years, prematurely born children have been found to have more deviations from the "normal" right eye and hand bias than children born at term (Eames, 1957).

Quite at odds with these perspectives from the psychological literature are those that emerge from the medical–clinical literature on neurological development in infancy (e.g., Andre-Thomas & Saint-Anne Dargassies, 1960; Beintema, 1968; Casaer, 1979; Prechtl, 1977; Saint-Anne Dargassies, 1977; Touwen, 1976). In marked contrast to the experimental psychologist, the pediatric neurologist views the *presence* of asymmetries in neonatal reflexes as a signal of neurological dysfunction, particularly of a hemisyndrome (e.g., Beintema, 1968; Prechtl, 1977). Furthermore, Prechtl (1977) describes the normal supine posture of the newborn as symmetrical; he labels as pathologically deviant "the head turned constantly toward one side and an asymmetrical posture [p. 20]." One clue to these divergent interpretations may be found in the contrasting focus of these investigators. The experimental psychologist seeks differences in the overall incidence of left and right responses in particular populations (e.g., full term, premature) or individuals, whereas the clinical neurologist searches out the few individuals who show lateral differences in the presence of specific reflexes or in the strength of these reflexes. Moreover, different realms of neonatal behavior are typically sampled—the neurologist focuses on standardized assessment of the primary reflexes and the psychologist favors tasks developed specifically for research.

Even when the same behaviors are sampled, differences in the method of response elicitation and scoring are likely to be substantial. For example, Turkewitz *et al.* (1965) elicited rooting by stimulating the perioral region with a camel's hair brush. This contrasts with the standard neurological procedure of stimulating the same facial region by stroking movements of the examiner's forefinger (Prechtl, 1977). Moreover, Turkewitz and his associates recorded turns only, whereas Prechtl rated the relative strength of the response (the vigor and extent of turning and the presence of grasping with the lips). Finally, Turkewitz *et al.* administered a predetermined number of trials or attempts on each side with each infant regardless of the response observed. This contrasts with the common clinical practice of terminating the trials once a good response has been seen at each locus of stimulation.

In our own research, we have been attempting to provide a partial bridge between the psychological and medical–clinical approaches. Our primary objective has been to provide further documentation of the presence or absence of lateral asymmetries in a number of behavioral responses by premature and full term infants in the early days of life. Our link with the neurological realm is via the inclusion of several primary reflexes or automatisms (Saint-Anne Dargassies, 1977) that comprise part of the neurological examination of the neonate and our use of carefully documented and widely accepted procedures for elicitation and scoring of these reflexes (Prechtl, 1977). Our point of contact with the psychological realm is via our focus on the relative incidence of right and left responses over a large number of elicitations. This focus contrasts with the typical clinical procedure of simply scoring the infant's best response on each side, without regard to the number of attempts or trials.

A further feature of our research is that it is longitudinal. Our premature infants are first seen at 33 weeks conceptional age; our term infants shortly after birth. We continue to see these infants through their first year and beyond, charting asymmetries in the appearance and disappearance of the primary reflexes, individual differences in such asymmetries, and relations between early asymmetries, if any, and later motor and language behavior. At the present time, data-gathering is nearly complete for the neonatal phase of the project, and our earliest participants are approaching 2 years of age. In this chapter, we will limit our presentation of methodology and data to the neonatal phase of the larger investigation.

Our expectation was that lateral asymmetries would be seen in a number of primary neonatal reflexes. If motor biases are genetically based (Liederman & Kinsbourne, 1980b), then such biases should be evident in a variety of inherited patterned movements or reflexes. Following the work of Turkewitz and his associates (Gardner *et al.*, 1977; Lewkowicz *et al.*, 1979; Turkewitz *et al.*, 1968), we also expected that premature infants would show less lateral asymmetry than full term infants. Finally, we expected that larger premature infants would show greater lateral differentiation than premature infants of lower birth-weight, who are at increased risk for later neurobehavioral disorders.

Method

We attempted to recruit 20 infants in each of three weight groups: normal (> 2500 gm), low (1500–2500 gm), and very low (1000–1499 gm). This report is based on a sample of 20 larger preterm infants (mean age at birth = 31.5 weeks, mean weight = 1707 gm), a sample of 20 smaller preterm infants (mean age at birth = 29.2 weeks, mean weight = 1251 gm) and a sample of 12 term infants (mean age at birth = 39.2 weeks, mean weight = 3380 gm). All infants were selected from those born in a major teaching hospital in Toronto, Ontario. Premature infants were included in the investigation only if they met the following criteria: (a) birth-weight appropriate for gestational age; (b) absence of physical malformations or congenital abnormalities; and (c) absence at 72 hr postnatal age of gross medical complications seriously compromising survival or normal cerebral functioning. Full term infants had to meet the following criteria: (a) gestational age greater than 37 weeks; (b) absence of physical malformations or serious medical complications; (c) spontaneous and noninduced delivery with low forceps or no forceps, and Apgar scores of 9 or 10 at 1 and 5 min, respectively. (It is interesting that advances in medical technology are making it increasingly difficult to satisfy this third criterion, hence our incomplete "normal" group.) Infants in the three weight groups were matched for sex, birth order, and socioeconomic status of the head of the household.

After extensive pilot testing, we constructed a test battery that included a number of primary reflexes and one additional response category (spontaneous head turn). The battery was administered in the hospital 3 days after birth for the full term infants and at 33, 34, 35, and 40 weeks gestational age for the premature infants. The test battery was administered again, in the infant's home, at 15 weeks following the expected date of delivery (i.e., at 55 weeks following conception). Whenever possible, each infant was tested twice (morning and afternoon) on each test day midway between feedings. Prior to testing, the infant was observed while sleeping, and his (or her) head orientation (right or left) was reversed for 10 min. The infant was then awakened. The examiners held the infant either upright with their hands under the infant's arms, or supine by supporting the whole body with their hands and forearms. They proceeded to rotate the infant through various planes for 10 to 30 min until the infant was awake and alert. Talking to the infants, obtaining eye contact, and undressing them were also part of the alerting procedure. This procedure was abbreviated for full term infants who could be brought to an awake–alert state more readily.

The order of evaluation of response categories in the first half of each session was as follows: rooting (left stimulation), plantar grasp (right), spontaneous head turn, palmar grasp (left), rooting (right), spontaneous head turn, arm recoil, rooting (left), crossed extensor (right), spontaneous head turn, lateral trunk incurvation (left), placing (right), stepping, and arm passage. For the remainder of the session, this order was repeated with the side of stimulation, where relevant, reversed.

Each reflex was elicited following Prechtl's (1977) protocol, and the scoring system was a modification of his system. Brief descriptions of all behavior categories and our scoring system follow:

Spontaneous Head Turn

Prestimulus state: 3 (eyes open, no movement); 4 (eyes open, gross movement); or 5 (crying). Position: supine, head midline, body symmetrical. The examiner supports the infant's head in midline for 5 sec with both hands. When the infant is not pressing its head to one side, the examiner gently releases the head. Direction of the first turn is noted.

Rooting (Cardinal Points)

Prestimulus state: 3, 4, or 5. Position: supine, head symmetrical in midline, infant's hands held above chest by the examiner. The perioral skin at the designated corner (right or left) of the mouth is tickled by the examiner's forefinger (five stroking movements). Responses: no response; 1 (lip movements on left or right side); 2 (weak turn to left or right side); or 3 (vigorous turn to left or right side).

Head Turn (Prone) and Arm Passage

Prestimulus state: 3 or 4. Position: prone, head centered and facing the examining surface with upper limbs extended along the trunk. Direction and latency of head turn and hand movement to face are noted.

Arm Recoil

Prestimulus state: 3 or 4. Position: supine, body symmetrical. The examiner passively extends both forearms simultaneously at elbow, then releases. Responses: none; 1 (slow, weak recoil of left and/or right arm); or 2 (quick, marked flexion in left and right arm).

Palmar Grasp

Prestimulus state: 3 or 4. Position: supine, body symmetrical, head midline, arms semiflexed. The examiner puts his or her index finger on the ulnar side of the designated (left or right) hand and gently presses the palm at the surface without touching the dorsal side of the infant's hand. Responses: no response; 1 (short, weak flexion); or 2 (strong, sustained flexion).

Stepping

Prestimulus state: 4. Position: as in placing response. The examiner keeps the infant upright and allows the soles of the feet to touch the examining surface. The examiner moves the infant forward to accompany any stepping. Responses: none; left or right initial step.

Placing

Prestimulus state: 4. Position: infants held upright with examiner's hands under their arms and around their chest, providing support for head and jaw. The examiner lifts infants so that the dorsal part of the designated foot lightly touches a protruding edge such as a table top. Responses: absent or present. The examiner records the number of trials to elicit a response on each side (with a maximum of five attempts).

Crossed Extensor

Prestimulus state: 3, 4, or 5. Position: supine, head centered in midline, legs semiflexed. The examiner passively extends designated (left or right) leg, pressing knee down, and, with a finger, stimulates the sole of this leg. Responses: none; flexion, extension; and/or adduction.

Plantar Grasp

Prestimulus state: 3, 4, or 5. Position: supine, head centered in midline, toes in resting position. The examiner presses thumb on ball of designated (left or right) foot. Responses: no response; 1 (weak and unsustained); or 2 (strong and sustained).

Lateral Trunk Incurvation (Galant)

Prestimulus state: 3, 4, or 5. Position: infant held by examiner's hand in prone suspension. The examiner draws his or her thumbnail along the designated (left or right) paravertebral line about 3 cm from midline down from shoulder to buttock. Responses: none; 1 (weak, short incurvation movement); or 2 (good incurvation of whole vertebral column).

Recording of responses by a second observer was not feasible since most of the testing was carried out in a busy hospital nursery. It is our impression, however, that the side of response was typically clear but that the degree or intensity of response was sometimes less clear.

Results and Discussion

The results from the reflex battery are organized in terms of responses involving the head (spontaneous head turning, rooting, and prone head turn), the arms and hands (arm passage, arm recoil, and palmar grasp), the legs and feet (stepping, placing, crossed extensor, and plantar grasp) and the torso (lateral trunk incurvation). Results are reported for each of the three groups of infants included in the design (the two preterm groups and the full term group). In some cases, data have been collapsed across the 33-, 34-, and 35-week observations, or across the two preterm categories when these were highly similar. Although the data were also examined in terms of the variables of sex and parental handedness, no positive results emerged, so these analyses are not reported.

Spontaneous Head Turning

The data from the 12 trials on a single day were summed for each preterm infant at the 33-, 34-, 35-, and 40-week postconceptional observations and for the full term infants at 40 weeks. The mean percentage of trials on which infants in the three groups turned right is given in Table 12.1.

The percentages are fairly close to the chance level of 50%, although they are marginally biased toward right responding. The rightward bias reached significance only in the larger preterm infants (1500–2500 gm) at

Table 12.1
Spontaneous Head Turning: Percentage of Right Turns Out of Total Turns

	Percentage of right turns			
Groups	33[a]	34	35	40
< 1500 gm	55	53	57	54
1500–2500 gm	60	50	58	59
> 2500 gm	—	—	—	55

[a]Conceptional age (in weeks).

the 33-week observation. In terms of individual infants in this group, 16 of the 20 infants directed more turns to the right than to the left ($p < .05$, by a two-tailed binomial test). If turning bias is defined by a more stringent criterion of two-thirds of the trials (i.e., 8 or more right turns out of 12), the bias is still evident for this group. According to this criterion, 9 infants demonstrated a right-turning bias, 2 infants had a left-turning bias ($p < .05$ by a one-tailed binomial test), and the remaining 9 infants did not show a strong bias in either direction.

There was little evidence of stability in the head-turning bias of individual infants across the four observation periods in either of the preterm groups. For example, if infants are defined by the stringent criterion above as right biased, left biased, and unbiased, then 12 of 20 infants in the larger preterm group changed category between 33 and 40 weeks. The same degree of instability was also seen across shorter periods such as 33–34 weeks, and even from the six trials in the morning to the six trials in the afternoon. Although it has been reported that the head-turning bias is stable among full term infants during the first week of life (e.g., Saling, 1979), we found no clear evidence of such stability when we compared responses in the morning and afternoon trials for our full term group.

The overall absence of dramatic head-turning preferences is consistent with Gardner et al.'s (1977) findings with premature infants but at odds with other reports of strong rightward biases in the self-initiated turns of full term infants (Saling, 1979; Turkewitz & Creighton, 1974; Turkewitz et al., 1965). However, significant biases in spontaneous head turning have been absent in much of the other work with term infants reported by Turkewitz and his associates (Moreau, Helfgott, Weinstein, & Milner, 1978; Turkewitz et al., 1967).

Rooting

Rooting includes a head-turning component but differs from spontaneous head turning in that it is elicited by lateralized stimulation. Nevertheless, the head-turning component of rooting also demonstrated the same marginal but nonsignificant rightward bias seen in spontaneous head turning. This general picture can be seen in the preterm groups when trials are summed across the 33-, 34-, and 35-week observations without regard to side of stimulation; 54% of all turns were to the right, and turns occurred on more than 97% of the trials. This same trend carried into the 40-week observation; 55% of turns were to the right, and turns occurred on 97% of the trials. The figures contrast with the 48% rightward responses and 40% head turning reported by Lewkowicz et al. (1979) for premature infants at 36–37 weeks gestational age. For our full term infants at 40 weeks, 58% of turns were to the right, and turns were observed on 91% of the trials. Across all three groups at 15 weeks (55 weeks conceptional age or 15 weeks corrected age for premature infants), a weak rightward bias was still evident—54% across all turns, although turning now occurred on only 27% of the trials.

Although we found marginally more ipsilateral turns to right stimulation than to left stimulation, ipsilateral turns were much more common than contralateral turns regardless of the side of stimulation. Summing across the early observations (33, 34, 35 weeks) of the preterm groups, 61% of all turning was ipsilateral in relation to the side of stimulation. This value agrees closely with that reported by Lewkowicz et al. (1979). At the 40-week observation, we found the percentage of ipsilateral turning to be 79% for the smaller preterm group, 74% for the larger preterm group, and 68% for the full term infants. Thus, we have some indication of a possible link between postnatal, as opposed to conceptional, age and the incidence of rooting, suggesting some effect of extrauterine experience.

This view differs markedly from Turkewitz and his associates, who report 93% ispilateral responding for full term infants (Turkewitz et al., 1968) versus 63% for premature infants (Lewkowicz et al., 1979). Lewkowicz et al. (1979) suggest the persistence of a more primitive tendency to turn away from stimulation in premature infants as well as in full term infants in poor physiologic condition. Accordingly, they argue that contralateral turning is likely to become laterally differentiated prior to ipsilateral turning. We found no evidence for such differentiation in contralateral turning in our premature or full term samples. There are, however, a number of sampling differences between their studies and ours. No selection criteria were reported for their premature sample except for birth at or before 37 weeks estimated gestational age. They do, however, report that 20% of the premature infants were below the weight norms for their gestational age. It is conceivable, then, that some of their premature infants had gross medical complications that might have altered their performance relative to a healthier premature sample. Indeed, 40% turning on stimulation trials (25% ipsilateral turning) compared to 97% turning in our premature sample may reflect, in part, such sampling differences. Furthermore, their requirement of responding within 1 sec of stimulus application contrasts with our response interval of 1 min (although the typical response time was 1–5 sec) and may have posed particular difficulties for their premature sample. The implications of these procedural differences can be seen in another study of rooting from their laboratory, in which 45% of stimulation trials resulted in head turning by full term infants (Turkewitz et al., 1969). Finally, most of the premature infants contributing to their comparison with term infants were at 36–37 weeks gestational age rather than 40 weeks.

Given the marginal right bias that we found in both head-turning responses, we looked at possible relations between the two. For example, would the percentage of spontaneous right turns be correlated with the percentage of right turning to ipsilateral (right) stimulation or to contralateral (left) stimulation? Correlations were computed on the basis of data from the early observations (33, 34, 35 weeks) of all 40 preterm infants. The percentage of spontaneous right turns bore no relation to the percentage of right turning to right stimulation ($r = .069$, $df = 38$, n.s.). Thus, infants do not have a generalized right-turning bias that spans self-initiated and right-stimulated trials. However, spontaneous right turns did correlate with right-turning to left stimulation ($r = .317$, $df = 38$, $p < .05$, two-tailed), suggesting the presence of a motor bias in unsuccessful rooters. Finally, we correlated the two types of right turning to stimulation: ipsilateral to right stimulation, and contralateral to left stimulation. These percentages were inversely correlated ($r = -.448$, $df = 38$, $p < .01$, two-tailed), indicating that the rooting reflex has some degree of bilateral integrity. In other words, the tendency to respond ipsilaterally, (i.e., appropriately) to stimulation on one side is positively related to the tendency to respond ipsilaterally to stimulation on the other side.

A possible link between rooting and neurological maturation or integrity has some support from our data. The average percentage of ipsilateral turns out of total turns increased from 61% in the early observations (33, 34, 35 weeks) to 77% in the 40-week observation of the preterm infants. Furthermore, the percentage of ipsilateral turns in the 33–35-week observations was associated with 1-min Apgar scores. We selected 1-min rather than 5- or 10-min Apgar scores for two principal reasons.First, the range of scores generally narrows considerably from initial to later tests. This may not mean that the early scores are unreliable, but that some difficulties that are initially apparent are soon masked or overcome. Second, Turkewitz et al. (1968) have reported relations between 1-min scores and asymmetries in rooting. When infants in our preterm groups were divided (arbitrarily) into those with scores of 7 or above and 6 or below, the high-Apgar group (12 infants) responded ipsilaterally on 70% of the trials, whereas the low-Apgar group (28 infants) responded ipsilaterally on only 52% of the trials. Thus, there is some relation between difficulties in evidence immediately following premature birth and the ability to root some weeks later, well before the time of normal delivery.

Successful rooting or ipsilateral turning to perioral stimulation seems to be governed both by postnatal age and by neurological integrity or maturity. When there is some degree of neurological disorganization, as reflected in low Apgar scores, a rightward motor bias may become apparent and override the tendency to respond in the direction of perioral stimulation.

Given the traditional focus on handedness in the psychological literature on lateralization, neonatal reflexes involving the arms and hands assume special interest and are now examined.

Head Turn (Prone) and Arm Passage

The head turn (prone) and arm passage reflex, which has not been evaluated previously for lateral asymmetries, takes the form of a head turn to one side followed by movement of the arm on the same side to the vicinity of the face. In contrast to spontaneous head turning and head turning to perioral stimulation, head turning from the prone position was not even marginally biased to the right. In fact, among the smaller preterm infants there was a nonsignificant trend toward left turning between 33 and 35 weeks, with head turning and arm raising on the right side in only 38.5% of all trials. In contrast, right turning for the larger preterm infants between 33 and 35 weeks was 48%, and rightward turning for all three groups of infants at 40 weeks was 50%. The absence of asymmetries in this reflex is in line with the general absence of prone position preferences in newborns (Michel & Goodwin, 1979).

Arm Recoil

The arm recoil reflex was elicited with slightly greater frequency in the left arm than the right, particularly in the early observations of the preterm sample. At 33 weeks gestational age, the smaller preterm infants recoiled their left arm on 77% of the trials, their right arm on 74%. At 34 weeks, these figures were 75% for the left arm, 73% for the right. At 35 weeks, the incidence was 92% for both arms and, at 40 weeks, 85% for the left arm, 83% for the right. For the larger preterm sample, recoil for the left and right arms was 86% and 79% at 33 weeks, 83% and 79%, respectively, at 34 weeks, 92% for both arms at 35 weeks, and 85% for both at 40 weeks. For the full term infants at 40 weeks, the left arm recoiled on 94% of the trials, the right arm on 93% of the trials.

The strength of recoil in the right and left arms differed in a minority of infants. For the combined preterm sample, asymmetric recoil strength was observed in 16 of 40 infants at 33 weeks, 7 infants at 34 weeks, 15 infants at 35 weeks, and 8 infants at 40 weeks. Of those infants with such asymmetries, the majority showed greater and more rapid flexion in the left arm: 81% at 33 weeks ($p < .05$ by a two-tailed binomial test), 57% at 34 weeks, 53% at 35 weeks, and 75% at 40 weeks. For the full term sample at 40 weeks, 4 infants differed in relative strength of recoil, with 3 showing greater flexion in the left arm.

There was little stability in the relative strength of recoil across observations. Greater stability was seen in the incidence of the response across sessions.

Palmar Grasp

Since the palmar grasp response was elicited on all trials, we focused on its strength, as rated by the examiner. Results for the two preterm groups were similar and were therefore combined. Across the four observation periods, fewer and fewer preterm infants were rated as differing in the strength of grasp in the two hands: 28 of 40 infants at 33 weeks, 25 at 34 weeks, 12 at 35 weeks, and 9 at 40 weeks. Of those infants showing asymmetric grasp strength, the majority were rated as grasping more strongly with the right hand: 68% at 33 weeks, 64% at 34 weeks, 83% at 35 weeks, and 67% at 40 weeks. This trend reached significance at 35 weeks ($p < .05$ by a two-tailed binomial test). In the full term group at 40 weeks, only 1 of 12 infants grasped more strongly with one hand. The side of stronger grasp was found to be unstable across the four observation periods.

Our findings failed to reveal the rather substantial differences in right-hand grasp previously reported for 17–105-day-old infants (Petrie & Peters, 1980). It should be noted, however, that our rating of palmar grasp, derived from Prechtl (1977), focused on arm as well as hand flexion, in contrast to Petrie and Peters (1980), who measured the application of force by the fingers. Moreover, Petrie and Peters did not control or record infants' head position. Thus, asymmetries in position may have influenced the strength of the grasp. Finally, their use of a nonstandard stimulus, a rubber bulb, resulted in a relatively brief grasp (2 sec) compared to the more sustained responses generally elicited in infants of that age.

Stepping

There was no evidence of lateral bias in the stepping reflex among the preterm infants. Across the four observation periods, these infants led with the right foot on 51% of the trials. On the other hand, the full term infants led with the left foot on 80% of the trials at 40 weeks, and 8 of 12 infants led with the left foot on the majority of the trials. Although the trend toward left-footedness is consistent with some views of right-handedness being associated with left-footedness (Von Bonin, 1962), it contrasts with recent reports of right-foot lead for infants 17–105 days of age (Peters & Petrie, 1979) and also for adults (Peters & Durding, 1979).

Placing

In the combined premature sample, the placing response was elicited within five trials in 72% of all attempts between 33 and 35 weeks and on 92% of the attempts at 40 weeks. The frequency of elicitation was similar in full term infants at 40 weeks. At 33 weeks, 32 of 40 premature infants placed within fewer trials for one foot compared to the other, but the bias favored the right foot in only 17 of these. At 34 weeks, 28 infants showed a bias, 12 for the right foot. At 35 weeks, 19 infants were biased, 11 in favor of the right foot. By 40 weeks, asymmetries were seen in 22 infants, with 10 biased rightward. In contrast, the full term sample showed marginal evidence for the bias, when evident, to be rightward. Only 6 of the 12 term infants showed such a bias, but 5 of the 6 favored the right foot. This trend could be seen in all three groups at a later test session administered at 15 weeks after the actual or expected date of delivery (for term or preterm infants, respectively). Approximately 33% of all infants showed a bias, and over 80% of the biases favored the right foot. There was no evidence of stability across observations either in terms of ease of elicitation or side of bias.

Crossed Extensor

The crossed extensor response was seen in most observations of the premature infants, but the form of the response differed at different ages. From 33 to 35 weeks, the typical response comprised flexion and extension, but, occasionally, only one of these occurred. By 40 weeks, the modal response was flexion, extension, and adduction, which occurred on 59% of the trials for the smaller preterm group, 78% for the larger preterm group, and 96% for the full term group. There were no lateral differences in the form or incidence of the response.

Plantar Grasp

The plantar grasp was elicited on all trials, and its vigor was generally equal in both feet. Some infants did show asymmetries, particularly in the early observations. Among the preterm infants, more vigorous responding in one foot was seen in 14 of 40 infants at 33 weeks, 15 infants at 34 weeks, 9 infants at 35 weeks, and 4 infants at 40 weeks. Similarly, 2 of the 12 full term infants differed in strength of plantar grasp. In these cases, however, there was no evidence of right–left bias, nor of stability across observations.

Lateral Trunk Incurvation

The lateral trunk incurvation response was elicited reliably on all trials, and no lateral differences in strength of incurvation were apparent.

Conclusion

Our findings with respect to lateral asymmetries can be summarized as follows. We found marginal, largely nonsignificant differences favoring rightward responses in the overall incidence of only 2 of the 10 responses evaluated: spontaneous head turning and rooting. Comparable differences favoring the incidence of leftward responses were seen in arm recoil and stepping reflexes. When differences in the relative strength or incidence of a response were seen in individual infants, the majority of these infants showed a rightward bias for spontaneous head turning, palmar grasp, and placing responses, and a leftward bias for arm recoil and stepping reflexes. When individual biases were seen, they were typically unstable across observation periods and tended to be more prominent for particular groups and age levels: spontaneous rightward (head) turning for larger preterm infants at 33 weeks, right-hand grasp at 35 weeks (combined preterm groups), rightward placing in full term infants, left recoil at 33 weeks (combined preterm groups), and left stepping in term infants.

The relatively low incidence of asymmetric responding in healthy, full term infants casts doubt on earlier interpretations of such asymmetries as indicative of superior neurobehavioral organization (Turkewitz & Birch, 1971). Moreover, the instability of lateral asymmetries across observation periods would preclude the diagnostic use of such asymmetries, even if they were apparent.

The marginal asymmetries in the incidence of supine head turning (with or without stimulation) offer weak support for earlier research with these responses (Liederman, 1977; Liederman & Kinsbourne, 1980a; Turkewitz & Creighton, 1974; Turkewitz et al., 1965, 1967). This may be related, in part, to our reduction of asymmetries in muscle tone and to somesthetic stimulation prior to testing (i.e., alterations of sleeping posture and our procedure of state preparation). There is much evidence to indicate a substantial contribution of prior posture to subsequent neonatal behavior (Casaer, 1979; Liederman & Kinsbourne, 1980a; Taft & Cohen,

1967; Turkewitz et al., 1967). Indeed, maintenance of the infant's head at midline for 15 min has been shown to reduce or even eliminate rightward biases in rooting and spontaneous head turning (Moreau et al., 1978; Turkewitz & Creighton, 1974; Turkewitz et al., 1969). Similarly, prior position differences may have contributed to the larger asymmetries in grasp strength observed by Petrie and Peters's (1980) infants compared to ours. It is less clear how postural differences could account for the right-foot lead in Peters and Petrie's (1979) infants and the left-foot lead in ours.

In any case, it is clear that the preprogrammed (rightward) motor bias postulated by Liederman and Kinsbourne (1980a, 1980b) cannot account for the weak and highly selective pattern of asymmetries seen in our sample. Although one might expect a less pronounced bias in unpracticed compared to highly practiced tasks (Annett, 1972), this could, at best, account for the minimal bias seen in some responses and its absence in others, but not for the leftward bias in arm recoil and stepping, for example. Fundamental differences between involuntary (reflexive) and voluntary motor responses may well be consistent with the absence of systematic asymmetries in the former domain and their presence or relatively greater strength in the latter. Developmental evaluation of such voluntary responses would necessarily be restricted to older infants and is, indeed, an integral part of our longitudinal investigation.

The cephalocaudal order of development (coupled with the notion of asymmetric function reflecting more mature neurobehavioral organization) leads to a prediction of asymmetries first in the head, then extending downward to the trunk, and finally to the extremities. This scheme is, however, inconsistent with our failure to find asymmetries in prone head turning together with their presence in placing. Consideration of the level of the nervous system that mediates these neonatal responses also fails to provide a coherent framework for organizing our results. Most of the responses tested have been localized to spinal segments, except for placing, which is believed to require cortical function (Taft & Cohen, 1967). It should be recalled that placing biases, however limited, were only seen in the full term sample at 40 weeks and in all three groups 15 weeks later.

We can only conclude that lateral asymmetry is not a general property of neonatal reflexive behavior, at least when the influence of postural asymmetry and state are controlled. Accordingly, the view that the left side of the brain predominates in the programming of motor output from birth (Liederman & Kinsbourne, 1980a, 1980b) must be rejected.

We must concede, however, that our control of prior posture introduced conditions that do not ordinarily prevail in the natural environment, where postural asymmetry (i.e., head rightward) is common. It is conceivable, then, that in the absence of postural manipulations, neonatal reflexive responding would be biased rightward. We are currently investigating this hypothesis.

Acknowledgments

Special thanks are due to K. Minde, D. McGregor, E. Hoskins, A. Shennan, and P. Fitzhardinge for their valuable support and advice. Thanks are also due to J. Stiefel for her help in data analysis.

References

André-Thomas, C. Y., & Saint-Anne Dargassies, S. (1960). *The neurological examination of the infant*. London: National Spastics Society.

Annett, M. (1972). Distribution of manual asymmetry. *British Journal of Psychology 63*, 434–458.

Apgar, V., & James, L. S. (1962). Further observations on the newborn scoring system. *American Journal of Diseases of Children 104*, 419.

Beintema, D. J. (1968). *A neurological study of newborn infants*. London: Heinemann.

Caplan, P., & Kinsbourne, M. (1976). Baby drops the rattle: Asymmetry of duration of grasp by infants. *Child Development 47*, 532–534.

Caputo, D. V., & Mandell, W. (1970). Consequences of low birth weight. *Developmental Psychology 3*, 363–383.

Casaer, P. (1979). *Postural behaviour in newborn infants*. Clinics in Developmental Medicine (No. 72). London: Heinemann.

Coryell, J. F., & Michel, F. (1978). How supine postural preferences of infants can contribute toward the development of handedness. *Infant Behavior and Development 1*, 245–257.

De Hirsch, K., Jansky, J. J., & Langford, W. S. (1964). The oral language performance of premature children and controls. *Journal of Speech and Hearing Disorders 29*, 60–69.

De Hirsch, K., Jansky, J. J., & Langford, W. S. (1966). Comparisons between prematurely and maturely born children at three age levels. *American Journal of Orthopsychiatry 36*, 616–628.

Drillien, C. M. (1964). *The growth and development of the prematurely born infant*. Baltimore, Maryland: Williams & Wilkins.

Eames, T. H. (1945). Comparison of children of premature and full term birth who fail in reading. *Journal of Educational Research 38*, 506–508.

Eames, T. H. (1957). Frequency of cerebral lateral dominance variations among school children of premature and full-term birth. *Journal of Pediatrics 51*, 300–302.

Ehrlich, C. H., Shapiro, E., Kimball, B. D., & Huttner, M. (1973). Communication skills in five-year-old children with high risk neonatal histories. *Journal of Speech and Hearing Research 16*, 522–529.

Gardner, J., Lewkowicz, D., & Turkewitz, G. (1977). Development of postural asymmetry in premature human infants. *Developmental Psychobiology 10*, 471–480.

Gesell, A., & Amatruda, C. S. (1945). *The embryology of behavior*. New York: Harper.

Gesell, A., & Ames, L. B. (1947). The development of handedness. *Journal of Genetic Psychology 70*, 155–175.

Gesell, A., & Halverson, H. (1942). The daily maturation of infant behavior: A cinema study of postures, movements, and laterality. *Journal of Genetic Psychology 61*, 3–32.

Goodwin, R. S., & Michel, G. F. (1981). Head orientation position during birth and in infant neonatal period, and hand preference at nineteen weeks. *Child Development 52*, 819–826.

Hammer, M., & Turkewitz, G. (1974). A sensory basis for the lateral difference in the newborn infant's response to somesthetic stimulation. *Journal of Experimental Child Psychology 18*, 304–312.

Harris, P., & MacFarlane, A. (1974). The growth of the effective visual field from birth to seven weeks. *Journal of Experimental Child Psychology 18*, 340–349.

Kawi, A. A., & Pasamanick, B. (1958). Association of factors in pregnancy with reading disorders in childhood. *American Medical Association 166*, 1420.

Lewkowicz, D., Gardner, J., & Turkewitz, G. (1979). Lateral differences and head turning responses to somesthetic stimulation in premature human infants. *Developmental Psychobiology 12*, 607–614.

Liederman, J. (1977). *Lateral head-turning asymmetries in human neonates: Hereditary, organismic, and environmental influences.* Unpublished doctoral dissertation, University of Rochester, New York.

Liederman, J., & Kinsbourne, M. (1980a). The mechanism of neonatal rightward bias: A sensory or motor asymmetry? *Infant Behavior and Development 3*, 223–238.

Liederman, J., & Kinsbourne, M. (1980b). Rightward motor bias in newborns depends upon parental right-handedness. *Neuropsychologia 18*, 579–584.

Michel, G. F., & Goodwin, R. (1979). Intrauterine birth position predicts newborn supine head position preferences. *Infant Behavior and Development 2*, 29–38.

Moreau, T., Helfgott, E., Weinstein, P., & Milner, P. (1978). Lateral differences in habituation of ipsilateral head-turning to repeated tactile stimulation in the human newborn. *Perceptual and Motor Skills 46*, 427–436.

Peters, M., & Durding, B. M. (1979). Footedness of left and right-handers. *American Journal of Psychology 92*, 133–142.

Peters, M., & Petrie, B. F. (1979). Functional asymmetries in the stepping reflex of human neonates. *Canadian Journal of Psychology 33*, 198–200.

Petrie, B. F., & Peters, M. (1980). Handedness: Left/right differences in intensity of grasp response and duration of rattle holding in infants. *Infant Behavior and Development 3*, 215–221.

Prechtl, H. F. R. (1977). *The neurological examination of the full term newborn infant* (2nd ed.). Clinics in Developmental Medicine (No. 27). London: Heinemann.

Rabinovitch, M. S., Bibace, R., & Caplan, H. (1961). Sequellae of prematurity: Psychological test findings. *Journal of the Canadian Medical Association 84*, 822–824.

Rubin, R. A., Rosenblatt, C., & Balow, B. (1973). Psychological and educational sequellae of prematurity. *Pediatrics 52*, 352–363.

Saint-Anne Dargassies, S. (1977). *Neurological development in the full-term and premature neonate.* Amsterdam: Excerpta Medica.

Saling, M. (1979). Lateral differentiation of the neonatal head turning response: A replication. *Journal of Genetic Psychology 135*, 307–308.

Stubbs, E. M., & Irwin, D. C. (1933). Laterality of limb movements of four newborn infants. *Child Development 4*, 358–359.

Taft, L. T., & Cohen, H. J. (1967). Neonatal and infant reflexology. In J. Hellmuth (Ed.), *Exceptional infant* (vol. 1). New York: Brunner/Mazel.

Touwen, B. (1976). *Neurological development in infancy.* Clinics in Developmental Medicine (No. 58). London: Heinemann.

Turkewitz, G. (1980). Mechanisms of a neonatal rightward turning bias: A reply to Liederman and Kinsbourne. *Infant Behavior and Development 3*, 239–244.

Turkewitz, G., & Birch, H. G. (1971). Neurobehavioral organization of the human newborn. In J. Hellmuth (Ed.), *Exceptional infant* (vol. 2). New York: Brunner/Mazel.

Turkewitz, G., & Creighton, S. (1974). Changes in lateral differentiation of head posture in the human neonate. *Developmental Psychobiology 8*, 85–89.

Turkewitz, G., Gordon, E. W., & Birch, H. G. (1965). Head turning in the neonate: Spontaneous patterns. *Journal of Genetic Psychology 107*, 143–158.

Turkewitz, G., Moreau, T., & Birch, H. G. (1966). Head position and receptor organization in the human neonate. *Journal of Experimental Child Psychology 4*, 169–177.

Turkewitz, G., Moreau, T., & Birch, H. G. (1968). Relation between birth condition and neuro-behavioral organization in the neonate. *Pediatric Research 2*, 243–249.

Turkewitz, G., Moreau, T., Birch, H. G., & Crystal, D. (1967). Relationship between prior head position and lateral differences in responsiveness to somesthetic stimulation in the human neonate. *Journal of Experimental Child Psychology 5*, 548–561.

Turkewitz, G., Moreau, T., Davis, L., & Birch, H. G. (1969). Factors affecting lateral differentiation in the human neonate. *Journal of Experimental Child Psychology 8*, 483–493.

Von Bonin, F. (1962). Anatomical asymmetries of the cerebral hemispheres. In V. B. Mountcastle (ed.), *Interhemispheric relations and cerebral dominance*. Baltimore, Maryland: Johns Hopkins Univ. Press.

Weiffenbach, J. M. (1972). Discrete elicited motions of the newborn's tongue. In J. F. Bosma (ed.), *Third symposium on oral sensation and perception*. Springfield, Illinois: Thomas.

Weiner, G., Rider, R. V., Oppel, W. C., & Harper, P. A. (1968). Correlates of low-birth-weight. Psychological status at eight to ten years of age. *Pediatric Research 2*, 110–118.

13

Familial Handedness, Prenatal Environmental Adversity, and Neonatal Lateral Organization

MICHAEL SALING

Introduction

Genetic variation and intrauterine adversity have been widely implicated as antecedents of the direction of manual specialization. But, despite a considerable research effort, a coherent view of the prenatal determination of hand preference has not emerged. Levy (1977) has pointed out that studies aimed at the elucidation of prenatal influences on manual specialization are likely to be frustrated by the fact that handedness is subject to various sociocultural pressures: Any prenatal influences on handedness that may exist are inevitably overlaid by years of transaction between lateral preferences and the postnatal environment.

An obvious strategy for minimizing postnatal environmental influences is to study the neonate. It has now been demonstrated in a number of laboratories that most supine newborns spontaneously prefer a right-sided head position (Casear, 1979; Gesell & Ames, 1950; Michel & Goodwin, 1979; Saling, 1979; Turkewitz & Creighton, 1974). This lateral bias is stable on an intraindividual level (Goodwin & Michel, 1981; Saling, 1979, 1982), is associated with infantile (Coryell & Michel, 1978; Goodwin & Michel, 1981) and perhaps childhood (Gesell & Ames, 1947) manual specialization, and does not seem to be primarily attributable to postnatal asymmetrical experiences produced by caretaker placement of the baby (Liederman, 1977; Prechtl, Fargel, Weinmann, & Bakker, 1979; Saling, 1982) or by maternal cradling preferences (Saling, 1978). Taken together, these findings suggest that neonatal asymmetry in head position is an appropriate model phenomenon for investigating the prenatal origins of human lateral organization.

MANUAL SPECIALIZATION
AND THE DEVELOPING BRAIN

Inheritance of the Neonatal Head-Position Bias

Liederman and Kinsbourne (1980) investigated the relationship between neonatal head-position preferences and parental handedness. Head position was biased toward the right in the offspring of two right-handed parents, but was essentially unbiased when one parent was left-handed, irrespective of whether the left-handed parent was the mother or the father. Liederman and Kinsbourne opted for a genetic explanation of their findings because of the minimal nature of parent–infant contact during the early neonatal period and because maternal and paternal handedness made equivalent contributions to the direction of the neonatal head-position bias.

Although there can be little objection to Liederman and Kinsbourne's explanation in terms of their findings, it seems to be incomplete in the light of recent speculations on the inheritance of lateral asymmetries. Morgan and Corballis (1978) have argued that the nuclear genome is incapable of coding left–right information because, in their opinion, there are no noncontroversial instances of the reversal of an asymmetry by the individual's own genome. Instead, they suggested that genome factors serve to "buffer the organism against influences, either systematic or accidental, that might otherwise result in asymmetries [Morgan & Corballis, 1978, p. 272]."

The idea of genetic buffering is central to the epigenetic theory of Waddington (1971) and its recent extension to the area of psychocognitive development (McCall, 1981; Piaget, 1971; Scarr-Salapatek, 1976). Waddington's model postulates that phenotypic variation is potentially unlimited, but in reality it is restricted by the canalization of development to a limited number of differentiated routes that are mutually interactive. In the normal course of events, a developmental process may deviate from its pathway as a result of external perturbations; however, it is returned to its former route by what Piaget (1971) refers to as "the interplay of coercive compensations [p. 19]." This self-stabilizing property of developmental pathways is brought about by coadapted gene complexes (Waddington, 1971). Variation in these gene complexes can reduce canalization, or buffering, to a point at which self-stabilization is lost, and environmental influences are able to produce a deviation that eventually consolidates into a new developmental pathway.

The generality of Morgan and Corballis's (1978) contention that genes are incapable of coding information about lateral asymmetries has been challenged (Levy, 1977; Nottebohm, 1979). Nevertheless, these objections do not militate against the possibility that, in some cases, genotypic variation does control the extent to which an asymmetry is buffered against environmental pressure, although it may not specify the direction of the asymmetry. In the data of Liederman and Kinsbourne (1980), parental sinistrality was associated with an *absence* of lateral bias in the offspring rather than a *reversal* of the usual rightward bias, suggesting that the genotypic variation implied by variations in parental handedness does not specify the direction of the lateral bias in neonatal head position, but that genotypic variation influences the degree of canalization in a developmental pathway that usually culminates in behavioral dextrality.

A strategy for assaying the nature of the genotypic influence on neonatal lateral organization is suggested by the properties of the buffered and unbuffered phenotype. One of the implications of genotypic buffering is what Scarr-Salapatek (1976) refers to as the "functional equivalence of environments [p. 66]." The strongly canalized phenotype is invariant over environments that have "distinctive, describable differences [p. 66]"; weak canalization allows the phenotype to vary with changes in the environment (Scarr-Salapatek, 1976). Therefore, an adequate empirical test of the genetic buffering hypothesis necessarily involves an examination of the *interactive* contributions of parental handedness and an effective, preferably prenatal, environmental pressure to the lateral bias in neonatal head position.

Intrauterine Adversity as an Effective Prenatal Environmental Influence

Turkewitz, Moreau, and Birch (1968) demonstrated that a suboptimal condition at birth, measured in terms of Apgar status, increases the probability that ipsilateral head turning to laterally applied perioral somaesthetic stimulation, a normally right-biased behavior, will be biased toward the left. Similarly, premature birth, which is associated with an elevated risk of perinatal brain damage, decreases the extent to which spontaneous neonatal head-position preferences are right-biased (Gardner, Lewkowicz, & Turkewitz, 1977; Kurtzberg, Vaughan, Daum, Grellong, Albin, & Rotkin, 1979). That this effect is the result of neurological nonoptimalities, rather than immaturity itself, is attested to by the findings of Prechtl *et al.* (1979): When preterm infants were selected on the basis of an undamaged nervous system, the rightward bias in spontaneous head position was present. Conversely, preterm infants with nervous system dysfunctions did not exhibit a rightward bias (cited by Prechtl *et al.*, 1979). Further evidence that could be interpreted as support for Prechtl's contention has been reported by Fox and Lewis (1982): These authors found that the rightward bias in the first head turn out of a midline position was absent in preterm infants with respiratory distress but was present in preterm infants with optimal neonatal histories. An absence of the rightward bias in spontaneous head position was also found in full term neonates who had three or more nonoptimal neurological signs during the first few days of postnatal life (Saling & Abkiewicz, n.d.). The effect of birth risk on head-position preferences may persist for at least six weeks after delivery (Liederman & Coryell, 1982).

The consistent finding of an association between birth stress and head-position biases supports the idea that variations in the adequacy of the intrauterine environment constitute a source of environmental pressure that is capable of disrupting neonatal behavioral dextrality.

A Hypothesis

It is suggested here that the association between parental handedness and the lateral bias in neonatal head position is mediated by differential birth-risk effects on the neonatal asymmetry in the offspring of two right-handed parents and the offspring of at least one left-handed parent. Specifically, birth stress will disrupt the neonatal rightward bias to a greater extent when one parent is left-handed than it will when both parents are right-handed. This interaction would tend to produce a difference in the degree of neonatal dextrality present in the two parental handedness groups as a purely secondary effect. In other words, parental sinistrality is associated with a reduction in the extent to which behavioral dextrality is buffered against the disruptive influence of early environmental pressure; genotypic variation specifies the degree of canalization, rather than the direction, of neonatal lateral differentiation.

Method

Subjects

The sample consisted of 210 consecutively born neonates. Any infant whose gestational age was less than 34 weeks, who was untestable for medical reasons, or who was the product of a multiple gestation was not included. The final sample consisted of 129 males and 81 females. The majority of infants (167) were born at term (38–42 weeks) and had a birth weight that was appropriate for gestational age (2300–3900 gm). Of the remaining infants, 27 were born at term but had nonoptimal birth weights, and 16 were born before term. Most of the preterm infants (15) had birth weights that were appropriate for their gestational age.

Procedure

Infants were observed on the third day of life, having been randomly assigned to a pre-, mid-, or postprandial observation period. The infants were observed in their own bassinets at normal room temperature.

Clothing likely to restrict movement was removed, and the bassinet was positioned so that lateralized light stimulation was eliminated. The infant was placed in a supine position and the observers then stationed themselves at the foot of the bassinet. By placing one hand on either side of the infant's head over the temporal region, the observers gently rotated the head to a midline position and maintained it there until it exerted no further lateral pressure on the restraining hands. The head was then released, and as soon as the infant made a perceptible turn out of the midline, a 5-min period of observation commenced. Head postures were recorded in terms of a seven-item taxonomy developed by the author (Saling, 1982). Essentially, this taxonomy provides for the coding of three rightward head positions, three leftward head positions, and a midline head position. The three rightward head positions, like the three leftward head positions, differ from one another in terms of the degree of head rotation involved. The most extreme lateral head posture is characterized by contact between an entire lateral surface of the infant's face and the substrate on which the infant is lying; the least extreme lateral head posture is characterized by an absence of contact between the infant's face or ear and the substrate. The lateral head posture lying between these extremes involves ear–substrate contact but no cheek–substrate contact. Each head posture spontaneously adopted by the infant was recorded, and the minute in which it occurred was noted. No attempt was made to interfere with the infant's ongoing behavioral state. In a pilot study carried out on 10 newborns, an interrater agreement of .80, measured in terms of Cohen's (1960) kappa coefficient, was obtained.

After the observation of head posture, the baby's mother was briefly interviewed in order to determine her preferred writing hand, and that of the baby's biological father. Thirty-seven newborns had at least one left-handed parent; of these, 16 had a left-handed mother, 17 had a left-handed father, and 4 had two left-handed parents.

The mother's hospital records were then perused, together with ratings requested from the medical staff, and birth risk was quantified by means of a 48-item birth-risk assessment scale derived in part from the Littman and Parmelee (1974a, 1974b) obstetric and postnatal complications scales. The scale yielded a birth-risk score that was defined as the sum of complications present in the infant's prenatal, intrapartum, and postnatal history. Of the 48 items comprising the birth-risk assessment, 10 items dealt with postnatal complications. In the present sample, birth-risk scores ranged from 1 to 16 with a mean score of 6.2 ($SD = 2.8$).

The inclusion of items relating to postnatal risk requires some explanation. The presence of clinical signs of an intrauterine anoxiogenic event does not necessarily imply a nonoptimal outcome for the infant (Brown, Purvis, Forfar, & Cockburn, 1974). However, when asphyxia, diagnosed by widely accepted clinical criteria, is followed by complications in the early neonatal period, its predictive significance is enhanced (Brown et al., 1974). Thus, although the present birth-risk assessment does not uniquely reflect intrauterine environmental variation, it does reflect the *adequacy* of the intrauterine environment with greater precision than it would if the postnatal factors were not included.

Results

Preliminary Exploration of the Data

The postural data were cast in the form of a 7 × 210 profile matrix, each entry representing the number of times a given posture was adopted by each neonate. The untransformed matrix was then subjected to a correspondence analysis (Hill, 1974) that may be regarded as a simultaneous R- and Q-mode principal components analysis for contingency data. The first, and most important, component extracted by this analysis scaled the seven postures along a continuum so that their positions along the continuum were monotically related to their positions in real space; the component was accordingly labeled *lateral differentiation* (LD), and constituted the dependent variable of the present study. The midline posture was associated with an LD scale value of .03; the most extreme rightward posture had an LD scale value of −1.00; and the most extreme leftward posture had an LD scale value of 1.87. The mean neonatal LD score was −.03 (SD = .86); as was expected, neonatal LD scores were significantly biased toward the negative (rightward) end of the scale (skewness = .82; $p < .01$).

In a previous study (Saling, 1982) carried out on 40 healthy full term neonates, neonatal LD scores were found to represent a stable individual characteristic (r = .80; p = .001) over the second and third postnatal days, despite considerable daily variations in behavioral state.

Main Findings

The contributions of parental handedness, that is, two right-handed parents versus at least one left-handed parent, neonatal sex, birth-risk score, and the Parental Handedness × Birth-Risk, and Sex × Birth-Risk interactions to neonatal LD scores were assessed by means of a linear multiple-regression analysis. Only interactions directly relevant to the genetic buffering hypothesis were investigated, as Cohen (1968, p. 438) suggested, because of the rapid loss of degrees of freedom with the inclusion of unnecessary terms in the regression equation.

The only significant contributor to neonatal LD was the interaction between parental handedness and birth risk, which increased the variance accounted for by the main effects from 1.06% to 6.55% [F (1, 205) = 12.08; $p < .01$]. The interaction was disordinal in nature and was the result of the following effects: In the offspring of two right-handed parents there was no relationship between birth risk and LD ($Y = -.02X + .04$; $r = -.06$; $p = .23$), however, in those newborns with a history of parental sinistrality, there was a positive relationship between birth risk and LD ($Y = .18X + -.95$; $r = .52$; $p < .001$), implying that increments in birth stress are linearly and continuously associated with an increasing leftward bias in neonatal position. Separate analyses indicated that the Parental Handedness × Birth-Risk interaction was primarily attributable to a *Paternal* Handedness × Birth-Risk interaction, which increased the variance accounted for by the main effects by 4.57% [F (1, 205) = 9.64; $p < .01$]. The Maternal Handedness × Birth-Risk interaction failed to increase the explained variation by a significant amount [F (1, 204) = 1.08].

Although the contribution of parental handedness to neonatal lateral differentiation was not significant, the mean LD score obtained by newborns with a history of parental sinistrality (.14; $SD = .92$) tended to be higher than the mean LD score obtained by the offspring of two right-handed parents ($-.06$; $SD = .84$).

Discussion

The present study failed to support Liederman and Kinsbourne's (1980) finding of a relationship between parental handedness and the neonatal lateral bias in head position. However, parental handedness did interact with birth risk to predict neonatal LD scores. In other words, LD was invariant over variations in birth risk, which in turn are predominantly attributable to variations in intrauterine environmental pressure, in babies with two right-handed parents, but varied positively with birth risk in babies with at least one left-handed parent. This finding offers little support for the idea that parental handedness primarily determines the direction of the neonatal behavioral asymmetry. The unequivocal involvement of paternal handedness in the interaction between parental handedness and birth risk suggests that the buffering effect is, in part at least, genetic. However, the present finding is compatible with the hypothesis that variations in parental handedness influence the extent to which neonatal lateral organization is buffered against the potentially disrupting effects of perinatal adversity.

To the extent that the lateral bias in neonatal head position can be regarded as a precursor of handedness, this conclusion must also apply to the prenatal determination of manual specialization. That handedness is a heritable trait is beyond doubt. However, the variance in offspring handedness that is directly and exclusively attributable to parental handedness, as opposed to environmental pressure, has not been determined. As Scarr-Salapatek (1976) has stated, "accounting for variability is logically prior to an adequate explanation of development [p. 60]." The findings of the present study point to the dangers of ignoring the Genotype × Environment interaction term in genetic analyses of lateral organization.

Although an elevated level of birth risk in a genetically susceptible population can be regarded as an important antecedent of behavioral sinistrality in the neonate, at least one other group of determinants of sinistrality must be recognized. In the present sample, a number of left-preferring newborns had two right-handed parents. The nature of the prenatal antecedents of this group's sinistrality is, as yet, unknown, but potentially includes genomic, cytoplasmic, or prenatal accidental variation. Whatever the exact identity of the latter group of determinants turns out to be, the classification of prenatal determinants of behavioral sinistrality suggested by the present findings is different from that suggested by current thought on the prenatal origins of the left handedness. According to Satz (1972) and Bishop (1980), for example, left handedness may be the result of either *natural* or *pathological* factors. The natural causes of left handedness encompass fundamental biological factors such as genetic variation, whereas the pathological causes include lateralized brain damage or dysfunction of perinatal origin. In terms of this view, natural left-handers have a history of familial sinistrality; however, because pathological left-handers are basically right-handed individuals who have changed their hand preferences following unilateral cerebral injury, they generally do not have a history of familial sinistrality. The present findings suggest that pathological left handedness is more likely to occur in individuals with left-handed relatives. This conflict further highlights the need for research on the interactive contributions of birth risk and parental handedness to manual specialization, preferably within a prospective methodological framework. It should be noted that infant data presented by Liederman and Coryell (1982) appear to support the Satz hypothesis: Perinatal insult was associated with a leftward head-position preference in the 6-week-old offspring of two right-handed parents, but not in offspring with at least one left-handed parent. However, this finding must be regarded with a degree of skepticism for two main reasons. First, a small sample of infants was observed (N = 32) of which only 9 had a left-handed parent. Second, there are likely to have been errors in the classification of infants into high- and low-birth-risk conditions: Liederman and Coryell considered a birth weight of about 4500 gm to be normal although this value actually extends into the high-risk range (see Lubchenco, 1976).

At the neonatal level, the present findings could be extended by investigating the interactive contribution of birth stress and parental handedness to head-position preferences in the offspring of two left-handed parents, and in twins. The genetic buffering hypothesis yields specific predictions for these groups. In the offspring of two left-handed parents it is expected that behavioral asymmetries are extremely poorly buffered and that the distribution of lateral preferences is influenced by the distribution of birth-risk scores to a greater extent than in the offspring of one left-handed parent. Twins constitute an interesting test case for the genetic buffering hypothesis because the second-born twin is often at greater risk than the first-born twin (Howard & Brown, 1970). It is predicted that the incidence of a leftward bias in head position will be greater in the second-born twin than in the first-born twin when at least one parent is left-handed: When both parents are right-handed, the twins are likely to be concordant for head-position preference.

Acknowledgments

The author wishes to express his appreciation to his supervisor, G. A. Doyle. The author also wishes to thank the superintendent of the Johannesburg Hospital for permission to carry out this study at the Queen Victoria Maternity Hospital, South Africa. The pediatric assistance of P. Jankowitz and C. Abkiewicz is gratefully acknowledged.

References

Bishop, D. V. M. (1980). Handedness, clumsiness, and cognitive ability. *Developmental Medicine and Child Neurology 22,* 569–579.

Brown, J. K., Purvis, R. J., Forfar, J. O., & Cockburn, F. (1974). Neurological aspects of perinatal asphyxia. *Developmental Medicine and Child Neurology 16,* 567–580.

Casaer, P. (1979). *Postural behaviour in newborn infants.* London: Heinemann.

Cohen, J. (1960). A coefficient of agreement for nominal scales. *Educational and Psychological Measurement 20,* 37–46.

Cohen, J. (1968). Multiple regression as a general data-analytic system. *Psychological Bulletin 70,* 426–443.

Coryell, J., & Michel, G. P. (1978). How supine postural preferences of infants can contribute towards the development of handedness. *Infant Behavior and Development 1,* 245–257.

Fox, N., & Lewis, M. (1982). Motor asymmetries in preterm infants: Effects of prematurity and illness. *Developmental Psychobiology 15,* 19–23.

Gardner, J., Lewkowicz, D., & Turkewitz, G. (1977). Development of postural asymmetry in premature human infants. *Developmental Psychobiology 10,* 471–480.

Gesell, A., & Ames, L. B. (1947). The development of handedness. *Journal of Genetic Psychology 70,* 155–175.

Gesell, A., & Ames, L. B. (1950). Tonic-neck reflex and symmetrotonic behavior. *Journal of Pediatrics 36,* 165–176.

Goodwin, R. S., & Michel, G. F. (1981). Head orientation position during birth and in infant neonatal period, and hand preference at nineteen weeks. *Child Development 52,* 819–826.

Hill, M. O. (1974). Correspondence analysis: A neglected multivariate technique. *Applied Statistics 23,* 340–354.

Howard, R. G., & Brown, A. M. (1970). Twinning: A marker for biological insults. *Child Development 41*, 519–530.

Kurtzberg, D., Vaughan, H. G., Daum, C., Grellong, B. A., Albin, S., & Rotkin, L. (1979). Neurobehavioral performance of low-birthweight infants at 40 weeks conceptional age: Comparison with normal full-term infants. *Developmental Medicine and Child Neurology 21*, 590–607.

Levy, J. (1977). The origins of lateral asymmetry. In S. Harnad, R. W. Doty, L. Goldstein, J. Jaynes, & G. Krauthamer (Eds.), *Lateralization in the nervous system.* New York: Academic Press.

Liederman, J. A. (1977). *Lateral head-turning asymmetries in human neonates: Hereditary, organismic, and environmental influences.* Unpublished doctoral dissertation, University of Rochester, New York.

Liederman, J. A., & Kinsbourne, M. (1980). Rightward motor bias in newborns depends upon parental right-handedness. *Neuropsychologia 18*, 579–584.

Liederman, J., & Coryell, J. (1982). The origin of left hand preference: Pathological and non-pathological influences. *Neuropsychologia 20*, 721–725.

Littman, B., & Parmelee, A. H. (1974a). *Manual for obstetrical complications scale.* Mental Retardation Center, Neuropsychiatric Institute, University of California at Los Angeles.

Littman, B., & Parmelee, A. H. (1974b). *Manual for postnatal complications scale.* Mental Retardation Center, Neuropsychiatric Institute, University of California at Los Angeles.

Lubchenco, L. O. (1976). *The high risk infant.* Philadelphia: Saunders.

McCall, R. B. (1981). Nature–nurture and the two realms of development: A proposed integration with respect to mental development. *Child Development 52*, 1–12.

Michel, G. F., & Goodwin, R. (1979). Intrauterine birth position predicts newborn supine head position preferences. *Infant Behavior and Development 2*, 29–38.

Morgan, M. J., & Corballis, M. C. (1978). On the biological basis of human laterality: II. The mechanisms of inheritance. *The Behavioral and Brain Sciences 2*, 270–277.

Nottebohm, F. (1979). Origins and mechanisms in the establishment of cerebral dominance. In M. S. Gazzaniga (Ed.), *Handbook of behavioral neurobiology* (vol. 2). New York: Plenum.

Piaget, J. (1971). *Biology and knowledge.* Chicago, Illinois: Univ. of Chicago Press.

Prechtl, H. F. R., Fargel, J. W., Weinmann, H. M., & Bakker, H. H. (1979). Postures, motility and respiration of low-risk pre-term infants. *Developmental Medicine and Child Neurology 21*, 3–27.

Saling, M. (1978). The significance of lateral compatibility for the early mother–infant relationship. *South African Journal of Psychology 8*, 35–42.

Saling, M. (1979). Lateral differentiation of the neonatal head turning response: A replication. *Journal of Genetic Psychology 135*, 307–308.

Saling, M. (1982). *Determinants of lateral organization in neonates.* Unpublished doctoral dissertation, University of the Witwatersrand, Johannesburg.

Saling, M., & Abkiewicz, C. (n.d.). *Neurological risk and head position preferences in newborns.* Unpublished data.

Satz, P. (1972). Pathological left-handedness: An explanatory model. *Cortex 8*, 121–125.

Scarr-Salapatek, S. (1976). Genetic determinants of infant development: An overstated case. In L. P. Lipsitt (Ed.), *Developmental psychobiology: The significance of infancy.* Hillsdale, New Jersey: Erlbaum.

Turkewitz, G., & Creighton, S. (1974). Changes in lateral differentiation of head posture in the human neonate. *Developmental Psychobiology 8*, 85–89.

Turkewitz, G., Moreau, T., & Birch, H. G. (1968). Relation between birth condition and neuro-behavioral organization in the neonate. *Pediatric Research 2*, 243–249.

Waddington, C. H. (1971). Concepts of development. In E. Tobach, L. R. Aronson, & E. Shaw (Eds.), *The biopsychology of development.* New York: Academic Press.

Postural Orientation in Human Infants: Changes from Birth to Three Months[1]

LAUREN JULIUS HARRIS
HIRAM E. FITZGERALD

Introduction

After nearly a century of research, a strong consensus has emerged that recognizes the fundamental biological character of lateralization of cortical function in human beings, of which the phenomenon of human handedness is the most public manifestation. What is less certain is our understanding of when and how this specialization is expressed in early development. Nearly all of the early empirical investigations were of very short-term longitudinal design, typically evaluated only a single infant, and sometimes (especially the baby biographies) employed methods of questionable sensitivity (see review in Harris, Chapter 10, this volume). Although there has been enormous improvement in methodology over the last few decades, most new research continues to be of cross-sectional or very short-term longitudinal design and to concentrate on a very small number of measures of laterality. Thus, we think it fair to say that, even today, there is insufficient information about how the expression of a full range of lateral differences, including hand use, might develop over time in individual infants.

In one sense, of course, the developmental outcome is known, or highly predictable, merely on the basis of family characteristics and base frequencies. That is, studies of the relationship between parental and child handedness indicate that children whose parents are right-handed (the vast majority in the population) will themselves be right-handed with a

[1]Parts of this report were presented at the First Biennial Meetings of the Merrill Palmer Society, Detroit, Michigan, May, 1982.

MANUAL SPECIALIZATION
AND THE DEVELOPING BRAIN

very high probability. When we say that there is insufficient information about development, what we mean is that we still have insufficient knowledge about the progress of this development over the formative early months. For instance, when does the expected right-hand preference first start to be expressed? How regular or continuous (or, as the case may be, discontinuous) is its course of development? Is regular use of the right hand preceded by a transient period of left-hand preference, as some early reports suggested? If so, does this represent a shift in cerebral control? Is later handedness reliably foreshadowed by asymmetries in other behaviors, for example, by early postural asymmetries? Finally, even accepting the essential biological character of handedness, might the development of lateral preference, culminating in true handedness, also be encouraged by the parents themselves, through their interactions with the child in play, feeding, and other everyday actions?

Infant Motor Skills Project

To try to answer some of these questions, we are studying a broad range of measures of lateral differentiation of function through the first 18 months of life. We chose this period because it marks the first appearance of many important motor skills, so that, by the end of this time, we could expect the infants to show lateral differences in some reasonably clear form. In this chapter, we would like to describe the study in general terms and then report some preliminary findings for two of the early measures.

Testing Periods

Our testing protocol calls for testing at 10 ages: within 3 days after birth (in hospital), at 14 days, and at 1, 2, 3, 6, 9, 12, 15, and 18 months of age. We chose these ages for both theoretical and practical reasons. We wanted to test frequently during the first 3 months because infant behavior changes so rapidly during this period and because one of our major interests was in studying possible early precursors of later hand differences.

Data Being Obtained

Our measures fall into several major categories: information on the family and the home environment, handedness of other family members, infant behaviors, and, finally, behaviors shown by the parents and the infant together.

FAMILY AND ENVIRONMENTAL MEASURES

Family demographic information (parental age, educational background, attendance at prenatal training programs, and the like) is obtained during a prenatal interview. At this time, we also obtain information through questionnaires about the parents' handedness and the handedness of other family members (including grandparents, parental siblings, and any other children in the family).

Home Environment Scale. Home environment measures are taken on every home visit throughout the entire study. In such measures, we hope to find additional clues for understanding any large discontinuities that may occur in individual infants' motor skill development or any differences between infants. So these measures include such things as the size and layout of the home, the number of people at home with whom the infant might interact, and the number and kinds of manipulatable toys available.

INFANT MEASURES

The infant measures fall into several categories and are administered at different times where appropriate.

Brazelton Test. To assess the infant's general physical status, we administer a Brazelton Newborn examination (1973) in the hospital and, as a reliability measure, at 1 month of age. We also obtain prenatal and perinatal hospital records on every infant.

Test of Laterality. The measures we have chosen as potential indices of laterality include postural orientation, stepping reflex, and, later, the infant's first steps and a variety of direct measures of hand use, very simple measures for the early months, and then progressively more complex measures as the baby grows older. The simpler measures include the duration of grasp of a wood barbell placed in one hand or the other, or in both hands at once (a task that we administer until about 6 months, at which time we have discovered that the baby is more likely to throw the barbell at us than to hold it in his hand); and various measures of reaching, either for a single object such as a yellow ball on a spring placed at the infant's midline, or for pairs of objects, one placed to the infant's left, one to the right.

For the older infant, we are assessing the hand used for such tasks as scribbling with a crayon, for feeding (both with the fingers and with utensils), and for the manipulation of complex toys where bimanual manipulation and coordination are required. For example, we show the baby a styrofoam ball in a bottle, demonstrate how to remove the ball, and then look to see which hand the baby uses to hold the bottle, which hand to reach inside to retrieve the ball.

SUBJECTS

Thus far, 37 infants and their families are enrolled in the project, all of whom are from the greater Lansing (Michigan) area. The parents have been recruited largely through the Michigan State University Clinical Center and prenatal clinics of Lansing-area hospitals. All of the pregnancies and births were normal and without any medical complications, as judged by hospital medical records; and all of the 37 infants (22 boys, 15 girls) were healthy and normal according to hospital records, Apgar scores (9 or above; Apgar & James, 1962), and the Brazelton newborn and 1-month evaluations.

We had been tempted to confine our study to FS− infants (no history of familial sinistrality), not only because they are more numerous, but because they are more likely to be homogeneous in cerebral organization than FS+ individuals (e.g., Hécaen & Sauguet, 1971). Nevertheless, we are not aware of any study that traces the expression of hand preference over this period of time in FS+ infants, so we are working to include at least a small number of FS+ infants in our sample. So far, in 29 of the 37 families, both parents and all other close biological relatives are right-handed; in the remaining 8 families, at least one parent is left-handed.

Postural Orientation, Birth to Three Months

For reasons of space, we shall confine our attention in this chapter to the postural-orientation measures, that is, the direction of the head while the infant lies supine.

That human beings show a preference for lying to one side more than the other has long been noted. Aristotle remarked on this, as did several nineteenth century writers such as Delaunay (1874) and Edouard Seguin (1875/1880). What is more, the consensus was that the preference was to lie on the right side rather than the left (see Harris, Chapter 10, this volume).

At least with respect to infants, the question of postural orientation has once again begun to attract interest, and the result has been ample corroboration of the early, largely anecdotal, reports. For instance, in 1938, Gesell noted, in reference to his investigations of the tonic neck reflex, that infants lie in the head-right position about 70–80% of the time. In 1965, Turkewitz, Gordon, and Birch reported that, in a sample of 20 newborn infants, 17 infants spontaneously oriented their heads predominantly to the right of midline while lying supine. In the same article, Turkewitz et al. also reported observations of spontaneous head position in several hundred other newborns. Only 3 infants were observed lying with their heads to the left. In 1971, Turkewitz and Birch reported that, of over 3000 observations made of 100 newborns lying supine, 88% had head-right positions, 2.8% midline positions, and 9.2% head-left positions. Turkewitz and Birch (1971) also found that the head-right posture appeared after the infants' heads had been held in midline and then released. With 2- and 3-day-olds, the head-right position was maintained 75% of the time during a 15-min observation period.

Given the approximate match between the proportion of neonates reported to show head-right preferences and the proportion of right-handers in the adult population, the question naturally arises whether this early postural preference is related to hand preference in later development. Among the early writers, many thought it was, although they disagreed about the nature of the relationship. Some argued that sleeping on the right side caused right handedness; others argued that handedness was the prior condition, that is, that we lie on the right side because we are right-handed. Neither group, however, subjected their views to empirical test. Among more recent authors, Gesell and Ames (1947) addressed this question and went on to make some strong claims that early head position predicted handedness in later childhood, or, to be more exact, that the "earliest manifestations of human handedness are in some way bound up with the phenomenon of the [asymmetry of the] tonic neck reflex [p. 171]." Gesell and Ames did not suggest the precise means whereby this link could be established, but if the later hand-preference measure were, say, reaching for a target, such an outcome would not be unreasonable to contemplate if we think of the head-turn preference as a manifestation of a basic, selective, orienting response involving inspection of a stimulus before approaching or withdrawing from it. Coryell and Michel (1978) have reported evidence consistent with this expectation. They found that when newborn infants were in the head-right position, the right hand was the hand more likely to be in the infant's field of view, and they went on to show that the hand more frequently in the field of view, whether left or right, was more likely to be used in a visually elicited reaching task when the infant was 3 months old. Coryell and Michel (1978) therefore suggested that handedness may arise from asymmetrical postural preference during early infancy, which "biases visual experience of the hands, giving one hand an advantage in eye–hand coordination tasks [p. 245]." We perhaps can recognize in this idea some continuity with an early proposal by Stevens (1908; see also Harris, Chapter 10, this volume) about the effects of eye movements on hand and arm movements in "left-" and "right-hemisphered" infants.

In our own research, we are looking at postural orientation in two different ways—first, the head position assumed by the infant after it is released from being held at midline and to either side (hereafter, *head orientation*); second, the head position that the infant has spontaneously assumed when it is inspected in its crib at various times during the day (hereafter, *spontaneous head position*). Because of the unobtrusive nature of this second measure in contrast to the "hands-on" method of the first measure, we saw an opportunity to expand our behavior sample well beyond what would have been possible on our home visits by asking the parents themselves to make the observations. All the parents readily agreed to this request.

In both instances, what we are trying to find out is, are the right-sided biases noted by others during the newborn period apparent in our sample too, and do the postural biases persist, at least through the first 3 months? Ultimately, we hope to find out to what extent, if any, these measures prove to be related to hand preference not only for reaching in early infancy, but also for later-developing hand-use skills.

Head Orientation after Holding

METHOD

The procedure that we are following for the measure of head orientation after holding is similar to that used by Goodwin and Michel (1981). Each baby is tested while lying supine with the experimenter positioned behind the infant. In the hospital, the infant typically is tested while in the bassinet, but sometimes at the foot of the mother's bed. In the home the infant is placed on a blanket on the floor. In all instances, in order to reduce potential biases, the mother and any other persons present are instructed to remain out of the infant's range of vision wherever the infant's head is positioned or wherever it may move when released.

We hold the infant's head in a midline position for 60 sec and then release it. At that moment, an observer, standing out of view of the infant at the foot end, records the infant's head orientation onto a coded form every 6 sec over the next 1 min, for a total of 10 observations. A stopwatch is used to time the behavior-sampling intervals.

Head orientation is being scored for three positions: in the infant's midline (nose–chin position between the right- and left-nipple lines), to the right (nose–chin position to right of right-nipple line), and to the left (nose–chin position to left of left-nipple line).

Immediately following the midline hold and observation period, we make three more 60-sec holds and observations in the following order: with the infant's head held to the left (so that the ear touches the bed or blanket), with the head held to the right, and finally a repetition of the midline condition. This procedure yields 40 observations per infant at each age. Under ideal testing conditions, the entire procedure is completed in just over 8 min.

The first test is made in the mother's hospital room when the infant is between 2 and 3 days old. All other observations are made in the family home at 14 days, 1 month, 2 months, and 3 months of age. Our original plan had been to make this observation at 6 months as well, but we have discovered that, by this time, most of the babies, after release, had begun to roll over—sometimes literally out of the video picture. All the home visits, but not the hospital visit, are videotaped.

RESULTS

Thus far, of our total sample of 37 infants, we have data through the third month on 23 of our 29 FS− infants and 5 of the 8 FS+ infants. Since we will not be completing detailed analyses of the results until our final sample is in, this chapter consists mostly of descriptive analyses of such trends and modal patterns as we think we are seeing in the data at this time.

We also note that, at this time, our data base consists of the written observation records made at the time of testing rather than analyses from the videotape records. After testing is completed with our full sample, we shall be making more detailed time-series analyses of the entire 60-sec observation period from the videotapes. Among other things, this will help us to determine whether such factors as changes in the infant's state are influencing the expression of lateralized functioning.

Finally, in this chapter, we shall confine our attention to the FS− infants, since our data set for FS+ infants is still so small. We can report, however, that preliminary examination of the scores for the FS+ infants fails to reveal any differences from the other subjects.

Modal Patterns across All Four Trials (Holds) across Age. The first question we have asked is, are any modal patterns emerging across the 3-month testing period that are consistent with a picture of a motor bias to the right as reported for the *newborn* period in earlier studies? The data obtained to date are summarized in Figure 14.1 for all five testing periods.

Figure 14.1*a* shows group data for the hospital observation period. Along the horizontal axis are the group scores for the 10 observations recorded during each of the 1-min periods. On the left are head-orientation observations in midline hold, followed by left hold, then right, and again the midline condition. The circles connected by the horizontal lines represent the mean score for each observation, and the vertical bars represent the variance around that mean. High scores indicate a trend for the infant's head to turn to the left, low scores to the right, and a score near the center indicates a tendency for the head to be in the midline. Thus, during the hospital visit, for the 60-sec observation period after positioning the head in midline, the trend is to *keep* the head in midline, with perhaps a slight bias to the right. After positioning the head to the left, infants tend to remain in the left position, and likewise to remain in the right position after holding the head to the right. Finally, after the second midline hold, the infants once again tend to remain in the midline position, again with a slight trend to the right. These trends seem to have persisted throughout the four subsequent testing periods to 3 months of age (see Figures 14.1*b*–14.1*e*).

Thus far, from these group scores, we do not see any very clear indications of a rightward bias in this group of babies. Rather, the initial position in which the infant's head is held tends to bias the direction of the head in the subsequent observation period.

Individual Patterns of Scores. Although the group scores suggest that the initial head position is the major influence on subsequent head direc-

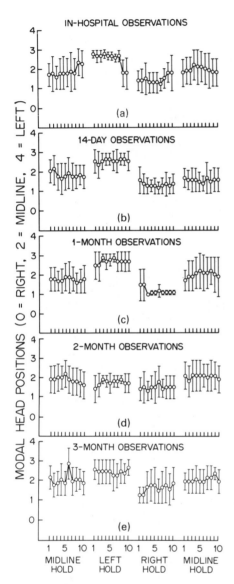

Figure 14.1. FS− infants' (no familial sinistrality; N = 23) modal head positions on each of 10 observations (one observation/6 sec) recorded during each of the 1-min observation periods following head-holding. Shown are scores for five different observation periods: (a) in hospital; (b) 14 days; (c) 1 month; (d) 2 months; and (e) 3 months. A score of zero indicates that the modal head position was to the right; 2 = head at midline; 4 = head to left. Circles represent the mean score for each observation; vertical bars represent the variance around that mean.

tion, inspection of Figure 14.1 also indicates a good deal of variability around the mean scores at every age. The question thus arises, to what extent may subgroups of infants depart significantly from these patterns in the group data? In formulating this question, we also were guided by the impressions of highly idiosyncratic and changeable patterns of development gained from some of the very early baby biography data mentioned earlier.

We have begun to tackle the problem of identifying different patterns of scores in several different ways. First, for each 60-sec trial, we have calculated the percentage of the 10 observations in which the infant turned its head in one of the three positions: left, midline, or right. From this percentage, we derived a statistic that seemed to reasonably represent an infant's modal, or most typical, head position after each initial hold condition. By this means, three subgroups have appeared.

In one subgroup are infants who appear to be extremely variable from one test session to the next. These infants typically shift over trials and over test sessions from one lateral position to the other. Another subgroup consists of infants who show little change over time, but rather keep their heads turned in the direction of initial positioning. These two subgroups are not necessarily independent. For instance, infant No. 14, whose scores are summarized in Figure 14.2, exemplifies both kinds of tendencies, but for different parts of the task.

Along the horizontal axis of each graph are the infants' ages when the observations were made; along the vertical axis, the plotted statistic represents the modal head position, where a high score indicates that the left direction best exemplifies the infant's head position after release, a low score the right direction, and a middle score either a midline preference or an equal shifting between left and right. For most infants, it is the former; that is, the midline is the modal position. We see the radical shifts in the first midline-hold condition but complete stability after the left and right holds.

Still another subgroup of infants show what appear to be neither extreme variability nor extreme confinement to the position in which they had been held. Rather, they show what we have decided might best be described as a decrease in lateral preference over age. This subgroup also

Figure 14.2. Subject No. 14: Modal head position during 60-sec observation period following each of the four head-hold trials (a–d) during each of five testing periods (in hospital, 14 days, 1 month, 2 months, 3 months). A high score indicates that the left direction best exemplifies the infant's head position after release; a low score, the right direction; a middle score, either the midline or an equal shifting between left and right. (a) First midline condition; (b) left condition; (c) right condition; (d) second midline condition.

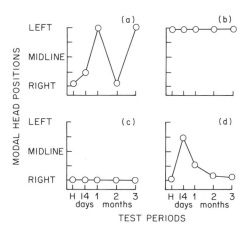

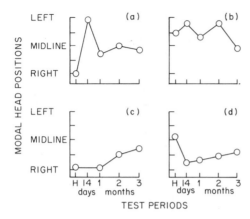

Figure 14.3. *Subject No. 25: Modal head position during 60-sec observation period following each of the four head-hold trials (a–d) during each of five testing periods (in hospital, 14 days, 1 month, 2 months, 3 months). A high score indicates that the left direction best exemplifies the infant's head position after release; a low score, the right direction; a middle score, either the midline or an equal shifting between left and right. (a) First midline; (b) left; (c) right; (d) second midline.*

includes the largest number of infants in the sample. Figure 14.3 illustrates this pattern for one infant, No. 25.

For infant No. 25, for the first midline-hold condition, the preferential head position has shifted from a strong bias to the right during the hospital visit to a strong bias to the left during the 14-day visit, after which there was no noticeable lateral preference. When this infant's head was held either to the left or to the right, the head tended to remain in that position during the early test periods but, like the results after the first midline hold, it shifted with age toward the midline position. For the second midline hold, which followed the right-hold condition, there seems to be some continuing preference for the right position.

In another infant, subject No. 5, whose scores are summarized in Figure 14.4, we can see something of this same tendency to shift away from the lateral pattern at the youngest ages toward the midline position at older ages. As we said, this is the most common pattern. The number of times we have found trends for decreasing lateral preference is greater than instances of increasing lateral preference by a ratio of 10:1. In other words, where there was a change, it is far more likely to be toward *decreasing* rather than toward *increasing* lateral preference.

First Turn from Midline after Initial Midline Positioning. Having found both in the group and individual scores only a slight rightward bias and a strong influence of initial head positioning at the youngest ages, we decided to consider only the *first* turn to either side from the midline after the first midline hold. Our thinking here is that the first turn after initial midline positioning of the head might more faithfully represent any *original* head-position bias that the infants might have. This, in fact, is the measure that Turkewitz used in some of his earlier studies of neonates (Turkewitz et al., 1965).

For the 1-min observation period after the first midline hold ended, we

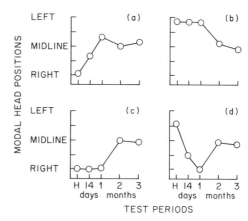

Figure 14.4. Subject No. 5: Modal head position during 60-sec observation period following each of the four head-hold trials (a–d) during each of five testing periods (in hospital, 14 days, 1 month, 2 months, 3 months). A high score indicates that the left direction best exemplifies the infant's head position after release; a low score, the right direction; a middle score, either the midline or an equal shifting between left and right. (a) First midline; (b) left; (c) right; (d) second midline.

therefore have noted which infants moved out of midline position during at least one of the ten observations and then simply recorded whether the first such occasion had been a move to the left or to the right. The results are summarized in the left half of Figure 14.5. Again, along the horizontal axis, the observation periods are listed for the five testing periods from hospital to 3 months of age. On the vertical axis, we show the percentage of individual infants in the sample who moved their heads out of midline, and then, among those infants, the percentage for whom the movement was to the right, and to the left.

For the hospital visit, when the infants were between 2 and 4 days of age, 22 of the 23 infants (96%) moved out of midline, of whom 19 (86%)

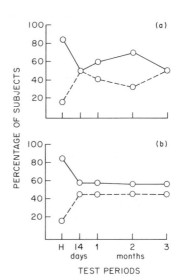

Figure 14.5. Direction of first observed head-turn from midline after (a) first and (b) second midline holds during each of the testing periods (in hospital, 14 days, 1 month, 2 months, 3 months). (Right = solid line; left = dashed line).

moved to the right, and 3 (14%) to the left (p < .001, binomial test). However, by 14 days (during the first home visit), as many babies moved to the left as to the right; by 1 month, the rightward bias is again in evidence, although less strongly than in the hospital; at 2 months, the rightward bias continues to increase; but then, at 3 months, the finding of "no differences" seen at 14 days has reappeared. The hospital data for the second midline hold (bottom half of Figure 14.5) are almost identical.

In summary, although we see evidence from all our data of an initial rightward bias (i.e., during the hospital visit), this initial bias apparently does not persist or become strengthened or consolidated over the first 3 months. Since, as we said, we expect nearly all of our FS− infants to become right-handed at least by early childhood, if not by 18 months, it becomes difficult, at least from these preliminary analyses, to make the case that postural asymmetry during the first 3 months is a first stage in a *linear* series of events culminating in established handedness. That it is a precursor of some kind seems clear enough given the in-hospital data, and also given Goodwin and Michel's (1981) findings, but the actual route to later handedness may not directly involve head turning beyond the youngest age periods. In other words, it may be that over the early months, the relative importance of head position for later hand preference declines, and that other behaviors take its place. The predictive validity of head-position measures thus might be found to vary as a function of the age at which they are made and, by implication, of the changing maturational status of the infant.

Spontaneous Head Position

The focus of our first measure is on the infant's head orientation after its head has been held in one position by the experimenter. As we have seen, preliminary evidence from that measure indicates an initial rightward bias, but there is no indication that this bias persists or becomes strengthened over the next 3 months. Rather, we are impressed with what seems to be, for the largest number of infants, actually a decrease in the strength or consistency of lateral position preference over age. We were interested, then, to see to what extent, if any, the same trends found with that experimental manipulation would be repeated in the parents' free observations of the infants' own head positions at rest.

METHOD

During the prenatal interview, parents received an explanation of the recording procedures. Written and oral explanations were repeated at the in-hospital testing period. The form used to record data contained stylized line drawings of supine and prone infants shown in midline, right, and left head positions. The resulting drawings appeared at the top of separate columns in which parents were to mark their observations. Thus, parents simply had to match their infant's head position to one of the drawings and to enter a check mark in the appropriate box on the data sheet. Observations were made twice daily for 6 days immediately following each research staff visit. In other words, parents recorded head-position data for the 6 days following the in-hospital visit, 6 days following the 14-day home visit, and so on through the 1-month, 2-month, and 3-month visits. In an effort to enhance the representativeness of the behavior position, we asked parents to make one observation in the morning and one observation in the afternoon or early evening. They also were asked to wait at least 30 min after placing their infant before making an observation. Finally, parents recorded infant state, prandial period, and whether the infant was prone or supine. On each home visit, we reviewed the procedure with parents in an effort to assure consistent data-collection practices. No parent expressed any difficulty in making these observations.

RESULTS

The morning and afternoon records proved to be essentially identical, so the scores have been combined in Figure 14.6, which summarizes infant head-position data for the FS− infants for the six observations made in the week following the staff visit for each of five age periods: in hospital, 14 days, 1 month, 2 months, and 3 months. In Figure 14.6, 21 of

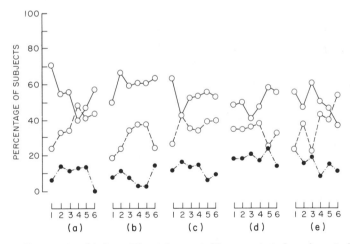

Figure 14.6. *Percentage of infants (N = 21) reported by parents to have been in head-right (solid line), midline (dashed line), and head-left (dotted line) positions during morning–afternoon combined observations for 6 days over five data-collection periods following each of the five testing periods. (a) After in-hospital visit; (b) after 14-day visit; (c) after 1-month visit; (d) after 2-month visit; (e) after 3-month visit.*

the 23 infants are represented since we have not yet received complete records from two families. The solid lines indicate head-right position, dotted lines indicate head-left position, and dashed lines indicate midline position. As can be seen in Figure 14.6, during the first day following the hospital test (i.e., the first day after the infant was taken home), 71% of the infants were lying in the head-right position when the parents observed them, 23% were in the head-left position, and 6% were in the midline position. By the second day, these percentages changed to 60% for head-right and 28% for head-left, and by the sixth day the head-left position constituted nearly 45% of the observations, whereas the head-right percentage was at 55%. Over the 3-month period there also was considerable day to day variation in percent distributions.

The data summarized in Figure 14.6 suggest several conclusions. First, despite day to day variation, infants initially tend to lie in the head-right position. However, by the second month, the head-right position preference weakens to about 50% and remains at approximately that level through the third month. On the other hand, there does not seem to be any very dramatic change in the head-left position data when we smooth out the curves. Rather, after the first month, there is a modest increase in midline positioning.

We are impressed by the similarity of these results to those obtained by our first measure—head orientation after holding. Our findings, however, are somewhat different from Coryell and Michel's (1978), which were obtained using a different measure (recording of percentage of time spent in head-right or head-left position during three 5-min observation periods). Over the same time period (birth to 3 months), the percentage of time their subjects were observed to lie in the head-right position increased from 55% to 60% to nearly 75% on days 7, 14, and 30. After that point, however, their results and ours are more compatible, since they found that, after 30 days, the percentage of time spent in the head-right position dropped and remained at approximately 50% between 2 and 3 months. As for time in the head-left position, in Coryell and Michel's infants, this score remained low (between approximately 15% and 30%) throughout; in our infants, the head-left score was slightly higher, but still lower than the head-right score at every age period tested.

Discussion

As we have seen, the spontaneous head-position data, like the results of the head orientation after holding procedure, suggest that for infants with right-handed parents, there is an initial rightward bias in the newborn period. This finding, as we have noted, is in agreement with a great deal of previous research. What our findings also indicate, however, is that head-position preferences change over the first 3 months of life, and possibly in different ways according to the method of observation used. Analysis of the scores for orientation after head hold suggests a rapid drop in the percentage of rightward positioning, whereas for the measure of spontaneous head position, the pattern of change looks less rapid. Obviously, at this stage of our research project we can advance neither of these developmental descriptions as firm patterns of biobehavioral organization. Rather, we view them heuristically and await additional data to see whether the patterns will persist.

Possible Exogenous Influences on Postural Orientation

Throughout the literature on postural orientation, a two-fold assumption seems always to have been made about the nature of the phenomenon: First, that it is fundamentally an expression of certain endogenous factors related to functional lateralization; second, that being "built in" in this sense, it is not appreciably influenced by, say, how the infant is placed in its crib or how the crib itself has been oriented in the nursery. Turkewitz and Birch (1971) have taken this position. Their study, mentioned earlier, of head position after midline-holding in 2- and 3-day-old infants, was undertaken specifically to determine whether the predominant head-right position shown in their free observations could have resulted from such factors as nurse placement or bassinet arrangement in the hospital nursery. Since the infants still turned their heads predominantly to the right of midline, Turkewitz and Birch thus concluded that, by the time the infant is 2 days old, asymmetrical placement is not required to produce a systematic preference for a head-right posture (Turkewitz & Birch, 1971, p. 31). Where deviations from the head-right posture occur, Turkewitz and Birch proposed that they may be symptomatic of neurobehavioral disorganization in the newborn. In support of this proposal, they reported a lower incidence of head-right positioning among low-Apgar newborns than among high-Apgar newborns.

Although we accept the first proposition that head position is fundamentally an expression of functional lateralization, at least in some rudimentary form, we think there are reasons why both the second proposition (about the influence of nursing practice or crib position) and the proposed significance of deviations from head-right posture might be questioned or at least qualified. To make the last point first, a recent comparison by Fox and Lewis (1982) of normal term infants with infants with clear perinatal complications (infants of 33 weeks or less gestational age tested at 38–39 weeks conceptional age who, moreover, had suffered from respiratory distress syndrome) failed to disclose any differences in the tendency to spontaneously assume the head-right posture. Where differences were evident was in the speed with which the affected infants resumed the head-right posture after their heads were held in midline. Only 20% of the affected infants turned to the right compared with 70% of the term infants. The differences were negligible. However,after 15 min, 80% of the affected infants and 90% of the normal term infants had as- sumed the right position. Thus, postnatal illness in premature infants can slow the lateral head-turn response after midline placement, but evi- dently does not disrupt the maintenance of the right postural asymmetry itself.

The manipulation in the Fox and Lewis (1982) study, like that used by Turkewitz and Birch (1971), consisted only of a midline hold. As we have already reported in connection with our first measure, when we added lateral-hold conditions, we found that newborn infants tended to remain in position, to the right if held to the right (which, of course, is under- standable assuming that the bias is to the right to begin with), but also to the left when held in *that* direction. Evidently, the head-right bias can be temporarily overridden, at least in the very young infant. This finding may shed some light on findings from an earlier study of spontaneous head-position preferences (Fitzgerald & Webster, 1979) that heretofore have been difficult to explain. The subjects in that study were 128 healthy Mexican newborns who were observed between one and four times a day on each of the first 3 postnatal days ($N = 128$ infants on the first 2 days with one to four observations per day but typically three per day; $N = 101$ infants on third day with one to four observations per day; $N = 30$ infants for all 3 days, four observations per day, no missing data). (There were no differences between infants who remained 2 days and 3 days.) The result was a predominant head-left position, in other words, the reverse of what has been reported in the literature as well as what we have described in the current report for FS− infants. Of the 30 infants observed over the entire 3-day period, 16 showed consistent head-left positions. Both for these infants and for the larger group, however, in only a few instances did the strength of the head-left position approach the 85% level found for the more usual head-right position as has been reported in the literature, including our current study. These anomalous findings could not be easi- ly accounted for in terms of either sex of infant, delivery procedure, or maternal parity. At most, it could be said that the strongest head-left positions were found to occur among girls delivered via Caesarean sec- tion, boys of primiparous mothers on day 3, and boys of multiparous mothers on day 1, variations for which we have no ready explanation.

How, then, to explain these findings? It happens that in the newborn nursery of the Hospital San Jose, where these observations were made, bassinets are positioned with one end facing the nurses' entrance and one side facing the nursery viewing window. The infants were always placed with their head at the far end, presumably so that from the nurses' entrance, all the infants' heads would be visible. Since the infants also were placed supine nearly all the time, this meant that the viewing window was to the infants' left side. Is it conceivable that when placing the infants in their bassinets, the nurses, deliberately or not, tended to turn the heads to face the viewing window? If so, an infant who did not resist the head-left placement therefore would be likely to remain as placed by the nurses. This could have accounted for a large proportion of the babies' preference for the head-left position since, as our current data on head orientation after initial holding indicate, when newborn infants are held in the right position or the left position, they tend to stay as placed in contrast to their head-orientation response following a midline hold.

In this connection, we would like to mention some other observations that illustrate another way in which nursing practice could influence head position. These are observations we have made of 200 infants not in our longitudinal study but in the newborn nurseries at the two hospitals at the time of our first observations in the longitudinal study. In both hospitals, the nurses' practice is to prop the baby on one side with a blanket after placing it in the bassinet. Of these 200 infants, 183 (92%) had been propped in this fashion, of whom 150 (82%) were propped under the left side so that the head was turned to the right. Under these circumstances, the infant could not easily change position. We do not know why this practice was instituted (it does not appear to have been done only a few years ago, and it was not the practice in the Mexican hospitals in the Fitzgerald and Webster, 1979, study mentioned earlier). We also have been unable to learn why the practice is to prop under the left side, but we wonder whether it is because, after the nurse places the infant in the bassinet, the infant spontaneously assumes the head-right position, thereby causing the nurse to place the blanket under the left side so as to not disrupt the infant's position.

Infant Biobehavioral State

We have adduced some reasons against the view that deviations from the predominant head-right posture necessarily reflect neurobehavioral disorganization. How, then, to account for deviations that cannot obviously be related to external causes, for example, practices like those that we speculated may have occurred in the case of the Mexican infants? To the extent that predominant head position is an early precursor of later hand preference, one possibility, of course, is that such deviations from the predominant position are a first sign of nascent left handedness rather than the modal right handedness. As we mentioned earlier, our preliminary examination of the results on the FS+ infants in our sample do not support this view, although given the sample size (N = 5), the variability of scores for all the infants, both FS+ and FS−, and the fact that familial sinistrality itself is no guarantee of left handedness but at most only raises its likelihood of occurrence, the question remains open. In this connection, we should mention that Liederman and Kinsbourne have reported finding that newborn infants with two dextral parents turn rightward significantly more often than infants with one left-handed parent (cited in Liederman & Kinsbourne, 1980, p. 224).

Another possibility is that deviations from predominant head-right preference reflect biobehavioral state changes within the normal range for infants at any given age. Some evidence for this possibility has already been reported by Michel and Goodwin (1979). They found that infant state was associated significantly with infant behavior in supine and prone positions. Newborns slept more and cried less when prone, and when supine spent more time in head-right positioning when alert or fussing than when drowsy or asleep. Liederman and Kinsbourne (1980) have obtained evidence consistent with this finding. Thus, certain variations in the observed incidence of head-right positioning, both between as well as within studies, might be related to variations in infant state at the time of testing.

Finally, the question can be raised whether certain group differences in newborn biobehavioral state will be shown to contribute to variations in postural orientation. For example, Freedman and Freedman (1969) found that when Chinese-American newborns were placed face down on their mattresses, they remained as placed and did not turn their heads from side to side nor lift their heads as European-American newborns did. Evidently, Navajo newborns are similar to Chinese-American newborns, whereas Nigerian and Australian aboriginal newborns are similar to European-American newborns in this situation (Freedman, 1976). To be sure, newborns in the Freedmans' research were placed in the prone position rather than the supine position. However, their data clearly illustrate organismic differences in activity level that may be related to differential reactions to caregiving practices. Brazelton (1977) has commented on the low levels of spontaneous activity among Mayan newborns. For example, Mayan newborns emitted few spontaneous startles and engaged in little hand-to-mouth activity. On the other hand, these infants, who were never observed to be placed in the prone position, maintained unusually long periods of quiet alertness. In contrast to the usual American practice of placing infants down in the horizontal position, Desert San newborns typically are placed in the vertical position (Konner, 1977). Vertical posture has been linked to increased production of adrenal medullary hormone via the orthostatic pressor reflex. Desert San caregivers insist that motor behavior is learned and adapt their caregiving practices to facilitate its development (Konner, 1977). Here, it is relevant to note that Zelazo, Zelazo, and Kolb (1972) found that as little as 12 min of daily exercise of the newborn's placing and walking reflexes facilitated the organization of voluntary walking.

All the aforementioned points suggest that, in the Fitzgerald and Webster (1979) study, both the inconsistent as well as the predominant head-left positions may reflect the ease with which a presumably exogenous factor (head positioning by nurses) was able to override the presumed biological predisposition for the head-right position. As we said, our new longitudinal data on head orientation after holding also suggest this conclusion. On the other hand, our data on spontaneous head position (parents' reports) suggest that organismic factors, such as the emergence of organized midline behavior, also assist in the overriding of reflexive head-right positioning.

Conclusions

We have presented preliminary results on two measures of head-position orientation from an ongoing longitudinal study of the development of lateral organization in the first 18 months of life. Results for the first measure—head orientation after initial head-holding—do not provide unequivocal support for a head-right bias for infant whose parents are right-handed (FS− infants). Rather, the infants tended to hold their heads in the direction in which they were placed by the experimenter. On the other hand, three subgroups of infants were identified on the basis of the most common head position to occur after each initial hold. One subgroup showed considerable variability across test sessions. A second subgroup showed little change over time; these infants tended to keep their heads turned in the direction in which it was placed initially. The third and largest subgroup showed a decrease in lateral preference over age; that is, these infants tended to shift from a lateral head-right pattern during the first few days of life to a midline pattern by 3 months of age.

Analysis of the direction in which infants turned their heads after initial midline holding generally supported the pattern for overall scores described above for the third subgroup: a strong rightward bias (19 of 22 infants) during the hospital visit (2–4 days of age) that, however, generally weakened over succeeding ages until it was no longer present by 3 months of age.

Results for the second measure—spontaneous head position—suggest a rightward bias for FS− infants that gradually weakens during the first 3 months. Thus, the developmental pattern for spontaneous head position in FS− infants seems to be similar to the development pattern for the initial head-turn response criterion for head orientation following an initial hold.

Our sample is still incomplete, and we have not yet finished all analyses of the data already collected, including the effects of state and prandial condition. Moreover, we have not yet begun to look at within-subject variation across dependent measures. Nevertheless, it is interesting to note how the results to date tend to support impressions gleaned from certain early biographical and early experimental studies that suggested that the development of hand preference for reaching and manipulation is highly ideosyncratic and variable over time within the same infant (see Harris, Chapter 10, this volume). At this point in our work, longitudinal data from the two measures of head orientation lend a similar impression. Perhaps, discontinuity at all stages of the development of lateral organization may prove to be a more general phenomenon than has been implied by contemporary cross-sectional studies.

Acknowledgments

This project would not have been possible without the help of many individuals and institutions. These include Carla Barnes, Douglas Carlson, Karen Cornwell, Dale Dagenbach, and Laura Kamptner; our colleague Thomas Carr, who is collaborating with us in certain later stages of the project not reported in this chapter; Margaret Hall, our secretary and "traffic manager," Esther Dienstag and Olga Hernandez, our Brazelton test examiners; and the many undergraduate student volunteers who are helping along the way. We also thank the medical and nursing staffs of the Michigan State University Obstetrics and Gynecology Clinic, Edward Sparrow Hospital (Lansing, Michigan), and St. Lawrence Hospital (Lansing, Michigan). We are grateful for the continuing support of The Spencer Foundation, and for earlier support for a pilot study from the Bio-Medical Grant Program of Michigan State University. Finally, we thank the families who gave and are giving their time so generously and enthusiastically to this project.

References

Apgar, V., & James, L. S. (1962). Further observations on the newborn scoring system. American Journal of Diseases of Childhood 104, 419.

Brazelton, T. B. (1973). Neonatal behavioral assessment scale. London: Spastics International Medical Publications.

Brazelton, T. B. (1977). Implications of infant development among the Mayan Indians of Mexico. In P. H. Leiderman, S. R. Tulkin, & A. Rosenfeld (Eds.), Culture and infancy. New York: Academic Press.

Coryell, J. F., & Michel, G. F. (1978). How supine postural preferences of infants can contribute towards the development of handedness. Infant Behavior and Development 1, 245–257.

Delaunay, C.-G. (1874). Biologie comparée du coté droit et du coté gauche chez l'homme et chez les êtres vivants. Paris: Blanpain.

Fitzgerald, H. E., & Webster, L. L. (1979). Lateral head posture in Mexican newborns. Academic Psychology Bulletin 1, 35–39.

Fox, N., & Lewis, M. (1982). Motor asymmetries in preterm infants: Effects of prematurity and illness. Developmental Psychobiology 15, 19–23.

Freedman, D. G. (1976). Infancy, biology and culture. In L. P. Lipsitt (Ed.), Developmental psychobiology: The significance of infancy. Hillsdale, New Jersey: Erlbaum.

Freedman, D. G., & Freedman, N. A. (1969). Differences in behavior between Chinese-American and European-American newborns. *Nature 224*, 1227.

Gesell, A. (1938). The tonic neck reflex in the human infant. *Journal of Pediatrics 13*, 455–464.

Gesell, A., & Ames, L. B. (1947). The development of handedness. *Journal of Genetic Psychology 70*, 155–175.

Goodwin, R. S., & Michel, G. F. (1981). Head orientation position during birth and in infant neonatal period, and hand preference at nineteen weeks. *Child Development 52*, 819–826.

Hécaen, H., & Sauguet, J. (1971). Cerebral dominance in left-handed subjects. *Cortex 7*, 19–48.

Konner, M. (1977). Infancy among the Kalahari Desert San. In P. H. Leiderman, S. R. Tulkin, & A. Rosenfeld (Eds.), *Culture and infancy*. New York: Academic Press.

Liederman, J., & Kinsbourne, M. (1980). The mechanism of neonatal rightward turning bias: A sensory or motor asymmetry? *Infant Behavior and Development 3*, 223–238.

Michel, G., & Goodwin, R. (1979). Intrauterine birth position predicts newborn supine head position preferences. *Infant Behavior and Development 2*, 29–38.

Seguin, E. (1880). *Report on education*. (2nd ed.). Milwaukee, Wisconsin: Doerflinger Book and Publishing. (Photoreproduction. Delmar, New York: Scholars' Facsimiles & Reprints, 1976.) (Originally published, 1875.)

Stevens, H. C. (1908). Right-handedness and peripheral vision. *Science 27*, 272–273.

Turkewitz, G., & Birch, H. G. (1971). Neurobehavioral organization of the human newborn. In J. Hellmuth (Ed.), *Exceptional infant* (vol. 2). New York: Bruner/Mazel.

Turkewitz, G., Gordon, E. W., & Birch, H. G. (1965). Head turning in the human neonate: Spontaneous patterns. *Journal of Genetic Psychology 107*, 143–148.

Zelazo, P. R., Zelazo, N., & Kolb, S. (1972). "Walking" in the newborn. *Science 177*, 1058–1059.

15

Methods for the Quantitative Analysis of Infant Limb Movements

JOHN M. DOWD
EDWARD Z. TRONICK

Introduction

Traditionally, the study of early motor coordination and manual specialization has focused on the normative ages at which well-defined purposive acts can first be performed (Gesell & Thompson, 1929; McGraw, 1969). One reason this "motor milestone" approach has been so prevalent and successful is that it provides an effective strategy for segmenting the infant's continuous flow of movements into valid, recognizable units of behavior. For example, the infant's reaching for an object, grasping it, and inserting it into his or her mouth can easily be recognized as a clear-cut behavior having a definite beginning and end. In contrast, we are hard put to know where to segment the active infant's flailing of arms and legs into units or events, or even whether these movements constitute behavior in the usual sense of serving a recognizable goal or purpose.

The milestone approach can be characterized as defining and studying the development of early coordination primarily in terms of the products or consequences of motor acts rather than attempting to deal directly with describing the dynamic process of *how* limb movements are executed. In addition to the advantages this approach offers in terms of segmenting the continuous flow of movement, it also greatly simplifies the task of describing the infant's behavior. For example, it is relatively easy to describe the consequences of an infant's reach for an object; the object is either successfully contacted or it is not.

In contrast, consider the difficulty of describing the component motions of the infant's arm during the reach. One of the infant's hands moves toward the object, falters, and starts again as the other hand makes a long,

MANUAL SPECIALIZATION
AND THE DEVELOPING BRAIN

wide swing, only to backtrack, start forward again, and so on through many beginnings of movements and partial movements—none actually touching the object, and all seeming to run together. Since these movements cannot be readily segmented into behavioral units and analyzed in terms of their consequences, they can only be studied directly in terms of their temporal and spatial dimensions, a difficult process indeed. Yet, despite the inherent methodological difficulties, the infant's earliest recognizably coordinated motor acts most likely emerge from these earlier, seemingly random, limb movements. Thus, if we are to understand the beginnings of limb coordination, we must find some way of describing and studying the earliest, spontaneous limb movements that are so common in the first months of life.

Three-Dimensional Cinematography

Fortunately, suitable methods for the direct, quantitative study of limb movements are now available. Recent advances in computer technology have stimulated the development of a number of relatively inexpensive techniques of computer-aided three-dimensional (3-D) cinematography (Abdel-Aziz & Karara, 1971; Dapena, 1978, 1981; Woltring, 1980). Using these methods, it is possible to determine from film data the actual three-dimensional location of any point on a subject's body while he or she moves about freely, completely unencumbered by any apparatus. One of the most important aspects of this methodology is the fact that the coordinate data represent a quantitative and virtually exhaustive transcription of both the temporal and spatial aspects of movement. Once the coordinate data for a particular movement sequence have been generated, this sequence can then be analyzed in an almost unlimited number of ways, with relative ease, and without having to rescore the original film data.

Such methods are rapidly being adopted in the fields of biomechanics and exercise science. Although these techniques are not yet widely used in other fields, they are ideally suited to the study of more fundamental issues concerning the development of limb coordination. As one example, Von Hofsten (1982) has used 3-D cinematography to study early infant reaching behavior. Previous studies using conventional methods (DiFranco, Muir, & Dodwell, 1978; Ruff & Halton, 1978) had suggested that infants show no evidence of coordinated reaching early in life. However, by using 3-D cinematography to derive accurate quantitative measures of the direction of infants' reaches, Von Hofsten (1982) was able to demonstrate evidence of rudimentary or prefunctional reaching in newborn infants. First, the direction of "forward-extensive" arm movements with respect to a target object was more accurate when infants were visually fixating on the object than when they were not. Second, more of such arm movements were made when the infants were visually fixating on the object. Furthermore, significant evidence for laterality was found, in that right-hand movements were more frequent than left-hand movements for nearly all of the infants.

Von Hofsten's application of this methodology represents the traditional research strategy of first identifying a well-defined behavior at one point in development and then attempting to trace its origins by looking for earlier and earlier evidence of the behavior (Von Hofsten, 1979, 1980, 1982). His elegant data concerning rudimentary reaching in neonates amply demonstrate the power of this approach and the superiority of 3-D methods over conventional methods of analyzing infant movements.

Our own application of these methods has been very different. Indeed, one of the most exciting aspects of this new methodology is that it opens up a wide range of possible approaches. However, new and quite foreign ways of thinking about how to analyze movement data are required if the full benefit of the advantages offered by these methods is to be gained. In what follows, we will therefore present our own research as one example, with an emphasis on the illustration of methods rather than the presentation of data.

Interlimb Dependencies

Rather than attempting to identify precursors of purposive behaviors such as reaching, we have sought to develop more global definitions of coordination that can be applied without the need for an observer to impose a segmentation of the infant's continuous flow of movement into units of behavior. We have chosen this approach in the hope that it will be more objective and have more generality for use early in development than more traditional approaches. The availability of quantitative measures of movement permits coordination to be defined in terms of the occurrence of specific relationships or interdependencies between right- and left-limb movements. If the infant's movements are uncoordinated, right-limb movements should be relatively independent of left-limb movements in both their temporal and spatial characteristics. In contrast, movements of the right and left arms must evidence some form of dependency if the movements serve a common goal. Thus, if specific kinds of interdependence between right and left movements can be found that are actively produced and show an orderly developmental progression in the degree of dependence, such measures may prove to be sensitive early indicators of coordination.

Temporal Interdependence

Several kinds of evidence suggested to us that interdependence in the timing of movements is a basic property of coordinated movement and, therefore, should develop very early in life. At least one study of adult limb movements has found a strong tendency for right- and left-arm movements to begin simultaneously and also reach peak velocity simultaneously (Kelso, Southard, & Goodman, 1979). Furthermore, simultaneous movements are inherently simpler in another way. Large limb movements produce significant unbalancing torques on the trunk of the body. A major aspect of coordination is the counterbalancing of such torques by opposing movements and postural weight shifts so as to maintain one's equilibrium. Simultaneous limb movements are inherently simpler to counterbalance, in this respect, than nonsimultaneous limb movements, because when several body parts are moved together, a single net torque is produced, rather than the trunk being shifted first in one direction and an instant later in another. Anecdotal evidence also suggests that symmetrical, simultaneous arm movements are easier to perform than movements having different temporal and spatial characteristics (for example, rubbing one's stomach while tapping one's head). Finally, Lashley (1954) has suggested that there are theoretical reasons to expect this kind of interdependence, based on the fundamental importance of rhythm to all behavior and the fact that rhythms are centrally generated.

We therefore conducted a study to determine if infants' right- and left-arm movements tend to occur simultaneously. We chose to investigate this hypothesis first with very young infants to determine if the method was suitable for use with this age group and also because a prior study had reported a strong tendency for synchronous movements in the neonatal period (Condon & Sander, 1974).

Method

Overview of 3-D Method

The details and principles of the method of 3-D cinematography we used are described completely by Dapena (1978). Briefly, the method requires filming the subject with two cameras oriented at roughly 90° to each other. The exact location, orientation, and lens magnification of each camera must also be determined. From these data, the original three-dimensional coordinates of any point common to both camera images can be reconstructed by computer analysis of the position of the point within each camera's image. The raw data required consist of the film coordinates of the body parts being scored. These coordinates are easily measured with the help of an X,Y coordinate digitizer. Using this computerized device, the film image being scored is projected onto the digitizer surface, and the observer records the coordinates of any point in the image simply by positioning a stylus over the point and pressing a button. The observer's task is thereby reduced from that of judging whether or not behaviors occur to that of simply pointing continuously at the image of the body part being scored, while slowly advancing the film. As a result, the actual procedure of scoring the film is extremely simple, requires little judgment on the part of the observer, and can therefore be done with virtually perfect objectivity and reliability.

In our adaptation of this method, two videocameras were positioned above and to either side of an infant subject. Each camera was aimed so that the image of the infant occupied only half of the field. A split-screen special-effects generator was then used to combine the two images of the infant, one from each camera, onto the left and right halves of a single, composite image, which was then recorded on a single videotape. This videotape was then professionally processed onto 16-mm film to facilitate frame-by-frame analysis. To analyze the film, we used a motion-analysis 16-mm film projector that could advance through the film one frame at a time and count frame numbers. The two images of the infant were projected onto an X,Y coordinate digitizer linked via telephone to a time-sharing computer. This permitted the entire data-scoring procedure to be done with no hand-transcription of any data. To enter all body points during a sequence of movement, repeated frame-by-frame passes through the film segment were made, digitizing one body point in one of the two camera's images on each pass.

Subjects

Using this system, we analyzed the arm movements of four healthy, full term infants (two male and two female) at 2 weeks of age and again at 10 weeks of age. All infants had uneventful medical histories, both pre-natally and postnatally. During videotaping, the infant was positioned supine on a foam rubber pad placed on the floor of the room within a symmetrical tentlike enclosure. At 2 weeks of age, two 37.5-sec sequences of active movement were analyzed for each subject. At 10 weeks, three such sequences were analyzed per subject.

Definition of Movement Events

Three independent components of arm movements were calculated from the 3-D coordinate data, including changes in the angle at the elbow (flexion–extension of the arm), movements of the upper arm causing the elbow to change its location in space, and rotational movements of the upper arm about its long axis extending from the shoulder to the elbow. Pilot work with these movement components showed that a simpler mea-sure of arm movement, namely wrist speed, considered independently of the other arm segments, was sufficient for our purposes. Since virtually all arm movements produced changes in wrist position, and hence in speed, changes in wrist speed provided an effective summary of all arm-movement components.

The wrist-speed data were then analyzed to determine three types of arm-movement events, including *starts* of movements, *abrupt changes in direction*, and *peaks in speed*. The last type of movement event was chosen because, although peaks in wrist speed are not salient from the observer's standpoint, they roughly correspond to internal events in terms of opposing muscle groups. For example, during an arm extension, a peak in wrist speed occurs when one muscle group stops acting (e.g., controlling extension) and the opposing group begins contracting (e.g., controlling flexion). We hypothesized that such internal events might be more fundamental than changes in direction and, therefore, right–left coordination might first be evident in this component, only later showing up in terms of external events such as changes in direction, which, although salient to observers, are not actually muscular events in the same sense as peaks in speed.

All three types of events were defined in terms of precise quantitative parameters. For example, "starts" of movements were located by first identifying all peaks in wrist speed greater than 40.0 mm/sec. Such peaks were considered to be the approximate midpoint of reliable arm movements. (Arm movements associated with peak wrist speeds of less than 40.0 mm/sec were found to be unreliable in independent scorings of the same movement sequence.) The start of the movement was then located by looking backward in time from the peak. Three criteria defined a start. First, the difference in speed between each film frame and the previous frame had to have fallen below a threshold of 2.0 mm/sec. This criterion was imposed to appropriately score instances where a movement began gradually. In such instances, the 2.0 mm/sec criterion located the first *reliable* increase in speed. The film frame identified by the first criterion was considered to be a tentative start, and the second criterion was then applied: The speed of the wrist at this point in time was required to be less than 10.0 mm/sec, or in other words, essentially stationary. Furthermore, by the third criterion, the wrist had to have been "at rest," defined as speed less than 10.0 mm/sec for at least 12 frames (.5 sec) prior to the start.

Criteria for all three types of events were chosen so as to maximize reliability, assessed by having two independent raters score the same film sequence and comparing the two sets of events that were generated. Reliability was high for all three types of events.

Figure 15.1 depicts a 2.5-sec movement sequence for one infant and illustrates both how movement events were scored, based on the wrist-speed data, and how the events related to the actual "shape" of the limb movements that produced them. The upper panel of Figure 15.1 depicts a series of line-segment drawings representing the position of the right and

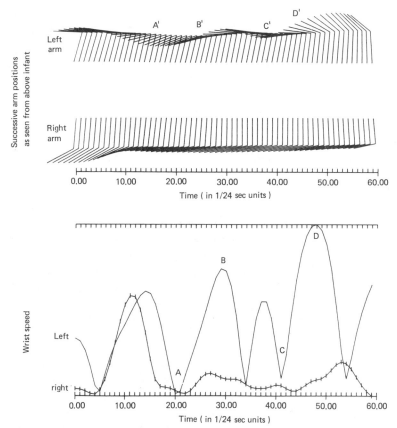

Figure 15.1. A 2.5 sec sequence of movement, as depicted by 3-D limb coordinate and wrist speed data. The upper panel summarizes the "form" of the movement sequence. Below, the corresponding wrist speed data are depicted, illustrating how movement events were scored. (See text for explanation.)

left arms of the infant, based on the 3-D coordinate data for each successive film frame. During the movement sequence, a number of flexion and extension movements can be seen to occur in the left arm, whereas only one movement occurs in the right arm. Directly below the drawings, the corresponding wrist-speed data have been plotted. Note that at points A and C, the speed of the left wrist (smooth line) drops abruptly and then increases just as rapidly. Such points would be scored as change-in-direction events. For the corresponding line-segment drawings immediately above, the left arm can be seen to be abruptly reversing directions, first from flexion to extension at A', and then from extension to flexion at C'. Similarly, the peaks in wrist speed for the left arm at points B and D in the speed data can be seen to correspond to points in the line-segment drawings (B' and D') where the wrist is rapidly moving. We have found careful examination of figures such as this to be invaluable, both in understanding the correspondence between quantitative measures of movement and their actual appearance and also for summarizing an infant's behavior, since the entire sequence can be read at a glance, or one aspect studied in great detail.

Results and Discussion

Statistical analyses of all three types of movement events were performed using the lag-sequential analysis method (Sackett, 1979) to measure whether there were either simultaneous or lagged dependencies between right- and left-arm movements.

No temporal dependencies between right and left movement events were found, for starts, changes in direction, or peaks in speed, despite our use of several definitions of simultaneity, ranging from co-occurrence within 1/48 sec (the same film frame) to co-occurrence within 7/24 sec (within ± 3 film frames). One infant at 2 weeks of age did evidence an imprecise type of synchronization of movements, in that there was a significant tendency for movements of one arm to co-occur within several seconds of movements of the other. Examination of the film for this infant showed that this was caused by the infant's behavior being organized into periods of activity, during which movement was likely to occur in both arms, and periods of inactivity, when no movements would occur.

Although these results are negative, they nevertheless give us some information concerning early limb coordination. These results suggest that, in the first weeks of life, there is little or no coordination in when movements are initiated. They lend no support to previous, controversial work suggesting that such movement coordination is fundamental and virtually always present (Condon & Sander, 1974). Furthermore, the absence of temporal coordination permits speculation that coordination over timing may be a relatively complex process and therefore does not appear this early in development. Alternatively, the data may reflect the immaturity of interhemispheric neural connections in the first weeks of life.

These findings may also reflect the fact that there was no necessity for the infants to move their arms in synchrony. Perhaps such dependencies are only apparent during movements that are constrained to serve some goal or task. We can think of no task in adulthood that is at all comparable to the "spontaneous" limb movements of infants, unless one were to ask adults to attempt to move their arms randomly, with no discernable pattern or timing structure. Whether or not adults could do this is uncertain. It is also uncertain whether the infants' movements early in life are truly spontaneous and random. Thelen (1981) has shown that the seemingly spontaneous kicking of infants in the first months of life is organized, stereotypical, and closely resembles movements seen later in development during walking. We remain confident that interdependence in the timing of limb movements must appear at some point during development. Certainly it is present to a high degree in adults' purposeful movements, as has been demonstrated by Kelso *et al.* (1979). This can also be easily demonstrated by attempting to tap a regular rhythm with one hand and a simultaneous random rhythm with the other. Despite all efforts, one pattern will be found to contaminate or "invade" the other. Given this endpoint, the question becomes one of when in development, and under what circumstances, interdependence in timing of movements is first evident.

Without more data, such speculations can only suggest hypotheses for future research. Only when enough pieces of the puzzle are present will there be enough constraints on hypothesis generation that a single coherent picture can emerge. In the present context, the pieces of the puzzle that need to be obtained consist of the testing of more types of dependencies at more ages. Interdependence in the *timing* of limb movements is but one of many kinds of interdependence that can be measured using this technique. For example, we could also have measured the tendency for limb movements to be symmetrical (both arms extending or both arms flexing) or alternating (one arm flexing while the other is extending) simply by changing the definition of the movement events. When we have identified a number of such interdependencies that are present in the adult under many different activities and have determined the ages at which such interdependencies first appear, a detailed picture should emerge of how coordination develops.

Limitations

Although the advantages of this methodology over more traditional, observer-based methods are many, we would not universally recommend it, for, as with any new methodology, when old problems are solved, new ones are created. The present method enables us to produce very detailed analyses of behavior, but at the expense of having to deal with large amounts of data. The study reported here utilized 18,000 film frames of data and required computer analysis of 216,000 pairs of film coordinates. This is a large amount of data by any standards. Without the availability of a large computer and associated data storage facilities, managing this amount of data would have been formidable. However, for many applications, much less data would be needed, and even a microcomputer would be adequate. Furthermore, as computer technology continues to advance, such limitations will become less and less significant.

Other Applications

In addition to using 3-D scoring methods to test specific hypotheses, as we have, a host of useful descriptive measures can also be developed, such as the average size, speed, and frequency of movements of each limb. Global measures can also be defined, for example, the characteristic posture held by the infant. Another useful stategy would be to use traditional time-series analysis methods. In the present context, calculating a spectral density function (Gottman, 1981) for the wrist-speed data of each arm would yield a detailed summary of the infant's movement that would specify the infant's characteristic proportion of slow versus fast movements. This approach could prove to be of use in quantitatively describing the degree of spasticity in infant's movements.

Many other possible applications could be mentioned. In fact, it is fair to say that the number of dependent measures of movement that can be derived using this method is limited only by one's ability to define the movement or pattern of movement in quantitative terms. Because of its advantages over conventional methods, we expect that 3-D analysis will become an increasingly common tool in the investigation of movement development.

References

Abdel-Aziz, Y., & Karara, H. (1971). Direct linear transformation from comparator coordinates into object space coordinates in close-range photogrammetry. *Proceedings of the ASP/UI Symposium on Close-Range Photogrammetry*, Urbana, Illinois, 1–18.

Condon, W., & Sander, L. (1974). Neonate movement is synchronized with adult speech: Interactional participation in language acquisition. *Science 183*, 99–101.

Dapena, J. (1978). Three-dimensional cinematography with horizontally panning cameras. *Sciences et Motricité 1*, 3–15.

Dapena, J. (1981). Three-dimensional cinematography with control object of unknown shape. *Journal of Biomechanics 15*, 11–17.

DiFranco, D., Muir, D., & Dodwell, P. (1978). Reaching in very young infants. *Perception 7*, 385–392.

Gesell, A., & Thompson, H. (1929). Learning and growth in identical infant twins: An experimental study by the method of co-twin control. *Genetic Psychology Monographs 6*, 1–24.

Gottman, J. (1981). *Time-series analysis: A comprehensive introduction for social scientists*. London and New York: Cambridge Univ. Press.

Hofsten, C. von (1979). Development of visually directed reaching: The approach phase. *Journal of Human Movement Studies 5*, 160–178.

Hofsten, C. von (1980). Predictive reaching for moving objects by human infants. *Journal of Experimental Child Psychology 30*, 369–382.

Hofsten, C. von (1982). Eye–hand coordination in the newborn. *Developmental Psychology 18*, 450–461.

Kelso, J., Southard, D., & Goodman, D. (1979). On the nature of human interlimb coordination. *Science 203*, 1029–1031.

Lashley, K. (1954). The problem of serial order in behavior. In F. A. Beach, K. Hebb, C. Morgan, & H. Nisson (Eds.), *The neuropsychology of Lashley*. New York: McGraw-Hill.

McGraw, M. (1969). *The neuromuscular maturation of the human infant.* New York: Hafner.

Ruff, H., & Halton, A. (1978). Is there directed reaching in the human neonate? *Developmental Psychology 14,* 425–426.

Sackett, G. (1979). The lag sequential analysis of contingency and cyclicity in behavioral interaction research. In J. D. Osofsky (Ed.), *Handbook of infant development.* New York: Wiley.

Thelen, E. (1981). Rhythmical behavior in infancy: An ethological perspective. *Developmental Psychology 17,* 237–257.

Woltring, H. (1980). Planar control in multi-camera calibration for three-dimensional gait studies. *Journal of Biomechanics 13,* 39–48.

IV

Infant Research

16

Is There a Stage of Left-Sided Precocity during Early Manual Specialization?[1]

JACQUELINE LIEDERMAN

Introduction

It has been suggested that there is a period during early infancy when the left hand is preferred for volitional, visually guided reaching (Anderson & McDonnell, 1979; McDonnell, 1979; McDonnell, Anderson, & Abraham, in press). This claim was based on the observation that infants presented with a target object move their left arms significantly more than their right arms, at age 2 months. When these infants were assessed a year later, they were found to be right-handed. If this were a reliable finding, it would be important because it suggests that left hemisphere–right-hand superiority takes time to develop and that there may even be an early period of right hemisphere–left-hand precocity.

Prior to McDonnell's reports, there were only a few investigators who suggested that there might be times during early infancy when left-sided, as opposed to right-sided, preference is normative (Cěrnáček & Podiviský, 1971; Coryell & Michel, 1978; DiFranco, Muir, & Dodwell, 1978; Gesell & Ames, 1947; Giesecke, 1936; Seth, 1973; Sounalet, 1975). The degree of left-hand superiority reported by some of these investigators was minimal and statistically insignificant where trends could be analyzed (Young, 1977). Thus, McDonnell's studies constitute the only documentation of a *significant* left bias during early infancy.

McDonnell's data permit more than one possible interpretation. McDonnell suggests that between the ages of 3 and 12 weeks, the left hand

[1]This research was supported by a Boston University Graduate School Grant.

is superior for volitional, visually guided reaching. His experiment, however, was limited by the lack of a baseline control condition during which extension movements could be measured in the absence of target presentation. Instead, a region was arbitrarily designated as baseline because it appeared to be the "normal resting" position for the hands when no target was visible. This description blurs an important distinction. Was a baseline established only for those periods when the arms were not extended? Or is it possible that the left arm moved more often than the right even when there was no target for which to reach?

High levels of left-hand activity do not necessarily indicate left-hand superiority, or even left-hand preference, in target-directed activity. An alternative explanation is that the left arm moves more than the right arm because it receives less downstream inhibition from supraspinal centers. Thus, high levels of left-arm movement may reflect diffuse activity that has spilled over from reflexive or associated movements. For example, Coryell and Michel (1978) reported the results of a longitudinal investigation showing that, at ages 4, 6, 8, and 10 weeks, infants activated their left hands in response to a visual stimulus slightly more often than their right hands. Although none of these differences were significant, when the greatest left "preference" occurred, it seemed to reflect a quieting of right-arm activity rather than an increase of left-arm activity (Coryell, personal communication).

A study by Liederman and Coryell (1981) supports this contention. During the first 3 months of life, in particular, turning the head and/or eyes to look at a laterally placed target triggers a synergism known as the asymmetric tonic neck reflex (ATNR). During the ATNR, the limbs extend on the side toward which the child faces (i.e., the face side). There is a lateral bias for this reflex during early infancy such that head turns to the left are more effective in eliciting the ATNR than are head turns to the right (Liederman & Coryell, 1981). Since the "face" arm moves more often than the "skull" arm while the ATNR is in effect (Coryell & Cardinali, 1979), these extension movements of the face arm during orientation toward a target could easily be mistaken for left-handed directed reaches.

McDonnell was aware that head movements could be a complication; he employed restraints that limited head and body movement. These devices could not have inhibited head movement totally since he used orientation of the head toward the target to decide whether the infant was attending. It remains possible, therefore, that the arms extended as part of the ATNR synergism either because (a) when the target was moved, the head turned to follow it; or (b) when the target was immobile, the head was turned to the preferred side. Indeed, in one study (McDonnell, 1979), targets were presented at the center of the infant's visual field and at various locations to the right and left of center. In a signal-detection analysis, the distribution of arm movements in response to a target in one position was used as a "noise" baseline and a change in the position of the target as the "signal." The only displacements that resulted in significant differences were shifts of the target from the most extreme left and right positions. Rather than reflecting visually guided reaching to a distant target, such arm extensions may have been reflex movements secondary to changes in head and/or eye position.

In another description of their series of studies, McDonnell et al. (in press) observed a higher proportion of left than right "reaches" even when the object was presented at midline. Here, too, it is possible that head position was a confounding variable. Hence, infants may have moved their heads back and forth slightly to the left and right, inducing more left-arm reflexive action during left head turns than right-arm reflexive action during right head turns, thereby accounting for the results. That is, McDonnell's data may not reflect precocity for reaching, per se, but may be due to a relative lack of inhibition on the left side producing more arm extensions in the context of reflexive activity on that side.

The present chapter questions whether more left-sided diffuse or reflexive activity early in infancy has been mistakenly interpreted as preferential left-sided reaching. Arm movements were observed in infants whose heads were turned away from the midline, either passively by the examiner when there was no target object to be reached for (Object Absent) or actively by the child, to enable him or her to view a laterally placed rattle (Object Present). In both conditions, the degree of head rotation was matched for left and right turns.

Method

Subjects

Thirty-eight infants (19 males, 19 females) were observed between 3 and 10 weeks of age (M = 6 weeks). According to maternal report, each child was between 2475 and 4500 gm at birth, had a gestational age between 38 and 42 weeks, and was without a history of labor or delivery complications. Subjects were not preselected according to family handedness. Lateral preference in spontaneous head turning was assessed by the procedure we will next describe. Subjects were selected to assure approximately equal numbers of right- and left-preferenced head turners within the male and female subgroups. Our sample included 17 left-preferenced infants (8 males, 9 females) and 21 right-preferenced infants (11 males, 10 females).

Procedure

The experiment was conducted in the parents' homes. Each infant was videotaped while lying supine on a cushioned wooden platform. Three sides of the platform were screened in order to provide an essentially symmetrical visual scene. Each infant was positioned with his or her feet toward the videorecorder, which was on a tripod at the edge of the open side of the platform. The camera was positioned so that the image of the child's body filled the field. An assistant sat behind the side of the platform opposite the open side (i.e., directly behind the infant). A small opening permitted the assistant to see the infant's head. Before each trial, the child's head was positioned in the midline for a brief time, with the extremities placed symmetrically in a semiflexed position.

The experiment consisted of two parts. One part involved the assessment of the infant's spontaneous turning preference. During the initial and final part of the session, the child's spontaneous movements were filmed for 20 sec. The infant's head was held symmetrically in the midline until there was no resistance against the examiner's hand. Then the head was released and filming began. The infants were alert and quiet at the start of each trial.

The rest of the experiment was designed to measure the effect of right and left head turning on arm movements. In the Object Absent condition, the examiner turned the infant's head 70° to the right or left and maintained it there for 25 secs. In the Object Present condition, the examiner induced head turning by presenting the child with a 9-cm spherical rattle covered with a red-and-white checkered pattern. The rattle was initially presented directly above the infant's face, within the infant's field of focal vision but beyond reaching distance. When the infant noticed the rattle, the assistant induced head turning by moving the rattle slowly to one side of the infant as his or her head followed the rattle. Thus, the rattle was usually directly in front of the infant. Filming began as soon as the child's head was oriented at 70° from the vertical. To standardize the degree of head turn, the back of the platform screen (facing the examiner) was marked at 70° from vertical. By continually shaking the rattle, the experimenter encouraged the child to keep his or her head turned for 25 sec. If the infant did not turn his or her head or maintain a lateral head position for at least 5 sec, the procedure was repeated.

Coding

The videotapes were paused at 2-sec intervals, at which time the infant's behavior at the end of the interval was recorded. The position of the head and arms was scored for the first 10 sec of each trial that the head was in the intended position, irrespective of state. A grid calibrated in 1-cm steps was placed in front of the monitor screen. The vertical axis was aligned with the child's body midline, and the horizontal axis was aligned with the infant's shoulders. The position of each arm was measured at the center of the wrist on the palm side. If the center of the wrist (palm side) was not visible, then the scorers imagined a bracelet around the wrist and found the midpoint of the "visible" part of the imaginary bracelet. To prevent a lateral bias due to the usual left-to-right method of reading, during half of the trials when the hand was positioned centrally within a grid area it was considered to have crossed the line of the left rather than the right side.

To assess reliability, the data from five subjects were scored independently by two judges. Agreement was 100% for judgments of head position; 93% for arm position, and 90% for the presence of an ATNR. Once reliability was established, one coder scored the left part of the screen and the other coder scored the right part of the screen.

Several dependent measures were generated: *spontaneous head turn preference:* the direction that the child most often turned during periods of spontaneous movement; *forward arm extension:* horizontal extension of the arm parallel to the shoulder axis; *diffuse movement:* the total amount of arm movement in the vertical and horizontal planes combined by the formula (vertical movement^2 + horizontal movement^2)$^{1/2}$; *midline crossing:* movement of the wrist across the midline of the child's body; *ATNR incidence:* the incidence of the ATNR, that is, extension of the "face" arm more than the contralateral ("skull") arm.

Results

A series of repeated measures analyses of variance were computed. Sex and lateral preference were used as between-subjects factors. The dependent measures on successive runs were: (a) mean degree of forward arm extension; (b) mean amount of diffuse movement; (c) proportion of trials during which midline crossing occurred; and (d) proportion of trials during which the ATNR occurred. For the first three dependent measures, a separate analysis was done with the ATNR as a covariate. Given the large number of analyses, the alpha level was set at .01.

In terms of forward arm extension, there was a significant lateral bias: The right arm extended more often than the left arm ($F = 13.90$; $p < .01$), especially when the head turned right rather than left [$F (1, 34) = 6.47$; $p < .01$] (see Table 16.1). There was also a significant effect of stimulus condition [$F (1, 34) = 6.91$; $p < .01$]. The arms extended further when there was a stimulus present than when there was no stimulus present (see Table 16.2). All three of these effects occurred even when the ATNR was used as a covariate in the analysis; the incidence of the ATNR did not covary with the degree of arm extension.

In terms of diffuse movement, the effect of stimulus condition was the opposite of that seen for arm extension: there was significantly *less* diffuse movement during the stimulus-present than the stimulus-absent tri-

Table 16.1

Lateral Asymmetries for the Degree of Forward Arm Extension and the Amount of Diffuse Arm Movement

| | Forward arm extension | | | |
| | Right arm | | Left arm | |
	Head turned right	Head turned left	Head turned right	Head turned left
M	6.27	5.83	4.99	5.65
SD	2.08	1.93	2.09	2.42

Diffuse arm movement

Girls

| | Right preference | | Left preference | |
	Turned right	Turned left	Turned right	Turned left
M	1.40	1.65	1.53	.80
SD	1.10	1.01	1.09	.83

Boys

| | Right preference | | Left preference | |
	Turned right	Turned left	Turned right	Turned left
M	1.29	1.24	1.17	1.68
SD	.77	.91	.96	1.28

als [F (1, 34) = 23.23; $p < .01$] (see Table 16.2). The direction that the head was turned modified this effect [F (1, 34) = 6.92; $p < .01$]. The effect of stimulus condition was stronger when the head was turned right rather than left.

There was also a significant difference between sexes with reference to how the direction of head turning affected the amount of diffuse movement: for direction of Head Turning × Sex × Lateral Preference [F (1, 34) = 8.33; $p < .01$]. In order to decompose the interaction, two analyses were computed with boys and girls as separate groups. The effect of direction of head turning, within the female sample, differed according to the infant's lateral preference [F (1, 17) = 8.17; $p < .01$]. There was more diffuse movement of both arms when the head was on the left side rather than the right side, in girls whose preference was right. Conversely, there was more diffuse movement on the right rather than the left side in girls whose

Table 16.2
*The Effect of Stimulus Condition on Forward Arm Extension and Diffuse
Arm Movement*

	Stimulus present	Stimulus absent
Forward arm extension		
M	5.90	5.36
SD	2.36	1.90
Diffuse movement		
M	1.03	1.65
SD	.97	1.10

lateral preference was left. When boys were considered separately, no significant interaction occurred (see Table 16.1).

There was no significant relation between the amount of diffuse movement and the incidence of the ATNR. Thus, the same pattern of results obtained when the ATNR was used as a covariate.

The incidence of midline crossing was very low (fewer than 2% of the trials). There were no significant effects of any independent measure upon the number of midline crossings until the ATNR was used as a covariate in the analysis. The incidence of midline crossing covaried with the occurrence of the ATNR [F (1, 33) = 7.38; $p < .01$];($\beta = -.02$). In addition, there was a significant Stimulus Condition × Sex × Lateral Preference interaction [F (1, 33) = 7.41; $p < .01$]. In order to decompose this interaction, two analyses were computed, with males and females as separate groups. There were no significant differences between the lateral preference groups when males and females were examined separately, leaving this result unclear.

In terms of reflex movement, there was a marginally significant laterality effect replicating Liederman and Coryell (1981): The incidence of the ATNR varied with the direction that the head was turned and with the lateral preference of the subject (Direction × Lateral Preference: [F (1, 34) = 4.20; $p = .048$].In right-preferenced infants, the ATNR occurred more often when the head was left rather than right; in left-preferenced infants, the ATNR occurred more often when the head was right rather than left.

Discussion

For arm extension of the sort that would occur during orientation toward a stimulus, a significant dextral bias was observed. The right arm extended further than the left arm, especially when the head was turned right rather than left. This right-arm activity took place not only when a stimulus was absent, but also when it was present, and no matter to which side the head was turned and to which side the head preferred to turn spontaneously. Greater right-arm activation during stimulus presentation has been reported in 1-week-old infants (Von Hofsten, 1982) and in 12-week-old infants (Coryell & Michel, 1978) but had not been previously demonstrated in infants 3–10 weeks of age.

The degree of forward arm extension did not just reflect random or reflexive movement. The result for arm extension was inversely related to one that was found for diffuse movement: Horizontal extension was most prominent when the stimulus was present; diffuse movement was most prominent when the stimulus was absent (especially when the head was turned to the right). Moreover, despite the surface similarity between the extension movement of the ATNR and the behavior that was coded as arm extension, the two measures did not covary significantly. For example, in right-preferenced infants, the right hand was extended further than the left, despite the predominance of the ATNR on the left side in these same infants.

The asymmetries in arm movement reported in this chapter do not parallel those observed by McDonnell (1979). For what we labeled arm extension, the significant dextral bias in our data is the opposite of the sinistral bias that he reported. When diffuse movement is considered, our data come closer to resembling his, at least for girls. Although we did not find a significant asymmetry in the amount of diffuse movement of the left versus the right arm, we did find a left-sided bias in terms of the effect of head orientation. In girls with a rightward head-turning preference, diffuse movement of *both* arms was greater when the head was turned left rather than right.

The discrepancy between McDonnell's findings and our own is intriguing, given that the two samples consisted of children in the same age range. One important difference was that the children in McDonnell's paradigm were seated at an incline, whereas children in our study were supine. Turning of the head when in an upright position may require more effort than when the head is supported by a mattress, and this may induce more intense activation of the muscle spindles that trigger the ATNR. Accordingly, there may have been a higher level of artifactual ATNR activity in McDonnell's paradigm than in ours. Alternatively, the freedom of arm movement afforded by placing the child at an incline may have enhanced the observation of movement asymmetries.

The important point is that our findings call into question McDonnell's interpretation of left-arm activity as a sign of left-sided precocity for visually guided reaching. Neither study provides evidence of visually guided reaching. In our study, the hand that extended was usually fisted rather than open, even though opening the hand would have permitted a closer approach to the stimulus. Similarly, in McDonnell's paradigm, the stimuli were within the infant's reach, yet the children made no attempt to actually contact or manipulate the object.

It seems likely that the sinistral bias observed within McDonnell's paradigm represented a kind of generalized disinhibition of movement during left, as opposed to right, head turning. The sinistral bias most likely reflected a combination of diffuse activity and spillover from reflex posturing and is most readily interpreted as a lag, rather than a lead, in development.

In conclusion, we did not find support for the notion of a stage of left-sided precocity during early target-related activity. Instead, during early infancy, orientation seems to trigger rightward movement, not only in terms of head turning (Liederman & Kinsbourne, 1980a, 1980b) but also with reference to preferential extension of the right arm. If future investigators identify contexts within which the young infant's left arm is more active than the right, we predict that this sinistral bias will be restricted to relatively diffuse movements that are unrelated to stimulus acquisition and manipulation.

Acknowledgments

I wish to thank Denise Stiassny, Amanda Johns, and Sylvia Martinez for their help with data collection and coding.

References

Anderson, V. E. S., & McDonnell, P. M. (1979). *The sinister infant: Unexpected laterality at 3–8 weeks.* Paper presented at a meeting of the Canadian Psychological Association, Quebec City, Canada.

Cěrnáček, J., & Podivinský, F. (1971). Ontogenesis of handedness and somatosensory cortical response. *Neuropsychologia 9,* 219–232.

Coryell, J., & Cardinali, N. (1979). The asymmetrical tonic neck reflex in normal full-term infants. *Physical Therapy 59,* 741–753.

Coryell, J., & Michel, G. (1978). How supine postural preferences of infants can contribute toward the development of handedness. *Infant Behavior and Development 1,* 245–257.

DiFranco, D., Muir, D. W., & Dodwell, P. (1978). Reaching in very young infants. *Perception 7,* 385–392.

Gesell, A., & Ames, L. B. (1947). The development of handedness. *Journal of Genetic Psychology 70,* 155–175.

Giesecke, M. (1936). The genesis of hand preference. *Monographs of the Society for Research in Child Development 1*(5, Serial No. 5).

Hofsten, C. von (1982). Eye–hand coordination in the newborn. *Developmental Psychology 18,* 450–461.

Liederman, J., & Coryell, J. (1981). Right-hand preference facilitated by rightward turning biases during infancy. *Developmental Psychobiology 14,* 439–450.

Liederman, J., & Kinsbourne, M. (1980a). The mechanism of neonatal rightward turning bias: A sensory or motor asymmetry? *Infant Behavior and Development 3*, 223–238.

Liederman, J., & Kinsbourne, M. (1980b). Rightward turning biases in neonates reflect a single neural asymmetry in motor programming. *Infant Behavior and Development 3*, 245–251.

McDonnell, P. (1978). Patterns of eye–hand coordination in the first year of life. *Canadian Journal of Psychology 33*, 253–267.

McDonnell, P., Anderson, V. E. S., & Abraham, A. (in press). Asymmetry and orientation of arm movements in three to eight-week-old infants. *Infant Behavior and Development*.

Seth, G. (1973). Eye–hand co-ordination and "handedness": A developmental study of visuo-motor behavior in infancy. *British Journal of Educational Psychology 43*, 35–49.

Sounalet, G. (1975). Emploi preférentiel d'une main et préhension fine entre 7 et 12 mois. *Enfance 2*, 133–149.

Young, G. (1977). Manual specialization in infancy: Implications for lateralization of brain function. In S. J. Segalowitz & F. A. Gruber (Eds.), *Language development and neurological theory*. New York: Academic Press.

Hand Differences
in Grasp Duration
and Reaching in
Two- and Five-Month-Old Infants[1]

PATRICIA R. HAWN
LAUREN JULIUS HARRIS

Introduction

Clinical reports of the relationship between age of unilateral cerebral injury and the likelihood of normal development or recovery of speech typically have been interpreted to mean that the cerebral hemispheres initially are "equipotential" for speech functions but become progressively lateralized over time (e.g., Lenneberg, 1967). Given the presumed link between handedness and cerebral lateralization, handedness likewise would be expected to be absent in early life and to develop only gradually—as speech itself becomes established. J. Mark Baldwin (1890) expressed this expectation when he wrote of the "fundamental connection between the rise of speech and the rise of right handedness [p. 65]," and Baldwin himself, as we saw in the review by Harris (Chapter 10, this volume), reported evidence for this view. Baldwin's own daughter showed a distinct preference for the right hand by the seventh and eighth months of age, but not before. Many subsequent investigators likewise

[1]Some of the research described in this chapter was reported at the Annual Meetings of the International Neuropsychology Society, New York, February, 1979, and at the Biennial Meetings of the Society for Research in Child Development, San Francisco, California, March, 1979.

P. R. H. was supported, during the conduct of this research, by Predoctoral Traineeship No. 14622 from the National Institute of Mental Health. The research was supported, in part, by a Michigan State University All-University faculty grant to L. J. H. The report was prepared by L. J. H. with the aid of grants from the Michigan State University Foundation and The Spencer Foundation.

have failed to find a reliable preference for right-hand reaching before about months 7–12 (Černáček & Podivinský, 1971; Giesecke, 1936; Lesné & Peycelon, 1934; Seth, 1973; Voelckel, 1913), and in some cases not until much later (e.g., Gesell & Ames, 1947).

Recently, the "equipotential," or "progressive lateralization," model has been challenged on several grounds. First, the presence of lateral asymmetries has been demonstrated in very young infants by measures other than reaching. For example, the newborn shows a predominant head-right position while lying supine (Turkewitz, Gordon, & Birch, 1965; Harris & Fitzgerald, Chapter 14, this volume) and, as early as the second or third month, the infant shows right- and left-ear advantages for dichotically presented speech and music sounds, respectively (Best, Hoffman, & Glanville, 1981; Glanville, Best, & Levinson, 1977). Second, keeping in mind the qualification that morphology may not always signify function, it is interesting to note that the brains of 5-month-old fetuses and newborns show gross morphological asymmetries in the temporal speech cortex comparable to those found in adult brains (e.g., Witelson & Pallie, 1973). Third, in preschool and school–age children, lateralization, as indexed by dichotic listening and other tasks, generally has not been shown to increase with age for either the encoding or decoding aspects of speech perception (e.g., Hiscock & Kinsbourne, 1977). Finally, the original clinical data on which the "equipotentiality" hypothesis depended have themselves been challenged. More careful testing of left-hemidecorticate infantile hemiplegics indicates that full right-hemisphere control of language causes difficulties with language structure in childhood as well as in adulthood (Dennis & Kohn, 1975; Dennis & Whitaker, 1976, 1977; St. James-Roberts, 1981). The two perinatal hemispheres thus do not seem to be equivalent substrates for language acquisition.

Given all these findings, the possibility therefore arises that functional cerebral lateralization exists from the outset and is relatively invariant over time. If so, the reported first emergence of dominant-hand preference by only 7–12 months or later, rather than indicating an absence of hand differences before this time, instead may reflect either deficiencies in the particular testing methods used or age changes in other behavioral systems. An argument of this sort has been made by Caplan and Kinsbourne (1976), who noted that in several studies of reaching, the object used was placed in front of the child in the midline (e.g., Gesell & Ames, 1947). Two problems with this method, according to Caplan and Kinsbourne, might have worked to mask underlying hand preference for reaching. The first is that young infants tend not to cross the midline of personal space when reaching for objects. Consequently, objects placed imprecisely (i.e., even slightly to the left or right of center of the infant's midline) might tend to be reached for by the hand on the same side. (Presumably, this same tendency would be enhanced when positioning is deliberately—and farther—to the side.) The second problem is that young infants may not have outgrown the synergistic tendency to reach with both hands together.

Caplan and Kinsbourne (1976) did not document either of these claims. The second is generally accepted (e.g., in Lesné & Peycelon's 1934 study, infants under 5 months of age almost invariably took hold of objects with both hands). The first, however, is open to question. Caplan and Kinsbourne might have had in mind Bruner's (1969) statement about the "mysterious midline barrier," wherein "[if] a toy is held before the hand of an infant after he has already grasped something in that hand, the contralateral hand will not reach across the midline to get it [p. 231]." According to Bruner (1969), the barrier is "a strict one at seven months [p. 231]." Provine and Westerman (1979), however, have found that by means of another method of restraining or otherwise engaging one limb (holding the arm beneath a blanket wrapped around the body), contralateral reaching was found. The percentage of infants succeeding in contacting objects presented on the restrained side (meaning that a contralateral reach is required) progressed from 0 to 71% over the age period 9–17 weeks, and to 100% by 18–20 weeks. The infants, moreover, were not observed to rotate their torsos and thus make the contact by reorienting their midlines (Provine & Westerman, 1979, p. 439). No significant differences, however, were detected, however, between the performance of the left and right arms (Provine & Westerman, 1979, p. 439).

Contralateral reaching involving midline crossing also has been reported when neither hand is engaged. Indeed, in his 1890 study, Baldwin found that during his daughter's eighth month, placement of objects from 2 to 6 in. to her left side even further enhanced her right-hand preference; as Baldwin (1900) said, "The right hand intruded regularly upon the domain of the left [p. 63]" (see Harris, Chapter 10, this volume).

These contrary findings aside, the general point of Caplan and Kinsbourne's (1976) argument is certainly sound: that the infant's level of cognitive and motor competence must be taken into consideration when devising any test of lateralized functioning. The question therefore arises whether, with appropriate measures, hand differences could be revealed in infants in the first 6 months.

Caplan and Kinsbourne (1976) themselves have introduced one such measure—the duration of the infant's grasp of a rattle placed in its hand. The subjects were 21 infants, ranging in age from 1 month 13 days to 4 months 1 day (M = 2 months 21 days), all without familial sinistrality (FS −) (i.e., no parent or sibling is left-handed). The result was that, on a unimanual task (each hand tested alone), the right-hand hold was significantly longer, on average (61.9 sec), than the left (40.7 sec). On a bimanual task (both hands tested together), the right-hand hold also was longer than the left, but the difference was smaller and nonsignificant (44.6 versus 35.6 sec). Caplan and Kinsbourne (1976) gave no information about age

differences in their infants, but their conclusion that "within the limitations of this experiment clear asymmetry between hands arose in 3-
month-old infants [p. 533]" seems to imply that the differences found
were due primarily to those infants 3 months of age or older at the time of
testing. Caplan and Kinsbourne also tested five familialy sinistral (FS+)
infants (ages not given but presumably in the same age range as the FS−
group) and found no significant hand differences on either task for the
group as a whole.

Results similar to Caplan and Kinsbourne's with FS− infants have been
reported in a short-term longitudinal study by Petrie and Peters (1980),
except that shorter average holding times on both the unimanual and
bimanual trials were obtained. The subjects were 28 infants (both parents
right-handed) first tested at an average age of 17 days (range 6–29 days)
and then at three subsequent sessions at 30-day intervals. On the unimanual trials, the average holding time for the right hand (36.6 sec) was
significantly longer than for the left-hand (29.0 sec). For the bimanual
trials, no significant hand differences were found (left hand: 25.2 sec;
right hand: 25.5 sec).

Petrie and Peters (1980) also measured the strength of the infants' grasp
on a rubber bulb and found that infants squeezed harder with the right
hand (cf. Gutzmann, 1911; Valentine, 1914; see Harris, Chapter 10, this
volume). In light of this difference, one might be tempted to identify grip
strength as the cause of the differences in *duration* of the grasps. This
possibility perhaps cannot be entirely excluded, but it seems unlikely,
since, as Peters and Petrie have noted, the response to the placement of
the rubber bulb (for the test of grasp strength) was very brief (about 2 sec),
whereas a much longer squeeze was needed to hold the rattle. The nature
of the response to the two stimuli therefore was quite different.

In summary, the results of these two studies clearly indicate that, at
least in FS− infants, manual asymmetry exists very early in life, long
before the onset of speech. Whether there are age differences over the age
period spanned in these two studies seems less clear. As noted, it seems to
have been primarily the older infants in Caplan and Kinsbourne's (1976)
study who had shown manual asymmetry. In Petrie and Peters's (1980)
study, however, a developmental trend in terms of systematic shifts of the
values of the asymmetry coefficients could not be detected over the four
test sessions (p. 217).

The question of age differences may be particularly important for re-
solving the different results of the unimanual and bimanual tests. For this
reason, we decided to repeat Caplan and Kinsbourne's grasp-duration
study on a sample of infants at ages 2 months and 5 months, these ages
being close to the lower and upper bounds of the range represented in
Caplan and Kinsbourne's study. We also, in effect, gave Bruner's (1969)
version of the "engaged hand" reaching test another try, although we
were unaware of Bruner's paper at the time, and Provine and Westerman's

(1979) had not yet appeared. Our primary purpose, instead, was to find a way to discourage bilateral reaching and even encourage contralateral reaching.

Method

Subjects

Names of potential subjects were drawn from Ingham County (Michigan) birth records and from birth announcements in local newspapers. Participation was solicited by letters to the parents, with follow-up telephone calls approximately 2 weeks later. By this means, 44 subjects were recruited, 40 of whom were from families with no left-handedness, or sinistrality (FS−), 4 from families with one or both parents left-handed (FS+).

FS− INFANTS

Of the FS− infants, there were 20 2-month-old (M = 62 days, range 59–66 days) and 20 5-month-old infants (M = 153 days, range 147–155 days), with 10 boys and 10 girls in each age group. Assessment of parental handedness was based on the parents' reports and confirmed by their answers to a 10-item handedness questionnaire (Raczkowski, Kalat, & Nebes, 1974). Further questions disclosed no left handedness in grandparents or siblings.

FS+ INFANTS

Of the four FS+ infants, there were two 5-month-old boys (both parents left-handed) and a 2-month-old boy and a 5-month-old girl (left-handed fathers). All four infants also had some history of left handedness in the paternal grandparents and in older siblings. These infants' performance will be discussed following presentation of the main results.

BIRTH-WEIGHT, GESTATION, PARITY

The mean birth-weight of the infants was 7.2 lb (3.27 kg), and the mean gestation period was 39 weeks. The sample included one postmature boy (birth-weight 10 lb [4.54 kg], gestation 44 weeks), and no premature or low-birth-weight infants. According to the parents, none of the infants had experienced any harmful prenatal experiences, complications at birth, or serious illnesses or injuries. None had been delivered by Caesarian section. Twenty-seven infants were delivered without the aid of obstetrical medications, of whom 5 had been delivered by the LeBoyer technique. Twenty-seven infants were first-born, 11 were second births, and 6 were third or later. None of the aforementioned variables was related to hand-use scores on any of the measures used.

TEMPERAMENT

Parents also were asked questions about the temperament of the infant (an adapted form of the Carey Questionnaire, [Carey, 1973]). Their answers indicated that all infants were well within established norms.

POSTURAL ORIENTATION

Finally, in light of the results of studies mentioned earlier on infant postural orientation, the parents were asked to observe and record their infant's head position on at least 15 different occasions over a 2-week-long period immediately following the experimental tasks. The procedure was similar to that described in Harris and Fitzgerald (Chapter 14, this volume). The parents recorded their observations directly onto a check-sheet illustrated with pictures of a supine infant with its head turned to the left and to the right.

Procedure

All infants were tested in their homes with one or both parents present. The entire test session was audio- and videotaped on a portable unit with zoom lens. The infant was positioned on the basis of preassigned posture, and the tasks then were presented in one predetermined order for each infant. The entire test session lasted from 20 to 30 min. Two to three weeks after testing, the experimenter returned to each home to pick up all questionnaires and the head-position observation records.

TESTING POSTURE

In Caplan and Kinsbourne's (1976) experiment, the infant was tested while leaning "against the knees of the reclining examiner [p. 533]." Presumably, this means that the infant sat on the floor, facing away from the examiner, with the examiner therefore placing the rattles in the infant's hands from behind. In Petrie and Peters' (1980) study, the infant was held by the mother and, therefore, presumably was in a seated posture.

In the current study, one-half the 2- and 5-month-olds of each sex were assigned randomly to a seated-posture condition like Petrie and Peters', thus on the parent's (always the mother's) lap, firmly supported, with the experimenter directly in front; the remaining infants, as a check on the potential effects of posture, were tested while lying supine on the floor, with the mother behind at the head end, the experimenter at the feet. In a small number of cases, infants assigned to the supine condition began to cry and could not be quieted; they therefore were shifted to a seated posture.

TEST MATERIALS

Instead of a rattle (used by both Caplan & Kinsbourne, 1976, and Petrie & Peters, 1980), we used noiseless balsa-wood barbells on the possibility that a rattle's potential for making noise when shaken could confound both hand and age comparisons. The barbells were dowels 1 cm in diameter and 5.1 cm in length, with a 2.5-cm cube attached to each end. Each barbell weighed approximately 1 oz (28.4 gm). Three pairs were made, with each pair painted a different color to help sustain the infant's interest. On each trial, choice of color used was random with the constraint that when two barbells were presented (bimanual grasp trials), they were the same color.

Tests of Hand Use

Three tests of hand use were given: unimanual and bimanual grasp duration, and a test of reaching. Except for the differences already mentioned, test procedures on the grasp duration tests were the same as those used by Caplan and Kinsbourne (1976).

UNIMANUAL GRASP

Unimanual grasp duration was defined as the number of seconds an infant held a barbell in one hand alone. Four trials were presented, in left hand–right hand alternation, each trial beginning when a barbell was placed in one hand and ending when it was dropped. For one-half the boys and girls in each age group, testing began with the right hand, for the remaining infants, with the left hand. If the infant held the barbell for 150 sec, it was removed and the next trial was presented. All durations were timed by a stopwatch.

BIMANUAL GRASP

Bimanual grasp duration was defined as the number of seconds the infant held the two barbells, one in each hand. Four trials were presented, each beginning when the barbells were placed in the infant's hands and ending when they were dropped. Each trial was scored for the time that each hand held the barbell. After the infant dropped one barbell, 60 sec were allowed to pass before the other barbell was removed. The 60-sec limit was the same as that used by Caplan and Kinsbourne (1976). If both barbells were held for 150 sec, they were removed and the trial was repeated. This time limit was imposed for practical reasons only.

"REACHING"

For the reaching task, a barbell was placed in one of the infant's hands (hereafter called the *occupied hand*), and an identical barbell was presented at approximately 30° from body midline on the side contralateral to the free, or unoccupied, hand, and approximately 20 cm from the infant's face, so as to be well within reach. Four trials were presented, alternating hands; one-half the trials began with placement of the barbell in the left hand, one-half with the right hand. Each trial was scored for the hand used for reaching, for crossing the body midline, and for the latency to reaching (elapsed time from presentation of the second barbell to full arm extension). *Reaching* was operationally defined as any movement of the arm toward the barbell. The hand could be either fisted or open and did not actually have to come in contact with the object (White, Castle, & Held, 1964). If 150 sec passed after the second barbell was presented and the infant did not look at or move his arm toward it, both barbells were removed and the trial was repeated. This means that if the time limit was exceeded on a particular trial, we discarded the trial and presented another, so that each infant would have the same number of scorable trials.

This new procedure was designed to accomplish several aims: First, it should discourage bilateral reaching, since only one hand would be free, one already engaged, and since the target object was displaced 30° from the midline. Second, on the supposition that infants would be more likely to reach with the free hand than with the occupied hand, we could determine whether infants would show contralateral reaching more reliably or faster when the free (i.e., contralateral) hand was the right hand than when it was the left hand. Finally, since one hand was occupied, the infant's attention, if biased in any direction at that moment, presumably would be in the direction of the occupied hand (i.e., in a direction opposite to that of the presumably more engaged, contralateral hemisphere). Thus, by placing the second object on the same side as the occupied hand, we hoped to be able to enhance the likelihood of contralateral reaching by the free hand (i.e., reaching across body midline).

This procedure should not, of course, preclude ipsilateral reaching by the occupied hand, but we felt that at least it should preclude two other possibilities: ipsilateral reaching by the free hand and contralateral reaching by the occupied hand, since, in both cases, the infant would be reaching in the wrong direction. In fact, we did not observe any instances of these latter two behaviors. (We are assuming, therefore, that when the infant reaches, his attention is on the object, not on his hand.)

TASK ORDER

In Caplan and Kinsbourne's (1976) study, the unimanual tests always preceded the bimanual tests, whereas in Petrie and Peters's (1980) study, the tests were presented in counterbalanced order. Pilot testing for the current study suggested, however, that the reaching, bimanual grasp, and unimanual grasp tests required, in that order, from most to least attention and physical exertion on the part of the infants. The tests therefore were administered in that order to all infants so as to diminish subject attrition through fatigue or lack of interest.

CONTROLS FOR INFANT STATE, AND FOR CAMERA, INFANT,
EXPERIMENTER, AND PARENT POSITION

Testing was carried out at times when, according to parents, the infants were most likely to be active and alert. Each infant's state was monitored throughout testing, and testing was conducted only when the infants were in a quiet awake or active awake state according to the Brackbill and Fitzgerald scale (1969). Three infants had to be rescheduled for later testing (2 were crying, 1 was drowsy). We also were nearly able to counterbalance the number of infants in each age group tested before and after eating (2-month-olds: 8 pre-, 12 post-; 5-month-olds: 11 pre-, 9 post-). Those infants tested preprandially showed longer grasp durations and shorter latencies to reaching than did infants tested postprandially. However, prandial condition did not account for the age difference found and was not correlated with the margin of hand difference on any of the tasks.

Throughout the study, an attempt was also made to minimize the potential biasing effects of the infant's, experimenter's, or parent's position on the infant's behavior. Toward this end, the equipment was placed directly facing the infant to discourage any asymmetric posture or attention; a trial was started only when the infant's head was in midline with hands and arms in approximately symmetrical positions (this sometimes meant repositioning by the experimenter); and all object presentations were made directly before the infant rather than from one or the other side. Finally, as noted earlier, the infant either sat on the parent's lap or lay supine with the parent at the head end. In both conditions, the parent was instructed to remain still so as not to cue the infant in any way. If both parents were present, the parent not directly participating was asked to stand out of the infant's range of vision. All parents were completely cooperative in these regards.

Results

Descriptive Analysis

We begin with a qualitative description of the infants' performance since there were age differences here that are not expressed in the quantitative data analysis. On both the unimanual and bimanual grasp tests, the 2-month-olds seemed quite passive, as though unaware that anything was happening. Infants tested in the supine position held the barbells quite loosely, with their arms usually bent at the elbow, so that their hands were close to their ears. Infants tested in a seated position also held the barbells loosely but typically held their arms straight down at their sides or toward their laps. In both positions, there was little arm movement. The 5-month-olds, in contrast, were far more active, moving their arms and grasping much more strongly. They also often looked at the barbells and vocalized at the same time.

On the reaching trials, the 2-month-olds again were quite passive, and the arm positions were much the same as noted on the grasp tests. The free, unoccupied hand usually moved a little, though it was finger motion only. Often it was hard to get the 2-month-olds to look at the second barbell. Once they did, finger movements began (often accompanied by a sucking motion of the mouth), and the arm moved toward the second barbell slowly, with frequent stops and starts. By contrast, the 5-month-olds were easily induced to look at the second barbell. When it was presented, the first movements nearly always were of the free hand, followed by a more rapid, almost ballistic, swiping reach. In the majority of instances, the second barbell was touched but only infrequently grasped.

There were very few bilateral reaches for the 2-month-olds, and none for the 5-month-olds. Finally, ipsilateral reaches (i.e., by the occupied hand) were more frequent in the younger than in the older group (38 versus 18), and when they occurred, they were different as well. The 2-month-olds did not drop the first barbell to allow for grasping the second barbell, and actual contact with the second barbell was infrequent (observed only three times). The 5-month-olds, in contrast, usually dropped the first barbell before or during the reach itself.

Our overall impression, then, was of considerably greater skill in the older group. On the reaching task, we therefore have some misgivings about describing the younger infants' responses in the same terms as those of the 5-month-olds. Probably a more appropriate description would simply be "limb activation and extension."

Quantitative Analysis

All videotapes were scored by the examiner and by two independent raters who were unaware of the purposes of the study. Interrater reliabilities (i.e., correlations between scores assigned by each rater) were above .90 for all measures (i.e., duration on the grasp-duration tests, and hand used for reaching and time to full arm extension on the reaching trials). Preliminary tests failed to disclose any differences between the scores for infants tested in supine position and those for infants tested in the seated position, so these scores were combined.

UNIMANUAL GRASP DURATION

The means and standard deviations for the unimanual duration scores are shown in Table 17.1. An analysis of variance, with age, sex, and order (left or right hand first) as between-subject variables and hand and trial as

Table 17.1
Mean and Standard Deviation of Duration of Grasp (in Seconds)

	2-month-olds (N = 20)		5-month-olds (N = 20)	
	Left hand	Right hand	Left hand	Right hand
Unimanual task	35 (4)	54 (4)	67 (14)	110 (10)
Bimanual task	29 (4)	35 (4)	55 (11)	85 (8)

within-subject variables, disclosed significant main effects for age and hand, with grasp duration longer for the 5-month-olds than for the 2-month-olds [F (1, 38) = 450.3, $p < .001$], and longer for the right hand than for the left [F (1, 38) = 670.7, $p < .001$]. The analysis also revealed a significant Hand × Age interaction [F (1, 38) = 94.54, $p < .001$]. Inspection of the mean scores indicated that the hand differences were larger in the older group, but simple effects tests indicated that the differences were still significant at both ages [2-month-olds: F (1, 19) = 12.69, $p < .01$; 5-month-olds: F (1, 19) = 21.73, $p < .01$]. It is noteworthy that the mean durations for the 2-month-olds—35 sec for the left hand and 54 sec for the right—were very close to the scores reported by Caplan and Kinsbourne (1976)—41 and 62 sec—with the difference between hands about 20 sec in each experiment.

BIMANUAL GRASP DURATION

The scores for the bimanual grasp-duration task are also shown in Table 17.1. The overall durations were shorter than for the unimanual trials, just as Caplan and Kinsbourne (1976) and Petrie and Peters (1980) had found. An analysis of variance of similar design to that used for the unimanual scores again disclosed significant main effects for age and hand. The 5-month-olds grasped significantly longer than the 2-month-olds, and for the combined groups, the right hand held on longer than the left [F (1, 38) = 181.4, $p < .001$]. Again, the Age × Hand interaction was significant [F (1, 38) = 151.8, $p < .001$]. Analysis of simple effects showed the hand difference to be significant for the 5-month-olds [F (1, 19) = 10.65, $p < .05$] but this time, in contrast to the unimanual test results, not for the 2-month-olds [F (1, 19) = 2.08, n.s.].

LATERALITY INDEX

For both grasp-duration tasks, the greater hand difference for the 5-month-old than for the 2-month-old infants suggests an increase in asymmetry with age. The age comparisons are confounded, however, since the older infants also had absolutely longer grasp-duration scores. The age comparisons therefore were repeated, with laterality indices substituted for raw scores so as to permit a control for overall grasp duration. The formula used was LI = (R − L)/(R + L), with R and L scores referring to right and left means, respectively, over the pertinent trials, where positive scores indicate an asymmetry in favor of the right hand and negative scores in favor of the left hand (Marshall, Caplan, & Holmes, 1975).

The result was that on the unimanual task (Table 17.1), the age difference did not appear. All individual laterality indices were positive, the 2-month-olds averaging .22, the 5-month-olds averaging .23, a nonsignificant difference ($p > .05$). So, by this index, there is no evidence of an age difference in degree of hand asymmetry on this task. On the bimanual task (Table 17.1), all individual laterality indices once again were positive, but this time the age difference revealed in the analysis of the total duration scores was confirmed. The mean laterality index for the 2-month-olds was .20, and for the 5-month-olds, .39. The difference was significant [$F (1, 38) = 13.78$, $p < .01$].

REACHING TASK

Analyses of scores on the reaching task revealed a significant increase with age in the total number of ipsilateral and contralateral reaches (point biserial $r_{(age\ and\ total\ number\ of\ reaches)} = .79$; $r_{(age\ and\ total\ number\ contralateral\ reaches)} = .88$; $p < .001$). But, as in previous investigations of infants in the 2- and 5-month-old age groups, we found no evidence of hand differences for either measure. In other words, 5-month-olds reached for objects more frequently and crossed body midline in reaching more frequently than 2-month-olds did, but neither age group showed a hand difference on these measures.

Both age and hand differences, however, were found for speed of reaching (i.e., the time to full arm extension). The results are summarized in Table 17.2. Age and hand main effects were significant, both for ipsilateral reaching and for contralateral reaching. For ipsilateral reaches (i.e., reaches by occupied hand to barbell on same side), this meant that the 2-month-olds showed slower extension than the 5-month-olds [$F (1. 38) = 10.47$, $p < .05$], and that right-hand ipsilateral reaches were faster than left-hand reaches [$F (1, 38) = 5.31$, $p < .05$]. For contralateral reaching (i.e., reaches with the free hand to the barbell on the opposite side), this meant again that the 2-month-olds showed slower extension than the 5-month-olds [$F (1, 38) = 23.15$, $p < .001$], and the right hand was faster than the left hand [$F (1, 38) = 13.47$, $p < .001$].

Table 17.2 also shows significant Age × Hand interactions for both ipsilateral and contralateral reaching. Simple effects tests indicated that for both measures (ipsilateral reaches by occupied hand and contralateral reaches by free hand), the hand difference was significant for the 5-

Table 17.2
Mean and Standard Deviation of Latency (in Seconds) for Reaching

	2-month-olds (N = 20)		5-month-olds (N = 20)	
	Left hand	Right hand	Left hand	Right hand
Ipsilateral reaching by occupied hand	20 (12)	18 (9)	13 (7)	4 (3)
Contralateral reaching by free hand	25 (13)	23 (10)	18 (8)	8 (3)
Contralateral reaching by free hand				
Trial 1	25 (14)	34 (13)	19 (10)	11 (8)
Trial 2	22 (13)	17 (12)	18 (10)	4 (3)

month-olds [F (1, 19) = 7.37 and 13.76, respectively; $p < .05$] but not for the 2-month-olds [F (1, 19) = 2.08 and 2.92, n.s.]. In the case of contralateral reaching (across body midline), this interaction was further modified by a significant Age × Hand × Trial interaction [F (1, 38) = 6.31, $p < .05$] shown in Table 17.2. From trial 1 to trial 2, right-hand speed of reaching increased significantly more than left-hand speed [F (1, 38) = 14.52, $p < .05$ for right versus left], but the effect seemed to be more marked in the 2-month-olds [F (1, 38) = 17.4, $p < .001$] than in the 5-month-olds [F (1, 38) = 12.83, $p < .01$]. However, the proportional, as distinct from the absolute, amount of change appears to be similar in the two age groups (see Table 17.2).

INFANTS OF LEFT-HANDED PARENTS (FS+)

Let us now compare the scores of the 40 FS− infants with those of the 4 FS+ infants. For the FS+ infants, durations of unimanual and bimanual grasp were comparable to those of the infants whose parents were right-handed. The hand differences, however, were in the opposite direction, with the left hand being favored but by a smaller margin than the margin of right-hand preference in the FS− infants. On the reaching task, there were no hand differences in frequency of reaches. Average latencies were comparable to those of the other infants, but the asymmetry was toward the left and was less marked.

HEAD POSITION

Of the FS− infants, all 20 2-month-olds were reported to show a strong preference for the head-right posture. Of all asymmetrical postures recorded, 87% were toward the right. In the 5-month-old group, 17 of the 20 infants were reported to show no preference in posture. The remaining 3 infants had a head-right preference, but not so frequently or so strongly as the 2-month-old infants. Parents of the 17 5-month-olds who observed no preference were asked to recall whether their infants had shown a preference at a younger age. In 14 cases the answer was yes, all to the right.

Discussion

The "Midline Barrier"

It seems clear that when one of the infant's hands is already engaged, even a 2-month-old infant will be able to extend its free hand across the body in the direction of, albeit short of actually contacting, a visual target. This finding agrees with Provine and Westerman's (1979) results and further challenges the notion that there is a "midline barrier" in young infants. The findings that ipsilateral reaches (that is, reaches by the occupied hand) were more than twice as frequent in the 2-month-old infants as in the 5-month-olds and that the total numbers of reaches and midline crosses were significantly greater in the older group are also consonant with Provine and Westerman's (1979) results in suggesting that the ability (or readiness) to cross the midline increases with age as the infant develops a greater range and variety of visually guided manual skills.

Manual Asymmetry

FS– INFANTS

The results also show that infants with no familial history of left handedness use the right hand preferentially. On the unimanual test of grasp duration, both the 2- and 5-month-olds showed reliable and comparable right-hand preference. However, on the bimanual test and the reaching test, only the older infants showed right-hand preference.

The results for grasp duration thus support Caplan and Kinsbourne's (1976) as well as Petrie and Peters' (1980) findings. The results on the reaching task, however, depart from those of Provine and Westerman (1979), who found no left–right differences. Assuming that the great majority of Provine and Westerman's infants came from right-handed families (information not given in their report), then scoring differences may be relevant in accounting for the differences in results. Provine and Westerman scored for number of touches and ended a trial either after the infant's hand touched the stimulus object or after 60 sec, whichever came first. By the most nearly comparable measure in our study (i.e., number of reaches), we likewise found no hand differences. Hand differences instead were evident only when speed was taken into account.

Still another difference, this time from Caplan and Kinsbourne's results, appeared for the FS+ infants. Whereas only one of their five FS+ infants grasped longer with the left hand, all four of our infants showed preferences for the left, although the hand difference was less pronounced than for the main group of FS− infants. Although there are far too few subjects to permit final conclusions, we can note the consistency of these findings, as well as Caplan and Kinsbourne's, with the generally acknowledged view that hand differences in usage and skill are less pronounced in left- than in right-handed individuals (e.g., Benton, 1962).

Progressive versus Age-Invariant Lateralization

How our results bear on the relative merits of the "progressive" and "invariant" lateralization models of development is unclear. The unimanual test results seem to be consistent with the "invariant" model, that is, that functional lateralization appears early in development and is invariant over time, at least within this limited age range and for these particular behavioral measures. By contrast, the results on the bimanual grasp and the reaching tests suggest that although lateralization is present at 2 months of age, it has progressed beyond this early stage, becoming more clearly differentiated by 5 months. How, then, to reconcile the findings with investigations cited earlier that have failed to find age differences in tests of lateralized functioning? The answer, we believe, is that the age differences in the current investigation at least partly represent effects of complexity—both in terms of task demands and in increasing skills of the developing infant.

Consider, first, the unimanual and bimanual duration measures. Recall that neither Caplan and Kinsbourne (1976) nor Petrie and Peters (1980) found hand differences on the bimanual task. In commenting on this, Caplan and Kinsbourne (1976) suggested that a basic preference for the right hand may be "more easily demonstrated when one hand at a time is used; but what may increase with age is the power of the left brain to inhibit the right brain when both are activated and compete for attention [p. 534]." Our results are consistent with this view, that is, on the unimanual task, we found longer right-hand holding by comparable margins in both 2- and 5-month-olds (as measured by laterality indices); on the bimanual task, we found longer right-hand holding only in the 5-month-olds. Another way of putting this may be to say that in 2-month-olds, the tendency to make mirror movements—for the hands to work together—is very strong, and the bimanual task brings out this disposition.

The age difference on the reaching task likewise does not necessarily support the progressive lateralization view. There is some evidence in adults that lateralized tendencies are brought out more clearly on more complex tasks or on tasks requiring greater skill (Steingruber, 1975). The same probably is true for infants and children, so that the greater lateralization our 5-month-olds showed for reaching (at least with respect to the *speed* component of reaching) may be related to the greater complexity of this task and to the 5-month-olds' greater measure of skill (cf. discussion of Baldwin in Harris, Chapter 10, this volume). What we may be seeing, then—as Caplan and Kinsbourne suggested about their own results—is behavior over time coming increasingly under fine motor and thus left-hemisphere control, although the underlying cerebral lateralization remains constant. Thus, the presence of age differences in the degree of functional lateralization across all tasks does not necessarily mean that the progressive lateralization model holds in these instances. Rather, a mixed model like the one just described may be more appropriate. A similar proposal about the interpretation of age differences in performance on tasks of lateralized skills has been made by Harris and Witelson (1977) and Kinsbourne and Hiscock (1977) and also by Porter and Berlin (1975) and Satz, Rardin, and Ross (1971) (see discussion in Young, 1977, especially pp. 294–297).

In this connection, it is interesting to note the general agreement between the head-position data, as provided by the parents' reports, and the data reported by Harris and Fitzgerald (Chapter 14, this volume). In both studies, by this measure, there is evidence of a waning of, or at least no increase in, strength of asymmetry with age. The fact that the 5-month-olds in the current study showed the stronger hand preference for holding and increased speed of reaching thus suggests a disjunction between the head position and hand-preference measures. This is not an unreasonable outcome if we think of the early head-right posture as a largely reflexive precursor of later lateralized behaviors that are under a greater measure of voluntary control.

Grasp Duration, "Reaching," and Handedness

Handedness means not only a preferential use of one hand (for, say, holding or reaching), but a clear differentiation of function and skill. The so-called dominant hand is preferred and more skillful in tasks requiring fine motor coordination and motor sequencing, whereas the nondominant hand generally serves a supportive role, notwithstanding its own special skills, such as for spatial relations (Harris, 1975, 1980). Like Caplan and Kinsbourne (1976), we are tempted to conclude that hand differences in grasp duration during early infancy (and now we can include differences in speed of arm extension) are precursors of these dimensions of handedness in older individuals. But since we are not yet able to identify the functional relationships between these measures over time—something that could be accomplished only through long-term longitudinal studies—we perhaps should restrict ourselves, as Caplan and Kinsbourne did, to a more modest statement—that, within the limitations of our experiment, manual asymmetries are present in young infants at least as early as 2 months of age and, in any case, well before the onset of speech.

Acknowledgments

Thanks are due Gayle White and Shirley Cahill for their help in scoring videotape recordings, and Margaret Hall for typing the manuscript.

References

Baldwin, J. M. (1890). Origin of right or left handedness. *Science 16*, 247–248.

Baldwin, J. M. (1900). *Mental development in the child and the race* (2nd ed.). New York: Macmillan.

Benton, A. L. (1962). Clinical symptomatology in right and left hemisphere lesions. In V. B. Mountcastle (Ed.), *Interhemispheric relations and cerebral dominance*. Baltimore, Maryland: The Johns Hopkins Univ. Press.

Best, C. T., Hoffman, H., & Glanville, B. B. (1981). Development of infant ear asymmetries for speech and music. *Perception & Psychophysics 31*, 75–85.

Brackbill, Y., & Fitzgerald, H. (1969). Development of sensory analyzers. In L. P. Lipsitt & H. W. Reese (Eds.), *Advances in child development and behavior* (vol. 4). New York: Academic Press.

Bruner, J. S. (1969). Eye, hand, and mind. In D. Elkind & J. H. Flavell (Eds.), *Studies in cognitive development: Essays in honor of Jean Piaget*. London and New York: Oxford Univ. Press.

Caplan, P., & Kinsbourne, M. (1976). Baby drops the rattle: Asymmetry of duration of grasp by infants. *Child Development 47*, 532–534.

Carey, W. B. (1973). Measurement of infant temperament in pediatric practice. In J. C. Westman (Ed.), *Individual differences in children*. New York: Wiley.

Černáček, J., & Podivinský, F. (1971). Ontogenesis of handedness and somatosensory cortical response. *Neuropsychologia 9*, 219–232.

Dennis, M., & Kohn, B. (1975). Comprehension of syntax in infantile hemiplegics after cerebral hemidecortication: Left hemisphere superiority. *Brain and Language 2*, 475–486.

Dennis, M., & Whitaker, H. A. (1976). Language acquisition following hemidecortication: Linguistic superiority of the left over the right hemisphere. *Brain and Language 3*, 404–433.

Dennis, M., & Whitaker, H. A. (1977). Hemispheric equipotentiality and language acquisition. In S. J. Segalowitz & F. A. Gruber (Eds.), *Language development and neurological theory*. New York: Academic Press.

Gesell, A., & Ames, L. B. (1947). The development of handedness. *Journal of Genetic Psychology 70*, 155–175.

Giesecke, M. (1936). The genesis of hand preference. *Monographs of the Society for Research in Child Development 1*, Study No. 2.

Glanville, B. B., Best, C. T., & Levenson, R. (1977). A cardiac measure of cerebral asymmetries in infant auditory perception. *Developmental Psychology 13*, 54–59.

Gutzmann, H. (1911). *Beobachtungen der ersten sprachlichen und stimmlichen Entwicklung eines Kindes. Monatsschrift für die gesamte Spracheilkunde.*

Harris, L. J. (1975). Neurophysiological factors in the development of spatial skill. In J. Eliot & N. J. Salkind (Eds.), *Children's spatial development.* Springfield, Illinois: Thomas.

Harris, L. J. (1980). Which hand is the "eye" of the blind?—A new look at an old question. In J. Herron (Ed.), *Neuropsychology of left-handedness.* New York: Academic Press.

Harris, L. J., & Witelson, S. F. (1977). *The analysis of cognitive processes in children through the study of hemispheric specialization in different perceptual systems.* Paper presented at Biennial Meetings of the Society for Research in Child Development, New Orleans, Louisiana, March.

Hiscock, M., & Kinsbourne, M. (1977). Selective listening asymmetry in preschool children. *Developmental Psychology 13,* 217–224.

Kinsbourne, M., & Hiscock, M. (1977). Does cerebral dominance develop? In S. J. Segalowitz & F. A. Gruber (Eds.), *Language development and neurological theory.* New York: Academic Press.

Lenneberg, E. H. (1967). *Biological foundations of language.* New York: Wiley.

Lesné & Peycelon, -. (1934). A quel age un enfant cesse-t-il d'etre ambidextre pour devoir droitier? *Bulletin de la Societé de la Pediatrie 32,* 436–439.

Marshall, J., Caplan, D., & Holmes, J. (1975). The measure of laterality. *Neuropsychologia 13,* 315–321.

Petrie, B. F., & Peters, M. (1980). Handedness: Left/right differences in intensity of grasp response and duration of rattle holding in infants. *Infant Behavior and Development 3,* 215–221.

Porter, R., & Berlin, C. (1975). On interpreting developmental changes in the dichotic right-ear advantage. *Brain and Language 2,* 186–200.

Provine, R. L., & Westerman, J. A. (1979). Crossing the midline: Limits of early eye–hand behavior. *Child Development 50,* 437–441.

Raczkowski, D., Kalat, J., & Nebes, R. (1974). Reliability and validity of some handedness questionnaire items. *Neuropsychologia 12,* 43–47.

Satz, P., Rardin, D., & Ross, J. (1971). An evaluation of a theory of specific developmental dyslexia. *Child Development 42,* 2009–2021.

Seth, G. (1973). Eye–hand coordination and "handedness": A developmental study of visuo-motor behaviour in infancy. *British Journal of Educational Psychology 43,* 35–49.

St. James-Roberts, I. (1981). A reinterpretation of hemispherectomy data without functional plasticity of the brain. *Brain and Language 13,* 31–53.

Steingruber, H. J. (1975). Handedness as a function of test complexity. *Perceptual and Motor Skills 40,* 263–266.

Turkewitz, G., Gordon, E. W., & Birch, H. G. (1965). Head turning in the human neonate: Spontaneous patterns. *Journal of Genetic Psychology 107,* 143–148.

Valentine, C. W. (1914). The colour perception and colour preferences of an infant during its fourth and eighth months. *British Journal of Psychology 6,* 363–387.

Voelckel, E. (1913). Untersuchungen uber die Rechtshandigkeit beim Saugling. *Zeitschrift fur Kinderheilk 8,* 351–358.

White, B. L., Castle, P., & Held, R. (1964). Observations on the development of visually-directed reaching. *Child Development 35,* 349–364.

Witelson, S. F., & Pallie, W. (1973). Left hemisphere specialization for language in the newborn: Neuroanatomical evidence of asymmetry. *Brain 96,* 641–646.

Young, G. (1977). Manual specialization in infancy: Implications for lateralization of brain function. In S. J. Segalowitz & F. A. Gruber (Eds.), *Language development and neurological theory.* New York: Academic Press.

Laterality in Manipulatory and Cognitive-Related Activity in Four- to Ten-Month-Olds[1]

CAROLYN J. MEBERT

Introduction

An understanding of the developmental relationship between lateralization of cerebral function and manual activity has been the aim of considerable research and speculation in recent years. Gazzaniga (1970), for example, described how each hemisphere might establish "its own experience base and control system for behavioral operations [p. 1]." He suggested that the sensorimotor schemes developed by the right hand of an infant form the bases for the neurological mechanisms in the left hemisphere necessary for language functions. In this way, the left hand would, similarly, contribute to the laying down of "engrams" in the right hemisphere. But, since the right hand is predicted to be more active than the left, the left hemisphere would become more knowledgeable and would ask more questions of its environment, manifested in increased right-hand activity. In this way, Gazzaniga proposed, a relationship arises in which hand and hemisphere mutually reinforce each other.

Though this proposition is attractive, one could question Gazzaniga's emphasis on a generalized greater activation of the right-hand–left-hemisphere system. It may be the case that one hand is more often in the infant's visual field early in life (Coryell, 1977) and consequently develops a lead in *visually guided* manual activity; it does not necessarily follow that the other hand is less active, or that the other hemisphere is asking fewer questions of its environment. The two hands may be interacting with the environment with equal frequency, though their modes

[1]The research for this chapter was supported by a predoctoral fellowship from the National Institute of Mental Health (No. MH07239). Portions of this study were presented at the 1980 meetings of AAAS, San Francisco, California, and EPA, Hartford, Connecticut.

349

of interacting (i.e., how they handle objects—grasps used, manipulatory activities engaged in) may differ, perhaps as a function of the degree of visual "guidance" or concomitant visual experience that each hemisphere obtains. From early in life, therefore, each hand may be effecting the establishment of different kinds of sensorimotor schemes in the hemisphere contralateral to it. So that, just as the right hand "teaches" the left hemisphere to "talk" (in Gazzaniga's terms), the left hand may be providing the type of experience necessary for the organization of the processing operations characteristic of the right hemisphere. In this way, each hemisphere would be developing its own system for interacting with the environment. This, in essence, is the proposition examined in this chapter.

To this end, a variety of manual activities were examined in infants 4–10 months of age as they manipulated toys presented to them. It was predicted that the right hand (left hemisphere) would predominate in more refined exploratory activity (e.g., precision grasping, fine motor behavior), whereas the left hand (right hemisphere) would excel in more global spatial activity (e.g., gross motor behavior), although there would be no differences between the hands in overall amount of activity displayed. This hypothesis fits a current view of the specialized skills of the hemispheres (and presumably the contralateral hands–fingers, to which they are exclusively connected [Brinkman & Kuypers, 1973]), that is, that the left hemisphere excels in more time-dependent, sequential, or analytic processes, whereas the right excels in less sequential (e.g., Gestalt, spatial) processes (Bradshaw & Nettleton, 1981). Tasks designed to assess object permanence (Piaget, 1954) were also included, as performance on such tasks requires the use of sensorimotor schemes presumably no different from the ones to which Gazzaniga referred. Successful performance on object permanence tasks requires not only a mental representation of a hidden object, but coordination of eye and hand as in visually guided reaching, as well. Furthermore, visually guided reaching has been related to the development of preferred-hand use and neurobehavioral development in infancy (e.g., Castner, 1932; Černáček & Podivinský, 1972; Coryell, 1977; Sherick, Greenman, & Legg, 1976). Therefore, the relationship between hand use in reaching on various cognitive tasks and hand use in toy manipulation was investigated in an attempt to determine the extent to which reaching behavior observed in somewhat constrained tasks generalizes to manual activity more broadly defined.

Method

Subjects

A total of 40 infants were included in the final sample; 10 at each of the following ages: 4 months (M = 4 months, 5 days; 5 males, 5 females), 6 months (M = 6 months, 3 days; 6 males, 4 females), 8 months (M = 8 months, 6 days; 5 males, 5 females), and 10 months (M = 10 months, 4 days; 4 males, 6 females). These subjects were all white, from middle-class homes (as determined by parental occupation), and had at least one parent who had completed college. All infants included in the study had right-handed parents and siblings, were born at term with a birth-weight over 2500 gm, and had no medical problems up to the time of testing.

Procedure

Infants were tested in a laboratory setting at times parents thought best for the infant (e.g., after a nap or feeding). Parent(s) were permitted to remain in the room throughout the session and remained quiet and seated behind the infant during testing. Testing began when the subject appeared calm and alert. If the infant became distressed during testing, the session was interrupted until the infant was calm enough to begin again. All sessions were videotaped for later coding.

Four-month-old infants were placed in an infant seat that was secured at a 60° angle in a plastic hospital bassinet. A board was placed across the top of the bassinet, above the infant's legs, serving as a tray. The 6-, 8-, and 10-month-olds were seated in an infant feeding table.

The procedure involved four tasks. Performance on the last three tasks listed (i.e., cognitive tasks [CT] 1–3) was used to determine the subject's hand preference in reaching, as well as for the purposes stated in the task descriptions. During task administration, the experimenter stood to the right of the infant when placing a toy in the infant's right hand, and to the left when placing a toy in the left hand. After presenting the toy, the experimenter sat in front of the infant, under the videocamera, which was positioned at the subject's midline. Descriptions of the four tasks used follow.

MANIPULATION OF TOYS

Two different toys, a white plastic ring with a red key attached and a green nut-and-bolt toy, were placed, one at a time, in the infant's right or left hand. Behavior directed at the toy was recorded for 2 min. There were four trials of this task, accounting for all combinations of hand and toy. The order in which the toys were used and the hand of presentation were systematically varied across subjects within an age group. If a dropped toy was not retrieved by the infant, the experimenter replaced it in the hand to which it was initially presented.

COGNITIVE TASKS

Three types of cognitive tasks were administered: (a) standard object permanence; (b) object permanence with restriction; and (c) modified object permanence. These tasks will be referred to as CT 1, CT 2, and CT 3, respectively.

CT 1. With the infant seated, a teething toy composed of six different colored disks held together with a string was dangled in front of the infant and tapped on the tray until the infant's attention was caught. The toy was then covered completely with a cloth. The infant's behavior was recorded for 30 sec or until the cloth was removed and/or the toy obtained, whichever occurred first.

CT 2. In order to determine if the two hands differ in performance on standard object-permanence tasks, two additional trials of the test described above were conducted. These trials differed from the first in that a sock was put on the infant's hand and forearm prior to presentation of the toy. Umansky (1973) found, in infants of the same ages as those tested here, that the sock effectively immobilized the infant's arm, thereby affording use of only or primarily the unrestricted arm. In one trial, the right hand was restricted, in the other, the left was restricted. Order was counterbalanced within cells.

CT 3. In order to determine whether the two hands use similar or different strategies to remove a cloth from a grasped object, a modified version of Gratch's (1972) object-permanence test was conducted. A plastic hammer was tapped on the tray in order to attract the attention of the infant, and was then placed in the infant's hand. Hand and toy were then covered with either a transparent cloth or an opaque cloth. Placing the toy in the infant's hand ensured that the response of each hand to this situation could be recorded, and it was in this respect that our procedure differed from Gratch's. (He had the infants reach for the toy, not controlling for hand use, and had designed the task as a way of assessing the relative dominance of vision and touch.)

There were four trials in this task: right hand–opaque cloth, left hand–opaque cloth, right hand–transparent cloth, and left hand–transparent cloth. Presentation of these trials was systematically varied across subjects within an age group. Each trial was terminated after 30 sec had passed or when the infant removed the cloth, whichever occurred first.

The order of presentation of the four tasks was the same for all subjects, although the order of right–left and transparent–opaque presentations did vary. CT 1 was administered first, followed by one trial of CT 2 and two trials of CT 3. The entire manipulation task was then administered, followed by one trial of CT 2 and, finally, the last two trials of CT 3. Pilot testing indicated that a presentation order such as this promoted good cooperation from subjects, decreasing the likelihood that boredom or fatigue would interfere with performance. Intertrial and intertask intervals were kept as short as possible in order to maintain the infant's attentiveness.

Coding

MANIPULATION TASKS

The manipulation tasks were coded for relevant behaviors during every 3-sec interval of the 2 min the subject had the toy and for whether those behaviors occurred with or without visual contact. The original coding scheme included 27 different categories of behavior. On the basis of low frequencies of occurrence and/or similarity in hand or arm actions involved in the behaviors, these categories were collapsed to form the following 11 categories:

Power Grasp. Palmar contact with the object and no intrinsic movements of the hand. (Based on Connolly's [1973] description of different types of grasps, this category includes ventral, opposed palmar, and transverse palmar grasps.)

Precision Grasp. Grasps that afford some degree of intrinsic movements and no palmar contact. (Connolly's transverse digital and adult [pincer] grasps.)

Fine Motor Activity. Movements of the hand and fingers alone, excluding grasping and any behaviors in which the whole arm was active.

Gross Motor Activity. Activity that involves the whole arm only, such as in shaking, hitting, and so on.

To Mouth. Bringing a toy to the mouth and/or holding the toy in the mouth.

Away from Mouth. Removing the toy from the mouth.

Approach. Movement of hand and arm in the direction of the toy (which is either held by the other hand or on the table). No contact with the toy by the approaching hand is implied.

Contact Toy. Touching the toy with the finger tips or with the whole hand (but not hitting or other gross movements on the toy); this involves neither holding the toy nor movement of the fingers over the toy.

Toy Transfer. Transferring the toy from one hand to the other. The hand indicated was the one to which the toy was transferred.

Release. Throwing or dropping the toy onto or off of the table. This could involve only hand (as in dropping the toy onto the table top) or full-arm movements (as in tossing the toy aside).

On Table. This is the only category of inactivity coded. It was scored when the arm(s) were lying inactively on the table top.

In addition to these behavioral categories, the amount of time, in seconds, that the infants held each toy in the right and left hands prior to dropping or transferring them was recorded. This was included as a partial replication of Caplan and Kinsbourne's (1976) study of grasp duration as an index of hand preference in young infants. The overall amount of activity of each hand both with and without visual contact was also recorded, in order to determine whether hand differences in visually guided activity were manifested in this situation. All grasps and activities observed were coded either R (right), L (left), or B (both) to indicate the hand use involved. (B was very rarely coded.) Agreement between coders averaged 92% (per coding sheet) after training, with a range of 82–97%.

COGNITIVE TASKS

All trials of the standard and restricted object-permanence tasks (CT 1 and CT 2) were scored ordinally (Uzgiris & Hunt, 1975) for cloth removal and attention to toy. Subjects received a score of 1 if they did not remove the cloth covering the toy, a 2 if they removed the cloth and played with it but did not attend to the toy, and a 3 if they removed the cloth and retrieved the toy.

The behaviors displayed in the modified object-permanence task (CT 3) were coded with a 1–3 scoring system as well. If the cloth covering the infant's hand and toy was not removed, the subject received a score of 1. If the cloth was shaken off, a 2 was scored, and if it were pulled off by the hand not holding the hammer, the score received was 3. These scores are assumed to be ordinal since Gratch's study suggest that shaking off a cloth to regain visual contact with an object is a lower-level response than is pulling off the cloth. Agreement between coders on the cognitive tasks was 99%.

Data Treatment

The frequency of occurrence of each of the behaviors just described was tabulated for each subject's two hands in both toy (ring-and-key, nut-and-bolt) and both presentation (right, left) conditions. These frequencies were converted to represent percentages of the total number of 3-sec periods the toy was interacted with, both with visual contact and without visual contact.

Preliminary analyses of variance were conducted on the manipulation data and included the factors of sex and reaching preference. For the reaching-preference factor, subjects were divided into right- and nonright-reachers on the basis of the reaching behavior displayed in the cognitive tasks (i.e., if a majority of reaches was executed with the right hand the subject was considered a right-reacher, otherwise the subject was placed in the category of nonright-reachers. Within each age group, subjects were divided almost evenly into these two reach categories. All main effects and interactions involving these two factors were nonsignificant; they were therefore excluded from further analyses. The results reported are from separate five-way analyses of variance performed on each category of behavior. The five factors are: age (4, 6, 8, 10 months), hand (right, left), toy (ring-and-key, nut-and-bolt), presentation (right, left), and visual field (in, out).

Because the data used in these analyses were in the form of frequencies converted into percentages, it cannot be assumed that all of the assumptions underlying the analysis of variance model have been met in all cases. Therefore, only those results significant at at least the .01 level will be reported. A significance level of .01 for an F value when the assumptions of the test have been violated is approximately equal to an associated probability of .05 for an F value calculated when all assumptions have been met (McNemar, 1957).

Post hoc comparisons of means were performed with the Newman–Keuls test and, where appropriate, with post hoc trend analyses. Any differences reported were significant at the confidence level of 95% or better.

Results

Manipulation Tasks

Presented in Table 18.1 are the means for right- and left-hand activity in each age group. Table 18.2 is a summary of the results of the ANOVAs in terms of significant main effects and interactions for each behavioral category.

An inspection of Table 18.2 indicates the presence of several main effects for age, toy, and field. Whereas power grasping significantly decreased over age [$F_{lin} (1, 36) = 14.92, p < .001$], both precision grasping and toy transfer increased with age [$F_{lin} (1, 36) = 23.09, p < .001$] and [$F_{lin} (1, 36) = 15.46, p < .001$], respectively. Thus, it appears that the infants increasingly use more refined behaviors as they get older and evidence a parallel decrease with age in less differentiated grasping.

With regard to differences between the two toys, no clear pattern emerges. Infants displayed the power grasp, fine motor activity, and to-mouth activity more often with the nut-and-bolt, but precision grasping and gross motor activity more often with the ring-and-key. Thus, for each toy, both more and less refined movements were observed. These toy main effects and the interactions involving toys do indicate that infants

Table 18.1

Mean Percentages of Right- and Left-Hand Activity in Each of the Behavioral Categories Analyzed in the Manipulation Trials for Each Age Group

Category	4 months		6 months		8 months		10 months	
	Right	Left	Right	Left	Right	Left	Right	Left
Power	27.30	32.57	22.88	27.74	21.64	20.49	23.41	16.10
Precision	25.03	13.39	31.82	20.22	33.48	27.40	33.92	28.93
Fine motor	18.95	18.25	22.94	25.99	27.44	25.04	23.26	20.72
Gross motor	36.34	27.68	23.89	23.86	22.87	20.16	27.99	16.15
To mouth	10.10	8.99	14.83	16.03	10.47	14.16	13.31	12.45
Away from mouth	5.38	4.05	7.98	7.40	4.89	5.59	5.82	4.65
Approach	7.71	5.31	6.07	7.30	5.93	7.15	6.96	8.82
Contact toy	10.28	13.86	8.21	12.06	11.96	11.46	7.67	11.21
Toy transfer	.31	.82	3.71	3.94	7.04	5.71	8.10	7.61
Release	6.05	4.73	4.81	4.10	7.23	4.85	4.01	3.86
On table	13.23	15.85	9.20	11.16	13.35	18.69	10.47	12.56
Initial grasp duration (in seconds)	34.56	35.80	16.30	15.09	14.96	15.38	9.34	8.42
Active in visual field	51.05	42.84	55.04	54.12	60.64	49.43	57.13	47.35
Active out of visual field	44.31	40.58	37.38	46.56	37.20	44.69	39.99	38.12

are able to distinguish between toys in both grasping behavior and other sorts of activities, suggesting that they are sensitive to differences in the characteristics of different objects.

A greater proportion of behavior in the categories of approach, fine motor activity, gross motor activity, transfer, away from mouth, and release occurred when the infant had visual contact with the toy than when the toy was out of their visual field. The result was in the opposite direction for only one behavior that necessarily took place much of the time out of the visual field—to mouth.

There was only one main effect for the hand. Overall, the right hand was used about 50% more often in precision grasping than the left (31.06 versus 22.48). As can be seen in Table 18.1, the right-hand advantage in precision grasping was evident in all age groups, a finding in marked contrast to that which emerged in the power-grasp category.

The predominant results, found in all but one category, were Hand × Presentation interactions. In the categories of power and precision grasping, to mouth, away from mouth, release, and gross motor activity, the hand to which the toy was presented was proportionally more active than the other hand. The reverse pattern was shown for approach, contact, transfer of toy, and on table: In these categories, the initially free hand

Table 18.2

Summary of Significant Results of the Analyses of Variance Performed on the Behavioral Categories from the Manipulation Trials

Category and main effects	F	df	Interactions	F	df
Power grasp					
Age***	7.55	3,36	Presentation × Hand***	95.78	1,36
Toy***	65.34	1,36	Age × Presentation × Hand***	17.15	3,36
			Toy × Presentation × Hand***	31.27	1,36
Precision grasp					
Age***	10.78	3,36	Presentation × Hand***	23.35	1,36
Toy***	55.34	1,36	—	—	—
Hand***	13.05	1,36	—	—	—
Fine motor activity					
Toy***	14.77	1,36	—	—	—
Field***	80.44	1,36	—	—	—
Gross motor activity					
Toy**	9.56	1,36	Presentation × Hand***	19.24	1,36
Field**	12.17	1,36	Presentation × Hand × Field***	18.64	1,36
			Age × Presentation × Hand**	5.09	3,36
Approach					
Field***	51.81	1,36	Presentation × Hand***	66.37	1,36
Contact toy	—	—	Presentation × Hand***	16.53	1,36
Transfer					
Age***	9.27	3,36	Presentation × Hand***	13.49	1,36
Field***	16.22	1,36			
To mouth					
Toy***	31.46	1,36	Presentation × Hand***	26.55	1,36
Field***	41.39	1,36	Age × Toy**	6.06	3,36
			Age × Toy × Field**	6.11	3,36
Away from mouth					
Field***	14.44	1,36	Presentation × Hand***	13.91	1,36
			Toy × Presentation × Hand**	11.66	1,36
Release					
Field***	18.23	1,36	Presentation × Hand***	24.21	1,36
On table	—	—	Presentation × Hand***	20.60	1,36
Initial grasp (duration)					
Age***	10.72	3,36	—	—	—
Activity in visual field					
Hand*	5.17	1,36	—	—	—

*p < .03.
**p < .01.
***p < .001.

displayed these behaviors more often than did the hand of presentation. Only fine motor activity seemed unaffected by presentation—both hands manifested equal frequencies of that behavior in both presentation conditions.

Three relatively isolated interactions were also found. A Presentation × Hand × Field interaction in gross motor activity indicated that when only out-of-visual-field activity is considered, the right-hand–right-presentation combination showed a higher mean percentage of activity than any other hand–presentation combination. For in-visual-field activity, the pattern was the same as that seen in the Presentation × Hand interaction. An Age × Toy interaction and an Age × Toy × Field interaction were found in the to-mouth category. These interactions indicated that, although there were no differences among the age groups in the frequency with which they brought the ring-and-key to their mouths, the 6-month-olds brought the nut-and-bolt to the mouth more often than any other age group, and the 10-month-olds brought the ring-and-key to their mouths significantly more often than the 4- and 10-month-olds, and did so more often with visual contact. The 8-month-olds did not differ from the 6- and 10-month-olds in this activity with the nut-and-bolt, but they did differ significantly from the 4-month-olds. When it was out of their visual field, the 4-month-olds brought the nut-and-bolt to the mouth significantly less often than any other age groups, and the 10-month-olds brought the ring-and-key to their mouths significantly more often than the 4- and 6-month-olds.

An Age × Hand × Toy analysis of variance of the amount of time (in seconds) each hand held the toy after it was presented before transferring or dropping it, revealed only an age main effect. There was a significant linear trend in the duration of initial grasp, decreasing from 4 to 10 months [F_{lin} (1, 36) = 25.7, p < .001].

Finally, two supplementary analyses, Age × Hand ANOVAs, were performed on overall amount of activity (a) with visual contact and (b) without visual contact. No significant interactions or main effects emerged at the .01 level. There did, however, appear to be a tendency for the right hand to be more active than the left with visual contact (see Tables 18.1 and 18.2).

Cognitive Tasks

Given the nominal and ordinal nature of the data in the cognitive tasks, nonparametric statistics only were used in these analyses. The scores obtained by each subject on CT 1 and the two trials of CT 2 were analyzed with the Friedman two-way analysis of variance (Siegel, 1956). These analyses were all carried out separately within each age group. For no group did significant differences emerge, either among the three conditions or when a comparison between the right hand and the left hand restricted conditions alone was undertaken. McNemar's test for the significance of change (Siegel, 1956) was applied to the data from CT 2. Again, the results for all age groups were nonsignificant.

Data obtained in CT 3, the modified object-permanence task, were also initially analyzed within age group with the Friedman two-way analyses of variance. Again, for any one age level, there were no significant differences found either among the four conditions (right hand–opaque, left hand–opaque, right hand–transparent, left hand–transparent), or between any two conditions that could be reasonably compared (e.g., right versus left transparent; right transparent versus right opaque).

In a second set of analyses, the frequency of subjects showing differences in the method of cloth removal when the toy was put in the right hand compared to when it was put in the left was examined by means of McNemar's test. No differences were found for any age group in the transparent cloth condition. In the opaque cloth condition the 4-month-olds and the 10-month-olds showed no differences ($\chi^2 = 1.4$ and 0, respectively). The 6- and 8-month-olds, however, did display significant differences in cloth removal as a function of the hand in which the toy was placed ($\chi^2 = 3.2$, $df = 1$, $p < .05$, and $\chi^2 = 4.16$, $df = 1$, $p < .025$, respectively). In both age groups there was a greater frequency of right-handed cloth removal. When the toy was in the right hand, the opaque cloth was shaken off; when it was in the left hand, the right hand pulled the cloth off. In the 6-month-old group there was only one instance of the left hand pulling off the cloth, and in the 8-month-olds there were none. The performance of each hand in the opaque compared to the transparent cloth condition was also analyzed by means of McNemar's test. No differences were found for either hand in any age group ($\chi^2 \leq 2.0$ in all cases).

Discussion

The infants manifested a wide variety of manipulatory activities when a ring-and-key or nut-and-bolt was placed in one hand or the other. There seemed to be an increase in the use of more refined behaviors with age (e.g., precision grasping and toy transfer increased with age, power grasping decreased), the behaviors were performed especially often when the hand was in view, and the free hand was typically used in approaching and contacting the toy. Both hands were equally likely to explore the objects, as indicated by the results of the fine motor activity category. Little laterality was evident in the infants' manipulatory behavior. Only precision grasping was manifested significantly more often by the right hand, and a supplementary analysis showed that overall activity during visual contact showed a trend for the right hand.

One of the interesting findings was that no difference was found between the two hands in the amount of time each one held the toys from the moment of presentation to the time the toy was transferred or dropped. Although the methodology and age of subjects differed (by 1 month at least) from those of Caplan and Kinsbourne's (1976) study of reflex grasping, the present findings can be contrasted with theirs. They found a longer duration of grasping by the right hand in 3-month-old infants, but if this does not hold up at 4 months (which it appears not to), the validity of duration of grasp as a measure of hand preference beyond the 3-month level must be questioned. These results may, in part, reflect a functional difference between reflexive grasping and the voluntary use of one hand in certain tasks.

With regard to the cognitive tasks, the results of the modified object-permanence task (CT 3) indicate that, under certain conditions (i.e., an opaque cloth covering the hand holding the toy), the hands do show differences in performance. Although there was no difference in the over-all frequency of cloth removal as a function of which hand was holding the toy and which was covered, for 6- and 8-month-olds the right hand was the one to perform more cloth removal; it shook off the cloth when it was covered and pulled the cloth off of the covered left hand. The left hand did shake the cloth off, but it did not pull it off the right hand. This difference was not evident in the 4- and 10-month-olds. However, whereas the results of this portion of the study do reveal hand differences in the manner in which a cloth can be removed from a covered hand at 6 and 8 months of age, the reaching behavior manifested in cognitive task performance did not seem to be related to other manipulatory behaviors, as evidenced by the lack of effects found in the analyses of manipulatory behavioral categories when subjects were divided into right- and non-right-reachers.

Overall, it appears, at least in the types of situations examined here, that neither hand had developed a particularly marked lead in dealing with the environment, except in the case of precision grasping. This would not be expected if lateralization in the nervous system were either preprogrammed (as Gazzaniga & LeDoux [1978] and Kinsbourne & His-cock [1977], among others, have suggested) or had progressed very far— lateralization as reflected in manual specialization, that is.

It could be that different situations or behaviors would show many more laterality results, unlike what was found here. However, although there were some changes across age in the behaviors examined, all behaviors were part of the infants' repertoire at 4 months (to a greater or lesser extent, depending on the behavior in question). It could be argued that these behavioral categories were too gross or primitive to afford a true picture of what the two hands were actually capable of and, therefore, of any differences between the two. However, the categories were in-cluded because they described infant behavior that had been observed, and no behavior was seen in the subjects examined that was not included as a coding category (except for putting the toy in the mouth and proceeding to climb out of the feeding table!). These categories as a group are therefore believed to characterize rather completely typical, single-object manipulation behavior in infants up to 10 months of age. It may be that it is only when infants are examined in relational play with toys (seen at 9–13 months of age, according to Fenson, Kagan, Kearsley, & Zelazo, 1976) or bimanual hand-preference tasks (Ramsay, 1980) that differential patterns of behavior in the two hands actually become distinguishable (i.e., when complimentary hand use becomes important in exploring the ways in which different parts of objects or two or more toys can be related to each other). That is, perhaps the tasks employed in the present study were not complex or demanding enough to adequately tap hand differences.

In any event, from the major class of results that emerged in this investigation (i.e., Presentation × Hand interactions), it appears that the two hands of infants do not, *of any inherent necessity*, differ in the frequency with which they interact with objects, or the behaviors they are capable of displaying. Power grasping, gross motor activities, bringing the toy to and away from the mouth, and releasing the toy were activities displayed, within both right- and left-presentation conditions, more by the hand to which the toy was presented than by the other. Conversely, approaching and contacting the toy were exhibited more often by the hand not presented with the toy, and the toy was transferred more often to that hand, as well. A higher frequency of inactivity was also found in the hand not given the toy. This pattern of results shows that the hand receiving the object explores it in a variety of ways, whereas the other hand eventually becomes involved, reaching over to touch and take it. The left and right hands equally performed these complimentary functions. In an experimental situation, it is possible to make sure that each hand has an equal opportunity for initial contact with objects; outside of the laboratory this is not possible. However, the infant may be effecting such a situation on his or her own.

One of the ways in which infants obtain objects in "real world" situations is through reaching. If one hand does develop an early lead in reaching and thereby dealing with the environment (as Gazzaniga, 1970, suggested), then it would be expected that that hand would have opportunities greater than those available to the other to develop sensorimotor schemes related to object manipulation and obtain whatever information these provide. As Gazzaniga further suggests, this would be manifested as more and more activity on the part of that hand. This does not seem to be the case, however, since evidence of this early lead would be expected to show up in the behaviors examined in the present study, but it did not. If, on the other hand, infants do not use one hand most of the time in most situations involving reaching until as late as early childhood, then the opportunities for sensorimotor scheme development might be more evenly distributed between the two hands. In this way it would be possible for each hand to develop similar types of operations in relation to objects, and so transmit to each hemisphere similar kinds of information. In essence, a naturally occurring balancing of left- and right-hand activity could be operating on the development of manual activity in infants.

Perhaps the prime bit of evidence in the data supporting this view concerns the especially relevant category of fine motor activities; there was no effect of presentation nor an effect of hand on this behavior. Both hands displayed the same amount of fine motor activity regardless of which hand initially had contact with the object. Therefore, it seems that *if* both hands are able to ask the same type of questions of their environment (of a sort that can be answered by fine motor behavior), then this would also be providing each hemisphere with similar sorts of information about the reality the infant is constructing (particularly if both hands actually *do* ask the same type of questions).

The equivalence of most of the behavioral categories examined is particularly significant because activities involving only the hands, wrists, and, especially, fingers are those most clearly under control of the contralateral hemisphere. In this way, it can be seen that at least the basic elements of the experimental base for behavioral operations in each hemisphere could be similar early in life. In addition, redundancy in the experience bases of the two hemispheres could actually be adaptive and may be one of the factors contributing to what is thought of as "plasticity" in the central nervous system in the first few years of life. That is, if the two hemispheres do not become markedly differentiated for some time and are acquiring similar knowledge of their environment, then it would be understandable how, in the event of damage to one hemisphere, the other could compensate.

Although the major portion of the findings that emerged in this investigation indicate little in the way of differential patterns of hand activity, a difference was found between the right and left hands in the proportion of precision grasping shown. The right hand used precision-type grasps more often than the left in all age groups, and precision-grasping-related behavior may be the type used by the right hand in the opaque cloth condition of the modified object permanence task. The predominance of the right hand in precision grasping may be developmentally related to the greater opportunity the infant has for seeing and manipulating that hand as the infant lies in a head-right supine position (Coryell & Michel, 1978). Also related to the phenomenon of infant supine postural preference may be the finding, here, of a greater amount of right- than left-hand activity with visual contact. That is, as young infants lie in a head-right position, looking at and manipulating the right hand, they may be developing a greater degree of flexibility in that hand (in terms of accommodating to the shapes and sizes of objects) relative to the other. The ways in which this could later be manifested are in the manner of holding objects and in the proportion of manipulatory behavior with visual contact displayed by that hand.

Furthermore, the right-hand lead in the precision-grasp category assumes particular importance in that precision grasping (more so than power) is a subroutine of skilled action patterns. As such it can be shaped and refined by practice, and becomes part of a motor syntax that can be used in a generative way (Connolly, 1973). According to Connolly, in order for skilled action patterns to develop, functional integration or modularization of subroutines is necessary, as is a rule system for combining the subroutines. Because of the right hand's early and continuing lead in the use of this type of grasp (most likely a contralaterally controlled act), it would have more practice in the application of precision grasps and more opportunities to refine them and learn the rules for combining them with other subroutines into skilled action sequences, relative to the left. And this would, according to the view of neurobehavioral development presented here, affect schema differentiation in the controlling left hemisphere.

If precision grasping is the type used in eating with forks and spoons and holding pencils, as Connolly suggested, then it is possible to see how the right hand could become the one preferred for acts necessitating a precision hold on objects. If, for example, caretakers consistently place a spoon in the right hand of infants learning to feed themselves, the infants will not only be afforded the opportunity to refine that grasp, but will also be afforded the opportunity to learn new things that that hand can do. The consistent placement of an object in one hand of the infant (in spite of any transferring the infant might do) could thus be seen as one of what Annett (1972, 1978) has called the "accidental factors" that contribute to the development of handedness, and are not really quite so accidental. Not only does this provide the right hand with specific experiences, but it also frees the left hand to engage in other types of activities and, in so doing, develop different rule systems for combining subroutines into skilled action sequences.

In summary, the evidence gathered in this study indicates that, in large part, the two hands of infants 4–10 months of age are able to engage in the same sorts of behaviors with fairly equal frequency as they manipulate objects, and that the relative frequency with which each hand interacts with toys is largely a function of which hand initially had contact with the object. Thus, in as much as manual activity affects the experience base and control system for behavioral operations of each hemisphere, these, too, will be similar. Some differentiation of control systems can also be seen to be taking place, however, in the differences found between the hands in type of grasp used and relative amount of activity engaged in with visual contact. The right-hand lead in precision grasping is notable in that consistent use of that hand in particular (skilled) acts involving that subroutine could contribute significantly to the development of different rule systems for each hand for combining subroutines into action patterns, thereby both reflecting and, through positive feedback, further contributing to the differential organization of the two cerebral hemispheres.

References

Annett, M. (1972). The distribution of manual asymmetry. *British Journal of Psychology 63*, 343–358.

Annett, M. (1978). Genetic and nongenetic influences on handedness. *Behavior Genetics 8*, 227–249.

Bradshaw, J. L., & Nettleton, N. C. (1981). The nature of hemispheric specialization in man. *The Behavioral and Brain Sciences 4*, 51–91.

Brinkman, J., & Kuypers, H. (1973). Cerebral control of contralateral and ipsilateral arm, hand, and finger movements in the splitbrain rhesus monkey. *Brain 96*, 653–674.

Caplan, P., & Kinsbourne, M. (1976). Baby drops the rattle: Asymmetry in duration of grasp by infants. *Child Development 47*, 532–534.

Castner, B. M. (1932). The development of fine prehension in infancy.*Genetic Psychology Monographs 12*, 105–193.

Černáček, J., & Podivinský, F. (1972). Changes of contralateral and ipsilateral somatosensory cortical responses during infancy. In J. Černáček & F. Podivinský (Eds.), *Cerebral interhemispheric relation*. Bratislava: Publishing House of the Slovak Academy of Sciences.

Connolly, K. (1973). Factors influencing the learning of manual skills by young children. In R. A. Hinde & J. Stevenson-Hinde (Eds.), *Constraints on learning*. New York: Academic Press.

Coryell, J. (1977). *Contribution of head position and the asymmetrical tonic neck reflex to the development of handedness in one- to twelve-week-old infants*. Unpublished doctoral dissertation, Boston University, Massachusetts.

Coryell, J., & Michel, G. (1978). How supine postural preferences of infants can contribute towards the development of handedness. *Infant Behavior and Development 2*, 245–250.

Fenson, L., Kagan, J., Kearsley, R., & Zelazo, P. (1976). The developmental progression of manipulative play in the first two years. *Child Development 47*, 232–236.

Gazzaniga, M. (1970). *The bisected brain*. New York: Appleton-Century-Crofts.

Gazzaniga, M., & LeDoux, J. E. (1978). *The integrated mind*. New York: Plenum.

Gratch, G. (1972). A study of the relative dominance of vision and touch in six-month-old infants. *Child Development 43*, 615–623.

Kinsbourne, M., & Hiscock, M. (1977). Does cerebral dominance develop? In S. J. Segalowitz & F. A. Gruber (Eds.), *Language development and neurological theory*. New York: Academic Press.

McNemar, Q. (1957). On Wilson's distribution-free test of analysis of variance hypotheses. *Psychological Bulletin 54*, 361–362.

Piaget, J. (1954). *The construction of reality in the child*. New York: Basic Books.

Ramsay, D. S. (1980). Beginnings of bimanual handedness and speech in infants. *Infant Behavior and Development 3*, 66–77.

Sherick, I., Greenman, G., & Legg, C. (1976). Some comments on the significance and development of midline behavior during infancy. *Child Psychiatry and Human Development 6*, 170–183.

Siegel, S. (1956). *Nonparametric statistics for the behavioral sciences.* New York: McGraw-Hill.

Umansky, R. (1973). The hand sock, an artificial handicap to prehension, and its relation to clinical disuse phenomenon. *Pediatrics 52*, 546–554.

Uzgiris, I., & Hunt, J. McV. (1975). *Assessment in infancy.* Chicago: Univ. of Illinois Press.

19

Lateral Bias in Reaching and Holding at Six and Twelve Months

MICHAEL PETERS

Introduction

The current search for indicators of lateral specialization in infants is based on the conviction that lateralization as a functional principle is operative very early in life (Kinsbourne & Hiscock, 1977). However, the search for early indicators of lateral specialization does not necessarily give a simple answer to the question: When does handedness emerge? During the first year of life, in particular, the central nervous system that guides movement is quite unlike the system that guides movement at later ages. The difference expresses itself rather directly in the capabilities of the motor system and, more indirectly, in the different meaning that movements have for infants at different ages. Herein lies one of the most difficult problems for developmental research in lateralization. Typically, investigators record certain movements, such as reaching and holding, with the intention of showing the presence or absence of lateral biases in such movement at different ages. This approach neglects, to an important extent, the changes of meaning that a topographically similar behavior can undergo at different ages. From a theoretical perspective, the conventional experimental approach appears to view lateralization of function as a sort of epiphenomenon that is superimposed on given behaviors once a certain degree of maturation has been reached by the infant. This chapter will stress an alternative interpretation, one that assigns great importance to the meaning of a given movement to the organism and that considers lateralization not as an epiphenomenon, but as an integral part of how movement intent comes to bear on movement execution.

MANUAL SPECIALIZATION
AND THE DEVELOPING BRAIN

The easiest way to present the arguments on which this latter interpretation is based is by way of describing the results of a rather conventional study of laterality in reaching and holding by infants of different ages. Although the data collected in this study do add to the body of information available on lateralization of function in infants (for a review see Young, 1977), the point of reporting this study lies in illustrating the difficulties of interpretation that arise once the question of what the movement means to the infant is introduced.

The Study

The data on lateral preferences were taken from videotapes recorded during a study of reaching and holding behavior of infants in the context of the Piagetian model of development (Greenberg, n.d.). Two groups of infants were studied. The first group consisted of 14 male and 15 female 6-month-old infants, and the second consisted of 15 male and 20 female 12-month-old infants. All infants were healthy, and there had been no selection in terms of parental handedness. Mothers held the infants under their arms, allowing them to move their arms freely. The infants were positioned so that they faced the table top on which the objects were presented. The table top had low vertical walls on the three sides away from the infant. The objects were felt-covered nonsense shapes 2 × 7.5 × 7.5 cm. The infants were presented with either a single object placed in the middle of the table or with two identical objects, one on each side of the midline. A single trial lasted 3 min, and two or four trials were given. The actual design of the study (which was not directed at handedness) was actually complex, involving manipulation of the single- or dual-object conditions, nature of the object, presence or absence of previous visual experience with the object, and number of trials. However, the experimental conditions were identical for each of the two groups. Here, only lateral preferences will be reported. These data were obtained by collapsing all experimental conditions to yield simple comparisons of the right and left hand in reaching and holding. The data were also collapsed over the sexes since there was no indication that the sexes differed in lateral preference.

Each incidence of the following behaviors was recorded: reaching directly for the object, holding the object with one hand, holding an object in each hand, and bringing the object to the mouth with one hand and with both hands. An attempt was made to score only those instances of reaching where the infant reached directly for the object; reaching that was used to line up the object so that the other hand could reach and grasp (de Schonen, 1977) or reaching without a discernible target were not included in the definition. *Holding* was defined as any instance when the hand grasped the object for at least 3 sec; touching in which the fingers did not grasp was not scored. If the object was transferred from one hand to the other, this was scored as holding for the hand that received the object. The record in such cases would show two consecutive instances of holding, first for one hand and then for the other. This way of scoring resulted in an apparent paradox in the data, which shows more instances of holding than of reaching. *Oral contacts* were defined as those instances where the object was clearly brought into contact with the mouth. The simplicity of the recorded behaviors and scoring scheme as well as the fact that doubtful cases could be rerun on the videotape allowed an average interobserver reliability of more than 80% for the recorded behaviors.

Results

Table 19.1 summarizes the results. The scores given in Table 19.1 present the average number of occurrences of the given behavior during a 3-min observation period (roughly one-third of the infants in each group had four observation sessions and the remainder had two observation sessions). It can be seen that there was no obvious lateral bias in holding and reaching in the 6-month-olds. This was confirmed by an ANOVA with repeated measures over the two hands (Hands × Behavior categories) that failed to yield a main effect for hands (F .44, $df = 1,28$, $p < .52$). In contrast, there was a clear trend toward a right-hand preference in the group of 12-month-olds. For this group, an ANOVA with repeated measures over hands (Hands × Behavior categories) showed a clear main effect for hands ($F = 24.1$, $df = 1,34$, $p < .0003$). The means in Table 19.1 indicate that the trends for holding and reaching were very similar.

Table 19.1 also shows that the younger group of infants had a higher frequency of oral explorations of the object. An additional ANOVA was

Table 19.1
Mean Frequency of Behavior (Three-Minute Period)

Age (in months)	N	M, SD	Reach Left	Reach Right	Hold Left	Hold Right	Mouth Left	Mouth Right	Two-handed actions[a] Hold	Two-handed actions[a] Mouth
6	29	M	4.6	4.5	6.5	7.5	2.3	2.6	6.3	3.6
		SD	2.9	2.7	3.7	3.4	2.0	2.3	4.1	3.9
12	35	M	4.7	7.5	8.6	12.3	1.5	1.5	6.2	1.7
		SD	2.1	4.0	3.3	5.2	1.9	1.7	3.7	2.6

[a]Holding object with two hands or bringing object to the mouth with two hands.

performed on data that compared unimanual and bimanual oral exploration (Age Group × Behavior with repeated measures over the behavior
categories) in the two groups. The data from six infants were randomly
dropped from the older group in order to gain equal numbers of subjects.
The main effect of age group was significant ($F = 6.36$, $df = 1.28$, $p <$
.016), in agreement with the data in Table 19.1, which shows a higher
frequency of oral explorations in the younger group.

Discussion

The results of the study are in agreement with the data reported by
Ramsay (1980). He recorded the number of unimanual contacts made with
a toy at ages 5, 7, and 9 months. Ramsay used both longitudinal and cross-
sectional samples, which yielded similar results. No lateral biases could
be identified in the 5-month-olds, whereas a clear right-hand bias
emerged for the 9-month-olds. The right-hand bias in the present sample
of 12-month-olds occurred in proportionately more subjects than in Ramsay's sample. The more clearly expressed bias in this study may be due to
two factors. First, that the infants in this study were 3 months older than
those in Ramsay's sample likely contributed to the difference. Second, the
much larger sample in the present study brought out the differences between left and right more clearly, due to smaller standard errors. The
results are also in agreement with a study by Bresson, Maury, Pieraut-Le
Bonniec, and de Schonen (1977). Their study showed a right-hand preference in what they called *direct reaching* at ages comparable to those in the
present study. The agreement between the present study and the one by
Bresson *et al.* can only be considered general, however, since their study
dealt with only very few infants and exact age comparisons are not
possible.

Thus, our results are straightforward and in agreement with comparable studies. How, then, are the results to be interpreted? Ramsay (1980)
concludes that different types of handedness emerge at different ages (i.e.,
that different behaviors develop lateralization at successive age levels).
There are activities that appear to show a lateral bias in unimanual movement (Caplan & Kinsbourne, 1976; Petrie & Peters, 1980) before 5 months
of age, and such bias supports Ramsay's conclusions. Our results also
raise the question of why there is no lateral preference in reaching and
holding at 5 months of age even though lateral biases in unilateral movement are present prior to that age. The answer depends on the meaning of
these activities for infants.

Piaget (1963) speaks of the centripetal tendency of infants at the age
that includes the younger group (6-month-olds) in the present study. This

tendency expresses itself in the infants' attempts to bring the object to their body or mouth, and is reflected by the high number of oral contacts shown in Table 19.1. At this age, the mouth is still "the limb of the head" (as Goethe had observed some time ago), and the infants use their hands in keeping with this interpretation: Reaching and holding serve as a simple intermediary that extends the range of oral exploration. In this situation, the movement intent is focused on the principal exploring organ, the mouth, and the question of which hand serves the subsidiary function of transporting objects to the mouth is perhaps not very important, which would account for the lack of a lateral bias.

The element of oral exploration is clearly less important for the older group (12-month-olds), in which there is a significantly lower frequency of oral contacts. More importantly, the behaviors of reaching and holding, although topographically similar to the same behaviors seen in the younger group, assume a different meaning for the older infants. Supplementary impressions of the infants' behavior will be given in order to show that the behavior of the 12-month-old differs quite clearly from that of the 6-month-old not only in frequency, but also in terms of meaning.

Infants in both age groups frequently released the object, but the manner of release differed for the two groups. For the younger group, Piaget's (1963, p. 220) observations still apply—object-dropping occurs by default; it is not intentional, but is due to a cessation of attention to the object. Although the schema of "releasing" is not fully developed in the 6-month-olds, the 12-month-olds showed a different behavior. They consistently observed their fingers while releasing the object, and watched it fall, so that they seemed to engage in a rather deliberate act. The further extension of releasing—throwing—was seen in some of the older infants but in none of the younger infants.

An additional indication of the difference in meaning of the activities for the younger and older group was in the overall pattern of activities. The younger infants dealt with the object at some length, rerunning familiar schemata. The older infants, in contrast, had a vigorous bout of activities with the object, abandoned it in favor of attending to their mother or some other aspect of the environment, and then returned to the object with some new activity.

Equally striking was the range of activities that the older group showed with the object itself. These infants, in Piagetian terms, were applying secondary circular schemata to new situations. They squeezed and shook the object, held it away from the body and brought it closer, waved it about, hammered it on the table, slapped it against one hand with the other, and dropped or threw it. Parker (1977), in her attempt to systematize Piaget's classification, considered the quality of volition at the younger age as *primitive voluntary*, and felt that the goal determination was "fortuitous" in the 4–8-month range, and labeled the quality of volition of infants past this age as *voluntary*, that is, with a deliberate goal determination.

It appears, then, that the change in meaning that takes place in reaching and holding is an important factor in the discussion of how and when lateral biases emerge. In the 12-month-old infant, reaching and holding reflect the deliberate intent of the infant to act on objects in the external world, and the outcomes of such actions are carefully observed.

A lateral bias in reaching and holding is not a superimposed quality, but an integral part of how attention is focused on the external world at this age. It can be stated that the processes of lateralization of function that underlie skilled manual movement are beginning to express themselves late in the second half of the first year of life. The absence of a lateral bias in the 6-month-old does not mean that lateralization as a functional principle is not operative at that age, only that it is not an important aspect of holding and reaching as studied in this particular experimental setting.

Another, and not mutually exclusive, interpretation of the absence of a lateral bias in reaching and holding at the earlier age is possible. There are reports in the literature that certain behaviors appear early in the developmental process, disappear, and finally reappear in a topographically similar form. For example, infants show early guided reaching that subsequently declines for some time, only to reemerge at a later stage (Bower, 1979). Another example concerns auditory cues. Infants orient toward a sound right after birth, and the behavior persists until approximately 80 days of age. The behavior decreases markedly between 80 and 100 days of age and then reemerges (Muir, Abraham, Forbes, & Harris, 1979). In these cases, the reemerging behavior has a different significance to the infant than the original behavior, even though the topography of the behavior is similar. It is quite likely that the intermediate period, during which the behavior is rarely seen, is a period in which marked structural and functional changes occur in the central nervous system and in which a sort of interregnum takes place.

Although the Piagetian timetable of development is not universally accepted, it is, perhaps, of more than passing interest in this regard that, according to Piaget, the stage of primary circular reactions extends from about 2 to 4 months. After this, a qualitative change presumably occurs, and the infants enter the stage of secondary circular reactions.

A similar interpretation can be applied to laterality in reaching and holding. Lateral biases in holding, for instance, have been observed soon after birth (Caplan & Kinsbourne, 1976; Petrie & Peters, 1980). Young (1977) mentions a right-hand preference for directed swiping movements of infants at the 3½-month level, and Coryell and Michel (1978) suggest that there is a significant right-hand bias in reaching among 12-week-old infants. As the number of infants both in the present study and in that by

Ramsay (1980) was considerably larger than the numbers studied by Young (1977) and by Coryell and Michel (1978), the lack of measurable right-hand bias in reaching at the 5–6-month level reported here and by Ramsay has to be taken seriously. It may well be that this lack of a measurable bias is a phenomenon similar to those mentioned earlier, in which a behavior is not seen during a period of marked change in structure and function.

Now that the basic observations relating to the expression of lateral bias have been described and interpreted, the central concern of this chapter, the change in meaning of the behaviors over time, can be addressed. Two separate problems relating to the discussion of meaning can be identified. The first concerns the way in which we arrive at our conclusions about meaning. It is quite clear that the interpretations of meaning are related only very loosely to the frequency counts made in this study. The problem encountered is common to that encountered with catalog recording methods. For reasons of efficiency and greater interobserver reliability, categories are kept simple and small in number. The methodological advantages gained are bought at a cost; many aspects of behavior are discarded. One solution is to extend the behavior catalog to the point where the behavior record comes close to a long-hand report (see Piaget). Once the observations are recorded in this manner, however, the implicit hypotheses determine how behavior is recorded and what aspects of behavior are recorded. Thus, the vicious circle closes: There can be no objective behavioral record without simplified and scientifically communicable methodology, and no identification of the more meaningful aspects of behavior without subjective interpretation of rich detail.

The second, and even more fundamental problem, is a question of interpretation that is of general significance for developmental research: How does one deal, both empirically and conceptually, with behaviors that remain similar in topography but change in terms of meaning to the organism? Piaget attempted to deal with the problem and struggled to find a term that would appropriately describe something that is and is not the same at different developmental stages. In the end, he proposed the term *partial isomorphism* to capture the essence of the process of transformation (Piaget, 1971, p. 58), but he recognized the inadequacy of the term. The overriding difficulty in talking about transformations that lead from one function to another is that suitable metaphors are very hard to find: It is easy enough to talk about the final outcome of a transforming process, and all but impossible to talk about the process of transformation itself.

Regardless of these conceptual difficulties, the conclusion to be drawn from this study is clear. When attempts are made to trace lateral biases in movement through the early stages of life, the meaning of given movements at given stages of development is an essential aspect of any interpretation concerning the presence or absence of lateral biases.

References

Bower, T. G. R. (1979). Human development. San Francisco, California: Freeman.

Bresson, F., Maury, L., Pieraut-Le Bonniec, G., & de Schonen, S. (1977). Organization and lateralization of reaching in infants: An instance of asymmetric function of hands collaboration. Neuropsychologia 15, 311–320.

Caplan, P. J., & Kinsbourne, M. (1976). Baby drops the rattle: Asymmetry of duration of grasp by infants. Child Development 47, 532–534.

Coryell, J. F., & Michel, G. F. (1978). How supine postural preferences of infants can contribute toward the development of handedness. Infant Behavior and Development 1, 245–257.

de Schonen, S. (1977). Functional asymmetries in the development of bimanual coordinations in human infants. Journal of Human Movement Studies 3, 144–156.

Greenberg, L. (n.d.). The effects of visual and manipulatory experiences on the recognition memory of infants.

Kinsbourne, M., & Hiscock, M. (1977). Does cerebral dominance develop? In S. J. Segalowitz & F. A. Gruber (Eds.), Language development and neurological theory. New York: Academic Press.

Muir, D., Abraham, W., Forbes, B., & Harris, L. (1979). The ontogenesis of an auditory localization response from birth to four months of age. Canadian Journal of Psychology 33, 320–333.

Parker, S. T. (1977). Piaget's sensorimotor series in an infant macaque. In S. Chevalier-Skolnikoff & F. E. Poirier (Eds.), Primate bio-social development. New York: Garland.

Petrie, B. F., & Peters, M. (1980). Handedness: Left/right differences in intensity of grasp response and duration of rattle holding of infants. Infant Behavior and Development 3, 215–221.

Piaget, J. (1963). The origins of intelligence in children. New York: Norton.

Piaget, J. (1971). Biology and knowledge. Chicago, Illinois: Univ. of Chicago Press.

Ramsay, D. S. (1980). Onset of unimanual handedness in infants. Infant Development and Behavior 3, 377–385.

Young, G. (1977). Manual specialization in infancy: Implications for lateralization of brain function. In S. J. Segalowitz & F. A. Gruber (Eds.), Language development and neurological theory. New York: Academic Press.

20

Relationships between Processing and Motor Asymmetries in Early Development

DAVID J. LEWKOWICZ
GERALD TURKEWITZ

Introduction

The relationship between motor and information-processing asymmetries is now well established in adults. Thus, speech is almost uniformly localized in the left hemisphere of right-handed individuals (Rasmussen & Milner, 1977), whereas its localization in left-handed individuals, although less well known, is more equivocal than is the case for right-handed individuals. This apparent association between handedness and hemispheric specialization for language raises questions concerning both the developmental course of these two asymmetries and the influences that one asymmetry may have on the other in development.

The principal aim of this chapter will be to address these questions. To do so, we will first review studies concerned with the development of various asymmetries in an attempt to glean some of the ways in which these different asymmetries may be related to one another in development. Then, we will present in some detail our attempt to examine this relationship in a more direct manner. Finally, we will discuss both the implications of our results for understanding the developmental relationships between motor and processing asymmetries, and the development of hemispheric specialization.

There are at least three different ways in which an association between motor and processing asymmetries may come about. First, it is possible that motor and information-processing asymmetries develop independently of one another and that any association between them reflects their association with a common mechanism or substrate. Second, it is possible that one asymmetry determines the other. Third, these two asymmetries

MANUAL SPECIALIZATION
AND THE DEVELOPING BRAIN

may be reciprocally related to one another, with each influencing the development of the other. Although these distinctions may be possible conceptually, further scrutiny reveals that they may not be empirically separable. For example, given a common substrate, it would be possible to have sequential as well as concomitant changes between two asymmetries. Sequential changes could come about if asymmetry a and asymmetry b were dependent on the maturation of region X but for asymmetry a the maturation of region X was both necessary and sufficient whereas for asymmetry b it was necessary but not sufficient. The same sequential relationship would be expected if the development of one asymmetry depended on the development of the other. In either case, the same sequential relationship might be observed but the underlying mechanism may be different. Because of the difficulty in separating cause and effect, we will ignore this issue and instead concentrate on an examination of the associations between motor and processing asymmetries at various stages of development.

Asymmetries in Early Development

The first well-documented evidence of anatomical asymmetries was provided by Geschwind and Levitsky (1968), who found that the planum temporale, which is in the posterior region of the temporal lobes and is part of the auditory association areas, was larger on the left in 65% and larger on the right in 11% of their sample of 100 adult brains. Since then, a number of studies have shown similar anatomical asymmetries not only in newborn full term infants (Witelson & Pallie, 1973), but even in pre-term infants (LeMay & Culebras, 1972; Wada, Clarke, & Hamm, 1975).

Asymmetries in motor responsiveness, as well as asymmetries in response to somesthetic, auditory, and visual stimulation, have been observed in newborn infants. Insofar as motor asymmetries are concerned, infants from birth, up until about 3 months of age, spend most of their time lying with their head on the right when supine (Coryell & Michel, 1978; Gesell, 1938; Turkewitz, Gordon, & Birch, 1965). Furthermore, not only do newborns maintain their head on the right, but they are more likely to turn their head to the right following its placement in the midline position (Turkewitz & Creighton, 1974).

When a light touch is applied to an infant's cheek, the overwhelming majority of responses made to stimulation of either cheek are head turns toward that stimulus and, of these, more "toward" turns are made in response to stimulation of the right than of the left side. Although the number of "away" turns is much lower, of these, stimulation of the left cheek produces more "away" turns than does stimulation of the right cheek. As a result, somesthetic stimulation of the perioral region produces a preponderance of right head turns. Although questions have been raised regarding the source of this asymmetry (Liederman & Kinsbourne, 1980), the bulk of the currently available evidence supports the view that both sensory and motor factors contribute to these asymmetries (Turkewitz, 1980).

Greater responsiveness to auditory stimulation of the right ear in newborns is evidenced by the fact that a lower intensity auditory stimulus (66 dB) elicits the same proportion of "toward" and "away" eye turns at the right ear as does a higher intensity (87 dB) sound at the left ear (Turkewitz, Birch, Moreau, Levy, & Cornwell, 1966). In other words, the right ear appears to have a lower auditory threshold. Asymmetries in visual responsiveness are evidenced by the fact that newborn infants spend more time looking to the right than to the left (Wickelgren, 1967).

A relatively sparse but growing body of evidence indicates that, beginning shortly after birth, infants exhibit asymmetries in processing of auditory stimulation that are similar in direction to those observed in adults. Several studies examining brain evoked responses to auditory stimulation in infants have found larger evoked responses in the left temporal lobe in newborns in response to clicks (full term neonates [Davis & Wada, 1977]), and in response to synthetic speech stimuli (both full term and premature [Molfese & Molfese, 1979, 1980]). Likewise, in older infants, speech stimuli have been found to elicit larger evoked responses in the left hemisphere than in the right, whereas nonspeech stimuli, such as white noise and musical chords, have been found to evoke larger responses in the right hemisphere than in the left (Molfese, Freeman, & Palermo, 1975). Psychophysiological data indicate similar effects for speech and music. Glanville, Best and Levenson (1977) found, in 3-month-old infants, that following habituation to a dichotic pair of verbal stimuli, presentation of a novel verbal stimulus at the right ear produced greater recovery of cardiac responding than its presentation at the left ear. The opposite effect was obtained for musical stimuli. Finally, behavioral measures have also indicated similar patterns of asymmetry. Entus (1977) showed that, in $1\frac{1}{2}$–3-month-old infants, recovery of high-amplitude sucking (HAS) was greater following habituation to a dichotic pair of verbal stimuli when the stimulus at the right ear was changed to a novel one than when the stimulus at the left ear was changed. The opposite ear effect was found for musical stimuli. However, a subsequent attempt to replicate Entus's findings for speech failed to indicate any asymmetry (Vargha-Khadem & Corballis, 1979). Hammer (1977) showed that 2-day-old infants make right eye turns to a binaurally presented speech stimulus, and left turns to a binaurally presented white-noise stimulus of equal intensity. Thus, despite the use of different techniques, the available data suggest that infants exhibit the same patterns of specialization observed in adults (Kimura, 1961, 1964), and that no developmental changes in specialization occur. Later in this chapter, we will suggest an alternative interpretation of these data.

The anatomical, motor, sensory, and processing asymmetries observed at or shortly after birth may be related to one another and may influence each other's development. Although there is no clear evidence concerning interrelationships among asymmetries during fetal life, it is at least possible to suggest ways in which such asymmetries could act during this time to produce the kinds of processing asymmetries found at or near birth.

In utero, the fetus seems to be insulated from the mother's external and internal auditory environment by the uterus, amniotic sac, and amniotic fluid. However, a number of studies indicate that, in mammals, sounds do pass through the abdominal wall (Bench, 1968; Bench, Anderson, & Hoare, 1970; Grimwade, Walker, Bartlett, Gordon, & Wood, 1971; Walker, Grimwade, & Wood, 1971) as well as the amniotic sac (Armitage, Baldwin, & Vince, 1980). In general, low-frequency sounds (below 1000 Hz) pass most easily through the abdominal wall, whereas high-frequency sounds become increasingly attenuated as their frequency increases. In addition, because of changes in the geometry of the mother during pregnancy, changes in the level of attenuation of externally produced sound have been observed (Bench et al., 1970). Although most investigators believe that the major sounds available to the mammalian fetus are cardiovascular sounds, Armitage et al.'s work, recording for the first time inside the amniotic sac, showed that, at least in sheep, cardiovascular sounds are not predominant. Both internal sounds generated by the mother and externally generated sounds were clearly audible. Thus, the fetus is exposed to both internal and external sounds whose characteristics may change during gestation. Since the fetal auditory system is functional prior to birth (Grimwade et al., 1971; Wedenberg, 1965; Weitzman & Graziani, 1968), the fetus's auditory system must register these sounds. With regard to speech sounds, the human fetus is likely to receive greater exposure to maternal speech than to any other. In fact, evidence suggesting that differential exposure to maternal speech may occur in utero has recently been provided by DeCasper and Fifer (1980), who found that human infants under 30 hours of age exhibit a preference for the maternal voice over a stranger's voice when the presentation of a given voice is made contingent on the infant's sucking. Thus, in utero exposure to speech sounds may interact with developing anatomical asymmetries that, as already indicated, are known to exist prior to birth, thus giving rise to hemispheric specialization with regard to processing of speech and nonspeech sounds. This scheme would account for the asymmetries found in the processing of auditory stimuli at birth.

Developmental Changes in Asymmetries

Although it is clear that asymmetries are present early in development and may have antecedents even prior to birth, the developmental fate of these initial asymmetries is less clear. As far as developmental changes in structural asymmetries are concerned, some evidence is available. There is no significant difference in the extent to which the relative size of the left planum temporale exceeds that of the right in fetuses, newborn infants, and adults (Witelson, 1977). This suggests that at least one potentially important structural asymmetry is stable throughout development. However, because of a limited database and a lack of standardized measurement techniques, no firm conclusions regarding age-related or developmental changes in structural asymmetries are possible. In addition, in the absence of data demonstrating a direct relationship between anatomic and functional asymmetries, and in view of the lack of concordance between the percentage of brains showing a larger planum on the left (about 70%) and the percentage of individuals showing left hemisphere lateralization of language (between 90 and 95%), it is unclear at this point what contribution the anatomic asymmetry makes to the development of hemispheric specialization.

With regard to developmental changes in motor asymmetries, there are two apparently separate bodies of data. One concerns postural asymmetries early in life, and the other concerns differential hand usage at some later ages.

Observations of the head-position bias of premature and full term infants at different ages indicate regular changes in the nature and strength of the head-position bias and have suggested a sequence in the development of this postural bias. By 35 weeks of gestational age, premature infants lie with their heads turned to the right more frequently than to the left (Gardner, Lewkowicz, & Turkewitz, 1977). This is the earliest age at which such an asymmetry has been detected. The strength of the positional bias first observed at 35 weeks of gestational age increases in a regular fashion until 39 weeks of gestational age, at which time premature infants exhibit a postural asymmetry comparable to that of full term infants. It should be noted that infants can exhibit a head-right posture in one of two ways. First, infants may assume a head-right posture because of a differential turning tendency such that they are more likely to turn their heads to the right than to the left. Second, they may be more likely to maintain a head-right than a head-left posture once they have assumed it. Although both premature and full term infants exhibit a marked head-right posture, the evidence suggests a different mechanism underlying the observed asymmetries in full term and premature infants. Thus, premature infants do not consistently turn their head to the right following release from a midline position, but rather are as likely to turn left as right. Full term infants under 12 hours of age, in addition to showing the marked postural asymmetry, are also more likely to turn their heads to the right following momentary maintenance of the head in the midline position, but not following maintenance of the head in the midline for 15 min. Finally, full term infants older than 12 hours of age lie with their heads to the right and turn right not only after momentary placement of their heads in the midline, but also after placement of their heads in the midline for 15 min. It is thus obvious that (a) the head-position bias consists of two separable components (i.e., assumption and maintenance of the head-right posture), (b) that the first of these components grows in strength with age.

In addition to the developmental changes in motor asymmetries associated with head position, changes in asymmetries of sensory functions have also been observed. As previously noted, the typical response of a newborn infant to a light touch of the cheek is a turn toward the side that is stimulated, with greater responsiveness manifested primarily in "toward" turns on the right side. This is the pattern observed in full term infants. Examination of responsiveness to somesthetic stimulation of the perioral region in premature infants, however, has revealed a general absence of lateral differentiation (Lewkowicz, Gardner, & Turkewitz, 1979). Although premature infants also make more "toward" than "away" turns, they make less of these than full term infants, and, unlike full term infants, they do not make more "toward" turns to stimulation of the right cheek. As a result, stimulation of the right and left cheeks in premature infants results in equivalent responding. The only evidence of lateral differentiation found in the premature infants is with regard to "away" turns. They make more "away" turns in response to stimulation of the left than the right cheek, and this proportion does not differ from that of full term infants. Thus, the data regarding development of lateral differentiation of head turning in response to somesthetic stimulation indicate that the earliest laterally differentiated response to develop is an "away" turning response.

The evidence for developmental changes in hand usage is considerably more equivocal. Early reports emphasized both the consistency across infants of the same age with regard to systematic differences in hand usage (Cohen, 1966) and the presence of cyclical changes in dominant hand usage with infants more likely to use one hand at one age and the other when younger or older (Gesell & Ames, 1947; Seth, 1973). Subsequent studies have suggested a consistent right-hand preference that emerges sometime during the second half of the first year (Ramsay, 1980b).

We have already indicated one way in which anatomic asymmetries may interact with differential auditory input in utero to produce processing asymmetries. Another instance of the dependence of one asymmetry on another is the relationship between the asymmetric head posture and other later-appearing asymmetries. There are several consequences of the head-right posture. First, differential tonus of the two sides of the neck is produced. Second, as a consequence of the head-right posture, the infant's cheeks are differentially stimulated. Finally, the head-right posture elicits the tonic neck reflex, which is characterized by extension of the limbs on the face side and flexion of the limbs on the skull side. The first two consequences of the head-right posture, namely differential tonus and differential stimulation of the two sides, have been shown to contribute to the lateral differences in response to somesthetic stimulation of the two sides of the infant's perioral region (Turkewitz, Moreau, Davis, & Birch, 1969). Induction of differential tonus by placing the infant's head on the right without at the same time allowing the right cheek to come in contact with the substrate produces lateral differences in responsiveness. Likewise, stimulation of the right cheek while holding the head in the midline, thus preventing induction of differential tonus, also produces a lateral difference in responsiveness to a subsequent touch. In connection with these two factors, it is important to note that, although the differential tonus in part reflects the operation of some motor mechanism, it has also been shown that the right perioral region has a lower sensory threshold than the left perioral region (Hammer & Turkewitz, 1974).

The third consequence of the asymmetric head posture is the tonic neck reflex. It has been suggested that the tonic neck reflex may contribute to the development of handedness (Coryell & Michel, 1978). The presence of the tonic neck reflex is generally observed in the first 3 months of life. Coryell and Michel's observations of infants during this time indicated that, because of the head-right posture, the infant's right hand is in his right visual field more often than his left hand. Furthermore, when visual stimuli were presented in the infants' visual fields at 12 weeks of age, their right hands were more active than their left hands. Thus, it appears that, as a result of the head-right posture, the tonic neck reflex is elicited more frequently on the right than on the left side of the body, leading to differential hand regard that, in turn, apparently leads to asymmetric use of the hands. By finding an association between differential experience with the two hands early in life and asymmetric use of the hands at a later point, Coryell and Michel have identified one possible antecedent to the development of handedness and have demonstrated the utility of considering the contribution of one type of motor asymmetry to the development of another motor asymmetry.

The Relationship between Motor Functions and Processing Asymmetries in Infancy

So far our discussion of different asymmetries and relationships between them in early development has not touched on the relationship between motor and processing asymmetries. This is because, with the exception of several studies by Ramsay (1980a, 1980b) and by Kinsbourne and his colleagues (Hicks, 1975; Hiscock & Kinsbourne, 1978; Kinsbourne & Cook, 1971; Kinsbourne & McMurray, 1975), no studies to date have examined this relationship in infants or children.

Ramsay has carried out a series of studies designed to assess the temporal relationship between the emergence of manual asymmetries and the emergence of different kinds of speech-production abilities in infancy. In a study of the temporal association between the onset of reduplicative babbling in 6-month-old infants and the onset of unimanual hand preference in a toy manipulation task, Ramsay (1980b) has found that the onset of babbling is closely followed by the onset of a right-hand preference in manipulation. In a study concerned with the relationship between the onset of bimanual hand preference and the development of speech in 1-year-old infants, Ramsay (1980a) found that the onset of bimanual hand preference was closely followed by the emergence of multisyllabic speech consisting of dissimilar consonant and vowel sounds across syllables. In 11 out of 12 infants, these kinds of expressions occurred for the first time in the same month as, or after, the onset of bimanual hand preference. On the basis of these two studies, Ramsay argues that the close temporal association between the various forms of manual asymmetry and the different milestones in speech development reflects the development of hemispheric specialization for articulatory and other motor functions in the left hemisphere. If that is the case, the data from these two studies suggest a change in the relationship between manual and speech-production (and presumably, processing) asymmetries in development. At 6 months of age, speech-production asymmetries precede the onset of manual asymmetries, whereas at 12 months the reverse is true. Thus, one possible interpretation of these data is that they reflect the existence of a reciprocal relationship between two functions in development that have changing patterns of antecedents at different ages.

Studies by Kinsbourne and his colleagues (Hicks, 1975; Hiscock & Kinsbourne, 1978; Kinsbourne & Cook, 1971; Kinsbourne & McMurray, 1975) with older children and adults provide more direct evidence for the interaction of motor and processing asymmetries and suggest a useful method for the investigation of relationships between these two asymmetries. In these studies, subjects were asked to tap as fast as possible with the index finger of one hand or the other. While tapping, the subject was asked to recite a verbal passage. Although speaking produced a decline in the rate of tapping in both hands, the decline was greater in the right hand. Based on a hypothesis in which competition for neural space was proposed, these results were interpreted as indicating a left-hemisphere specialization for speech. It is important to note, however, that although both Ramsay and Kinsbourne have used measures of motor functioning, in both their studies, these motor functions have been related to asymmetries of production. These asymmetries of production may be related to asymmetries of processing, but are, at best, indirectly related to these asymmetries. No studies to date have examined the effects of auditory input on the performance of a discrete motor response. Recently, we (Lewkowicz & Turkewitz, 1982) devised an extension of Kinsbourne's technique that permits assessment of the effect of incoming auditory stimulation on manual activity in infants.

To examine hemispheric asymmetries, we allowed infants to reach for an object while at the same time listening to monaural presentations of different types of auditory input. If mechanisms underlying manual activity are somehow associated with mechanisms concerned with the response to different types of auditory input, then performance of manual responses may be affected by auditory processing mechanisms. It was, therefore, expected that auditory input would engage the infants and, consequently, have an effect on the latency to reach, and that this effect would depend on both the type of auditory input and the ear to which it was presented. The direction of the effect, however, need not necessarily be the one suggested by Kinsbourne. For example, it is quite possible that activation of a region of the brain by the performance of one function may facilitate, rather than interfere with, the performance of another function subserved by the same side of the brain. Whether facilitation or inhibition was operating, it would be anticipated that activation of a particular hemisphere would have its greatest effect on the hand controlled by that hemisphere.

An alternative possibility is that presentation of auditory input would affect reaching because of generalized attentional effects. That is, input appropriate to the specialization of a given hemisphere may result in greater attention to that input than would be the case if the same input were presented to the other hemisphere. Deployment of attention to auditory input could then affect reaching with either hand by reducing attention to either the visually eliciting stimulus or to the visually guided motor performance. Therefore, in this case, unlike the previous one, the hand making the response would not matter. Thus, for example, hemispheric specialization for the processing of speech could lead to a different latency to reach if speech were presented to the right ear than if speech were presented to the left ear.

The general method consisted of presenting an object in the midline to infants who wore headphones and were seated on their mothers' laps. Just prior to the presentation of the object, a verbal or a musical passage was monaurally presented, and lasted until the infant made contact with the object. Each infant was presented with three blocks of four trials. The auditory input consisted of either a recorded segment of spoken verse or a recorded segment of flute and harpsichord music and measured between 65 and 75 dB (A scale) for each type of input at each ear. The testing sessions were videotaped, and the tapes were then scored for the latency to contact the object and the hand used in making the contact. Scoring of the videotape was done blindly, and agreement between observers for the latency measure (within .1 sec) was 97.3% and higher for the hand used.

The primary purpose of this study was to compare the effects of different auditory stimuli when presented to the right or left ear. Since any differences in effect would suggest specialization, independently of whether the effect was a facilitation or an inhibition, evaluation of the direction of effect was considered to be of secondary importance. To determine whether presentation of the auditory material had a facilitory or inhibitory influence on reaching latency, following the completion of the experimental trials, a subset of the infants were also presented with the object three times without accompanying sound.

The subjects in this study consisted of 24 6-month-olds and 24 8-month-olds, with an equal number of boys and girls at each age. All infants were in a quiet and alert state during the test session. Data concerning parental handedness were not obtained.

Because no support for the operation of a competition-for-space mechanism was found (e.g., there was no evidence of a differential effect on the two hands), the data were analyzed to assess the possibility of differential attentional effects. In these analyses, we examined the effects of both the nature and locus of stimulation, regardless of the hand used in reaching. The data consisted of the mean latency to contact for a given type of stimulus presented at a given ear.

To determine whether presentation of sound had a facilitory or inhibitory effect, the latency on experimental trials was compared with that on no-sound trials for the boys and girls at each of the two ages. Because the no-sound trials occurred after the experimental trials, and because there was a general decline in latency with time, the latency from the no-sound trials was compared with the latency from the last block of experimental trials. Each such comparison indicated a longer mean latency on sound than on no-sound trials, and in the younger girls and older boys, these differences were significant; $t(10) = 3.21$, $p < .01$, two-tailed, for the younger girls, and $t(9) = 2.59$, $p < .05$, two-tailed, for the older boys. It should be noted that, in view of the general decrease in latency with trials, comparison of the no-sound trials with the last block of experimental trials makes it easier to find facilitation and harder to find inhibition. Therefore, these data clearly indicate that any differential effect of type of material and/or ear of presentation would be based on inhibition, as any facilitory effect is ruled out by these comparisons.

Examination of latencies as a function of both ear of presentation and the type of auditory material presented revealed complex relationships among these two factors and age and gender. Both age- and gender-related differences in hemispheric specialization were found. Specialization was found in 6-month-old boys, whereas none was found in girls of this age. Thus, in 6-month-old infants, the effects of type of material and the ear to which it was presented depended on the gender of the infants (Figure 20.1), $F(1, 22) = 4.37$, $p < .05$. The source of this interaction was the differential effect of speech for boys and girls, $F(1, 22) = 6.63$, $p < .025$.

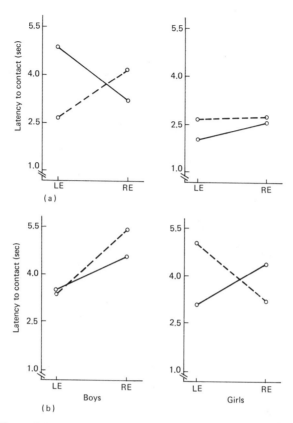

Figure 20.1. *Effects of different types of auditory input on the latency to contact an object.* (a) *6-month-old infants,* (b) *8-month-old infants. Solid line = speech; dashed line = music; LE = left ear; RE = right ear.*

Post-hoc analyses indicated that boys exhibited a marginally longer latency when speech was presented to the left ear than when it was presented to the right ear, $F (1, 11) = 4.43$, $p < .06$. Further post-hoc comparisons indicated that the boys took longer to contact the object when they heard speech in the left ear than when they heard music in that ear, $F (1, 11) = 5.29$, $p < .05$. None of the comparisons were significant for the girls. Thus, the data suggest a right-hemisphere specialization for the processing of linguistic input, but no specialization for the processing of musical input in 6-month-old boys. No specialization was evident for 6-month-old girls.

The pattern of results for the 8-month-old infants was markedly different from that obtained for the 6-month-old infants (see Figure 20.1). Once again, the effects of type of material and the ear to which it was presented depended on the gender of the infants, $F (1, 22) = 6.11$, $p < .025$; however, at this age, the interaction between ear of presentation and gender was found for music, not speech, F (1, 22) = 19.41, p < .001. Post-hoc comparisons indicated that, for boys of this age, presentation of music to the right ear resulted in a longer latency to contact the object than did its presentation to the left ear, F (1, 11) = 7.13, p < .025. There was no difference when speech was presented to the two ears. In girls of this age, the interaction between type of material and ear of presentation approached significance, F (1, 11) = 4.30, p = .06. Although none of the post-hoc comparisons were significant, it should be noted that the direction of differences (greater latency when speech was presented to the right ear than when it was presented to the left, and greater latency when music was presented to the left ear than to the right) suggests the emergence of left-hemisphere specialization for speech and right-hemisphere specialization for music in 8-month-old girls. Thus, the results for the 8-month-old infants suggest left-hemisphere specialization for the processing of music in boys, and a tendency for adultlike specialization in the girls.

Were it not for the previously noted finding that presentation of sound appears to increase the latency to contact, it would be possible to interpret the data as indicating the opposite pattern of specialization from the one we are suggesting. However, in view of that finding, the most conservative interpretation is that, for a particular type of input, the side producing the longest latency to contact is the one that is specialized for responding to that type of input.

The patterns of specialization we observed in boys are opposite to those found in a number of other studies: At 6 months, boys in our study exhibited right-hemisphere specialization for speech, whereas at 8 months, they showed left-hemisphere specialization for music. Not only are these results unusual with regard to the direction of the hemispheric specialization suggested, but they are also somewhat at variance with the typical finding of relative precocity in girls. That is, although the girls seem to be showing a tendency toward an adult-like pattern at an age (8 months) when boys still show a reversed pattern, the boys seemed to show some hemispheric specialization at an age (6 months) when the girls were still giving no indication of hemispheric differentiation. However, because there was a tendency for the girls to show an adult pattern of specialization earlier than the boys, and because of the generally reported earlier development of girls than boys, it seemed possible than one reason for the apparent lack of specialization in the 6-month-old girls was that they were in a period of transition. It therefore seemed possible that girls younger than 6 months would show more of a hemispheric difference than did the 6-month-olds, and, furthermore, that this hemispheric difference would be opposite to that seen in the 8-month-old girls. To examine this possibility, another study involving 24 5-month-old infants, with an equal number of boys and girls, was conducted (Klein, 1981). The infants were tested in the same manner as in the previous study. Results from this study failed to indicate any significant effect of type of material for either boys or girls, suggesting the absence of hemispheric specialization in processing verbal or musical material at this age. This effect was not simply due to the failure of the younger infants to reach, as all of the infants tested reached for the object.

It is, of course, possible that the findings we obtained did not reflect specialization for speech and music generally, but rather are specific to the exemplars of speech and music used in this study. This alternative is somewhat weakened by our use of a nonrepetitive tape, so that each infant experienced different exemplars of both types of auditory material on each trial.

A Developmental View of Hemispheric Specialization

It is still possible that the different patterns of specialization seen in boys and girls of the same age reflect gender differences in the ages at which hemispheric differentiation and specialization occur. However, the failure to find any evidence of a right-hemisphere specialization for speech or a left-hemisphere specialization for music in girls of any age suggests that it is not simply with regard to timing that boys and girls differ, but that the differences in hemispheric specialization may be more profound and may involve totally different developmental sequences. Yet, it must also be noted that few gender differences have been noted in adults, and those that have been reported have been questioned (Bryden, 1979). Thus, although initially the developmental path may be different for the two groups, by adulthood they seem to exhibit similar patterns of specialization.

The discrepancy between our findings and those previously reported for infants may be more illusory than real. It is quite possible that, at ages younger than 5 months, infants do indeed exhibit asymmetries in auditory responsiveness that are similar to those observed in adults. However, the basis for these asymmetries may, in fact, be different than that underlying asymmetries observed in adults. If this is the case, then, at some point in development, a shift in the mechanisms underlying responsiveness to auditory stimulation may take place, and our data may in fact represent a transition point from responsiveness based on one mechanism to responsiveness based on a different mechanism.

Thus, it is conceivable that, for young infants, asymmetries in auditory responsiveness are based on relatively primitive processing mechanisms. For example, the greater responsiveness to verbal stimuli found at the right ear in young infants may be due to the operation of mechanisms sensitive to the acoustic and phonetic properties of the stimuli rather than to the operation of mechanisms sensitive to more cognitively relevant properties of the auditory input. A recent study of the brain evoked response to synthetic speech and nonspeech stimuli in newborn infants provides support for this interpretation. Molfese and Molfese (1979) found an asymmetry in only the early component of the brain response to speechlike stimuli. Because higher levels of information processing require more time than lower levels of processing, the finding of an early, but not of a late, asymmetrical component suggests that, early in development, asymmetries in responsiveness are associated with lower, rather than higher, levels of processing.

Furthermore, in relating our results to prior studies, it should be noted that the reports of asymmetry in responsiveness to auditory stimulation in infants have so far been restricted to studies involving infants of three months or less.[1] The fact that there are no reports concerning asymmetries of auditory functioning in infants older than 3 months but younger than $2\frac{1}{2}$ years may not be simply a question of greatest availability of infants nor greatest relevance to theory, but may instead reflect prevalent research and publication practices. That is, data that seem either inconclusive or anomalous are less likely to be pursued and published than are those that are more readily interpretable within existing models. Without belaboring the point, in view of the generally greater ease of testing older than younger infants, it seems somewhat strange that there have been no reports of asymmetries during this period. We would, therefore, propose a developmental sequence in which an early-appearing and relatively robust asymmetry in responsiveness may begin to interact with a later-appearing asymmetry. This suggestion is compatible with similar suggestions made by a number of investigators. Thus, Studdert-Kennedy and Shankweiler (Shankweiler & Studdert-Kennedy, 1966, 1967; Studdert-Kennedy & Shankweiler, 1970) have suggested and provided considerable evidence for a presyntactic and presemantic processing difference involving a right-ear advantage in dichotic listening tasks. Moscovitch (1977) has suggested hierarchical processing mechanisms that may begin to operate at different periods in development. The most explicit model, however, that accounts for the discrepancies in studies that have examined age-related changes in listening asymmetries on dichotic tests is that of Porter and Berlin (1975). These investigators have proposed a hierarchical model of linguistic processing in which different levels of processing may be engaged, depending on the nature of auditory input. Thus, when the dicho-

---

[1] The study of Molfese et al. (1975) is the single example of infants older than 3 months being tested. However, in this study, only two infants were tested at 6 and 8 months, respectively.

tic material consists of either pairs of consonant–vowel syllables or of a short list of digits, a low-level process based on acoustic and phonetic properties of the input is called upon. However, when longer lists of digits or semantically meaningful material are presented, the acoustic–phonetic process is no longer sufficient to decode the input, and a higher-level process based on mnemonic and semantic properties of the input is engaged. Porter and Berlin propose that the acoustic phonetic process matures early and remains relatively stable during development, whereas the mnemonic–semantic process matures later and may, as a result, undergo developmental change. Moscovitch (1977) also proposes that lateralized processing based on phonetic properties of the stimulus is a low-level and developmentally earlier process than processes based on semantic, syntactic, and mnemonic properties.

The apparently anomalous data from our study become interpretable when they are considered in the context of a developmental model of lateralization. We would, therefore, concur with the view that processing of auditory input is not a unitary phenomenon, but rather consists of different processes that are dependent on the developmental status of the subject and the nature of the auditory input. Furthermore, we would agree that hemispheric specialization for the lower level of processing may come about early in development and remain relatively stable throughout life, whereas higher levels of processing may not develop until later and may change over time. It is possible that the presence of mechanisms that are responsive to acoustic and phonetic properties of a stimulus lay the groundwork for the development of the more complex mechanisms. Thus, it may be that the higher level mechanisms depend for their development on the prior development of the lower level mechanisms.

Given the proposed complex changes in specialization, it is possible that, at different stages of development, the same input would produce opposite patterns of specialization. Such a possibility, although clearly speculative at this time, is readily testable. Tasks requiring different levels of processing might be devised that would make it possible to look for shifts in the direction of asymmetry.

Our data concerning the effects of music on latency to contact, at least for the boys, also suggest reversed patterns of asymmetry when compared to those observed in adults. However, interpretation of the effects of musical input on manual activity becomes even more complicated than that offered for the effects of speech input, primarily because the data on hemispheric specialization for the processing of musical input are even more equivocal. As Gates and Bradshaw (1977) have noted, "the localization of musical function has not been demonstrated as consistently as in speech [p. 422]." They suggest that the seemingly inconsistent laterality effects that have been observed may best be explained by the operation of different processing mechanisms, resulting in either a left-ear or a right-ear advantage, depending on both the strategy adopted by the subject and the nature of the auditory material.

If a priori predictions about the direction of effect of musical input are to be made, the musical signal must first be understood in terms of both the processing strategy it calls forth in the subject, as well as its constituent properties. As far as properties of musical material are concerned, it has unique properties that set it apart from speech such as timbre, melody, and harmony, as well as properties that it shares with speech, such as intensity, duration, rhythm, pitch, and temporal order. Because musical material may engage processing mechanisms similar to those used in processing speech, it is quite reasonable to expect that some musical material may, under certain conditions, be processed in the same hemisphere as speech. For example, in some cases, rhythm may be the overriding feature of a musical passage. Given the evidence that rhythmic aspects of speech are processed in the left hemisphere (Robinson & Solomon, 1974), it would be expected that the left hemisphere would be better at processing musical input in which rhythm was the dominant characteristic.

The data from our studies obviously do not permit us to draw any conclusions regarding either the aspects of the musical input or the processing mechanisms responsible for the observed asymmetries. It is possible, however, that as was suggested for speech, changes in the processing mechanisms underlying response to the musical material may produce the observed asymmetries in responsiveness.

Relationship between Specialization and Preferential Use of the Hands

The current data indicate that ongoing manual activity may be modulated in subtle ways by auditory input and associated patterns of hemispheric specialization. However, the data do not indicate any relationship between the nature of auditory material, the way that material is processed, and the choice of hand used in reaching. The absence of such a relationship is only surprising if manual activity is considered as a unitary phenomenon. It is more likely, however, that manual activity consists of separate components, each underlain by a different mechanism. Consequently, it is possible that, in addition to contact latencies, manipulative activity following contact may also be affected by ongoing auditory input. Likewise, given different objects, differential processing initiated by auditory input might influence bimanual activity as, for example, in manipulating and supporting an object. This suggestion gains added plausibility in view of the fact that although there is some ipsilateral control of hand movements, fine finger movements are almost exclusively controlled by the contralateral hemisphere (Levy, Trevarthen, & Sperry, 1972). Thus, the presentation of monaural auditory input, as in this study, may have an even stronger effect on manipulative activity than on contact latency.

It is clear that the interpretation of the data offered by us is speculative and that the findings may be open to alternative interpretations. Since this study was our first attempt to test the utility of this technique for the investigation of hemispheric specialization in infants, we deliberately chose to present what would be considered ecologically valid auditory material. It goes without saying, however, that in future studies an attempt will have to be made to clarify the contribution that specific stimulus attributes make to the observed effects. Consequently, better controlled and more easily specifiable auditory material will have to be used. At the same time, it should be remembered that stripping the auditory material of its rhythmic, syntactic, semantic, etc. properties may, in fact, result in different patterns of specialization. In conclusion, our aim in this chapter was to address questions regarding motor and processing asymmetries and to present one possible way of answering such questions.

References

Armitage, S. E., Baldwin, B. A., & Vince, M. A. (1980). The fetal environment of sheep. *Science 208*, 1173–1174.

Bench, J. (1968). Sound transmission to the human foetus through the maternal abdominal wall. *Journal of Genetic Psychology 113*, 85–87.

Bench, J., Anderson, J., & Hoare, M. (1970). Measurement system for fetal audiometry. *Journal of the Acoustical Society of America 47*, 1602–1606.

Bryden, M. P. (1979). Evidence for sex-related differences in cerebral organization. In M. Wittig & A. C. Petersen (Eds.), *Sex-related differences in cognitive functioning*. New York: Academic Press.

Cohen, A. I. (1966). Hand preference and developmental status of infants. *Journal of Genetic Psychology 108*, 337–345.

Coryell, J. F., & Michel, G. F. (1978). How supine postural preferences of infants can contribute toward the development of handedness. *Infant Behavior and Development 1*, 245–257.

Davis, A. E., & Wada, J. A. (1977). Hemispheric asymmetries in human infants: Spectral analysis of flash and click potentials. *Brain and Language 4*, 23–31.

DeCasper, A. J., & Fifer, W. P. (1980). Of human bonding: Newborns prefer their mother's voices. *Science 208*, 1174–1176.

Entus, A. K. (1977). Hemispheric asymmetry in processing of dichotically presented speech and non-speech stimuli by infants. In S. J. Segalowitz & F. A. Gruber (Eds.), *Language development and neurological theory*. New York: Academic Press.

Gardner, J., Lewkowicz, D., & Turkewitz, G. (1977). Development of postural asymmetry in premature human infants. *Developmental Psychobiology 10*, 471–480.

Gates, A., & Bradshaw, J. L. (1977). The role of the cerebral hemispheres in music. *Brain and Language 4*, 403–431.

Geschwind, N., & Levitsky, W. (1968). Human brain: Left-right asymmetries in temporal speech region. Science 160, 186–187.

Gesell, A. (1938). The tonic neck reflex in the human infant. Journal of Pediatrics 13, 455–464.

Gesell, A., & Ames, L. (1947). The development of handedness. Journal of Genetic Psychology 76, 155–175.

Glanville, B., Best, C., & Levenson, R. A. (1977). A cardiac measure of cerebral asymmetries in infant auditory perception. Developmental Psychology 13, 54–59.

Grimwade, J. C., Walker, D. W., Bartlett, M., Gordon, S., & Wood, C. (1971). Human fetal heart rate change and movement in response to sound and vibration. American Journal of Obstetrics and Gynecology 109, 86–90.

Hammer, M. (1977). Lateral differences in the newborn infant's response to speech and nonspeech stimuli. Unpublished doctoral dissertation, City University of New York.

Hammer, M., & Turkewitz, G. (1974). A sensory basis for the lateral difference in the newborn infant's response to somesthetic stimulation. Journal of Experimental Child Psychology 18, 304–312.

Hicks, R. E. (1975). Intrahemispheric response competition between vocal and unimanual performance in normal adult human males. Journal of Comparative and Physiological Psychology 89, 50–60.

Hiscock, M., & Kinsbourne, M. (1978). Ontogeny of cerebral dominance: Evidence from time-sharing asymmetry in children. Developmental Psychology 14, 321–329.

Kimura, D. (1961). Cerebral dominance and the perception of verbal stimuli. Canadian Journal of Psychology 15, 166–171.

Kimura, D. (1964). Left–right differences in the perception of melodies. Quarterly Journal of Experimental Psychology 14, 355–358.

Kinsbourne, M., & Cook, J. (1971). Generalized and lateralized effects of concurrent verbalization on a unimanual skill. Quarterly Journal of Experimental Psychology 23, 341–345.

Kinsbourne, M., & McMurray, J. (1975). The effect of cerebral dominance on time sharing between speaking and tapping by preschool children. Child Development 46, 240–242.

Klein, P. E. (1981). The development of hemispheric specialization in infancy. Unpublished master's thesis, Hunter College, City University of New York.

LeMay, M., & Culebras, A. (1972). Human brain–morphologic differences in the hemispheres demonstrable by carotid anteriography. New England Journal of Medicine 287, 168–170.

Levy, J., Trevarthen, C., & Sperry, R. W. (1972). Perception of bilateral chimeric figures following hemispheric disconnection. Brain 95, 61–78.

Lewkowicz, D., Gardner, J., & Turkewitz, G. (1979). Lateral differences and head turning responses to somesthetic stimulation in premature human infants. Developmental Psychobiology 12, 607–614.

Lewkowicz, D., & Turkewitz, G. (1982). The influence of hemispheric specialization in sensory processing on reaching in infants: Age and gender related effects. Developmental Psychology 18, 301–308.

Liederman, J., & Kinsbourne, M. (1980). The mechanism of neonatal rightward turning bias: A sensory or motor asymmetry. Infant Behavior and Development 3, 223–238.

Molfese, D. L., Freeman, R. B., & Palermo, D. S. (1975). The ontogeny of brain lateralization for speech and non-speech stimuli. Brain and Language 2, 356–368.

Molfese, D. L., & Molfese, V. J. (1979). Hemisphere and stimulus differences as reflected in the cortical responses of newborn infants to speech stimuli. Developmental Psychology 15, 505–511.

Molfese, D. L., & Molfese, V. J. (1980). Cortical responses of preterm infants to phonetic and nonphonetic speech stimuli. Developmental Psychology 16, 574–581.

Moscovitch, M. (1977). The development of lateralization of language functions and its relation to cognitive and linguistic development: A review and some theoretical speculations. In S. J. Segalowitz & F. A. Gruber (Eds.), *Language development and neurological theory.* New York: Academic Press.

Porter, R. J., & Berlin, C. I. (1975). On interpreting developmental changes in the dichotic right-ear advantage. *Brain and Language 2,* 186–200.

Ramsay, D. S. (1980a). Beginnings of bimanual handedness and speech in infants. *Infant Behavior and Development 3,* 67–77.

Ramsay, D. S. (1980b). Onset of unimanual handedness in infants. *Infant Behavior and Development 3,* 377–385.

Rasmussen, T., & Milner, B. (1977). The role of early left-brain injury in determining lateralization of cerebral speech functions. In S. J. Dimond & D. A. Blizard (Eds.), *Evolution and lateralization of the brain.* New York: Annals of New York Academy of Sciences.

Robinson, G. M., & Solomon, D. J. (1974). Rhythm is processed by the speech hemisphere. *Journal of Experimental Psychology 102,* 508–511.

Seth, G. (1973). Eye–hand co-ordination and "handedness": A developmental study of visuo-motor behaviour in infancy. *British Journal of Educational Psychology 43,* 35–49.

Shankweiler, D., & Studdert-Kennedy, M. (1966). Lateral differences in perception of dichotically presented synthetic consonant–vowel syllables and steady-state vowels. *Journal of the Acoustical Society of America 39,* 1256a.

Shankweiler, D., & Studdert-Kennedy, M. (1967). Identification of consonants and vowels presented to left and right ears. *Quarterly Journal of Experimental Psychology 19,* 59–63.

Studdert-Kennedy, M., & Shankweiler, D. (1970). Hemispheric specialization for speech perception. *Journal of the Acoustical Society of America 48,* 574–594.

Turkewitz, G. (1980). Mechanisms of a neonatal rightward turning bias: A reply to Liederman and Kinsbourne. *Infant Behavior and Development 3,* 239–244.

Turkewitz, G., Birch, H. G., Moreau, T., Levy, L., & Cornwell, A. C. (1966). Effect of intensity of auditory stimulation on directional eye movements in the human neonate. *Animal Behaviour 14,* 93–101.

Turkewitz, G., & Creighton, S. (1974). Changes in lateral differentiation of head posture in the human neonate. *Developmental Psychobiology 8,* 85–89.

Turkewitz, G., Gordon, E. W., & Birch, H. G. (1965). Head turning in the neonate: Spontaneous patterns. *Journal of Genetic Psychology 107,* 143–158.

Turkewitz, G., Moreau, T., Davis, L., & Birch, H. G. (1969). Factors affecting lateral differentiation in the human newborn. *Journal of Experimental Child Psychology 8,* 483–493.

Vargha-Khadem, F., & Corballis, M. (1979). Cerebral asymmetry in infants. *Brain and Language 8,* 1–9.

Wada, J. A., Clarke, R., & Hamm, A. (1975). Cerebral hemispheric asymmetry in human. *Archives of Neurology 32,* 239–246.

Walker, D., Grimwade, J., & Wood, C. (1971). Intrauterine noise: A component of the fetal environment. *American Journal of Obstetrics and Gynecology 109,* 91–95.

Wedenberg, E. (1965). Prenatal tests of hearing. *Acta Oto-Laryngalogica 206,* 27–32.

Weitzman, E. D., & Graziani, L. J. (1968). Maturation and topography of the auditory evoked response of the prematurely born infant. *Developmental Psychobiology 1,* 79–89.

Wickelgren, L. W. (1969). The ocular response of human newborns to intermittent visual movement. *Journal of Experimental Child Psychology 8,* 469–482.

Witelson, S. F. (1977). Anatomic asymmetry in the temporal lobes: Its documentation, phylogenesis, and relationship to functional asymmetry. In S. J. Dimond & D. A. Blizard (Eds.), *Evolution and lateralization of the brain.* New York: Annals of the New York Academy of Sciences.

Witelson, S. F., & Pallie, W. (1973). Left hemisphere specialization for language in the newborn: Neuroanatomical evidence of asymmetry. *Brain 96,* 641–646.

21

Development of Manual Laterality and Language Function

THERESE TREVES
ITA GOLDSHMIDT
AMOS D. KORCZYN

Introduction

Ample evidence exists of hemispheric brain specialization in human beings. Among the various lateralized functions, those whose existence has been best established are related to manual behavior and language, which are both usually controlled by the left cerebral hemisphere (Kinsbourne & Hiscock, 1981, p. 130). The excerpt from the biblical psalms, "If I forget thee, O Jerusalem, let my right hand forget its cunning. Let my tongue cleave to the roof of my mouth" provides an interesting example. However, it is still unclear whether it is due to chance that the two functions reside in close anatomical vicinity, or whether a functional relation favors it.

An analysis of the relationship between manual dexterity and verbal function is complicated. The latter is obviously not existent at birth, although the anatomic substrate for its development is already established (Witelson & Pallie, 1973), and may reveal itself by functioning in some rudimentary form (Molfese, Freeman, & Palermo, 1975). Manual preference also does not manifest itself at this early age (Korczyn, Sage, & Karplus, 1978). These two functions may thus develop simultaneously over several years (Zangwill, 1975, p. 145), and merely because of this overlap in their development, some correlation between them is to be expected.

Cohen (1966) observed that the more advanced the developmental status of an infant, the more likely the infant will be to demonstrate hand preference. It is therefore possible that the degree of maturation achieved

MANUAL SPECIALIZATION
AND THE DEVELOPING BRAIN

by the central nervous system is responsible for this correlation. Alternatively, as suggested by Gazzaniga (1970), manual dexterity may be a factor responsible for speech lateralization (and thus possibly verbal development).

Some insight into the relationship between limb preference and language function may perhaps be gained through a comparison of the development of language function and manual asymmetry in young children. We hoped that, by extending our previous experiments (Korczyn et al., 1978) to ages where both verbal functioning and limb use have developed to a degree enabling meaningful examination, we could achieve a better understanding of the interrelationship between both processes.

Methods

In the present experiments, 61 normal 1–3-year-olds, 24 females and 37 males, were examined. Infants attending a well-baby clinic were included unless neurologic or any other serious diseases were known or suspected. Subjects were not preselected according to parental handedness. Each child was tested for leg, arm, and eye preference, the latter only in children 18 months and older.

Subjects were made to stand with both feet together and asked to start walking. The leg first lifted was recorded. Similarly, subjects were asked to kick a ball, and the kicking foot was noted. This test was repeated four times for each behavior, so that eight leg movements were recorded. For arm-preference testing, first a doll and then a toy car were presented to the child, and the hand used for grasping the object was observed. This test was also repeated four times with each object. Ocular preference was tested by letting the child look first through a cardboard cylinder and then into a kaleidoscope, again with four trials per object. It was decided that the child showed a lateral preference if he or she preferred the same side during six or more of the eight consecutive trials for a particular measure.

Our criterion of lateral preference was similar to that of Cohen (1966), who assessed hand preference in 8-month-old infants. Although several subjects could have been misclassified, preliminary testing showed that when more trials were applied, subjects became tired and less cooperative.

Verbal development was assessed according to Reynell's (1977) method, with separate scores given for comprehensive and for expressive language abilities. In this test, each subject obtains a raw score according to achievements. The adjusted score is determined using Reynell's norms, according to the age of the child, and thus reflects the child's verbal developmental status, corrected for age. Both laterality and verbal development were assessed in each individual by the same examiner. Preliminary tests did not show a discrepancy in the results between the two examiners, who gave identical instructions to the examinees.

Results and Discussion

Reynell's raw scores for language abilities increased with chronological age, both for verbal comprehension and for expressive language status, indicating the applicability of the Hebrew version of the test to the population studied. The regression of expressive language raw score (y) over age (x), measured in months, is given by the formula $y = 1.23x - 6.9$ ($r = .88$, $p < .05$), whereas for the comprehensive scores, $y = 1.63x - 17$ ($r = .9$, $p < .05$). The close similarity between the raw scores in each child is made obvious by comparison of their individual scores. Indeed, the correlation between the raw scores for comprehension and for expression is high ($y = .56x + .04$, $r = .58$, $p < .05$, where y is the expressive and x the comprehensive raw score). Subsequently, we shall

Table 21.1

Linear Regressions, Correlation Coefficients (r), and Significance Values (p) of Reynell Raw Score over Age, for Each Group and Subgroup

Group	N	Expressive Reynell score	Comprehensive Reynell score
All subjects	61	$y = 1.23x - 6.9$ $r = .88^*$	$y = 1.63x - 17.0$ $r = .90^*$
Right-handed	36	$y = 1.23x - 6.5$ $r = .85^*$	$y = 1.74x - 19.6$ $r = .91^*$
Left-handed	4	$y = .86x - 1.9$ $r = .96^*$	$y = .94x - 6.4$ $r = .92^{**}$
No hand preference	21	$y = 1.10x - 4.9$ $r = .85^*$	$y = 1.58x - 15.7$ $r = .88^*$
Right-legged	39	$y = 1.25x - 2.8$ $r = .86^*$	$y = 1.67x - 18.1$ $r = .92^*$
Right-handed and right-legged	27	$y = 1.21x - 6.4$ $r = .88^*$	$y = 1.64x - 18.7$ $r = .91^*$
Right preference, one organ or more	47	$y = 1.29x - 8.3$ $r = .87^*$	$y = 1.73x - 19.5$ $r = .92^*$
Right preference, two organs or more	34	$y = 1.19x - 5.0$ $r = .83^*$	$y = 1.70x - 20.0$ $r = .89^*$
Right preference, three organs	10	$y = 1.18x - 4.8$ $r = .57^{**}$	$y = 1.61x - 15.2$ $r = .75^*$

Note: x = the age (in months) and y = the raw score obtained in the expressive or comprehensive test; r = Pearson's coefficient.
$^*p < 0.05$.
$^{**}p < 0.01$.

present only the results of the expressive scores, since analysis according to comprehensive scores gave essentially identical results (see Table 21.1).

Ocular laterality could not be tested prior to age 18 months. In the 18–24-month-old group, only 17% of the subjects tested showed a clear eye preference (either right or left, see Table 21.2). This figure progressively increased, to 66% in the 24–30-month age group and to 86% in those 30–36 months old. Because a limited number of infants was tested, it is impossible to talk about the ratio between younger infants who prefer their right eye and those who prefer their left. At the 30–36-month age group, however, 69% of those with clear ocular preference favored their right eye. Arm preference showed a similar trend, with the percentage of children demonstrating a clear preference increasing from 19 to 86%. (Table 21.2). Here, however, there was a high percentage of subjects with right-arm preference even at the youngest age tested, and this was maintained throughout, reaching significance at 18–24 and 30–36 months. For leg preference, even at the youngest age group tested, the number of undetermined subjects was small, and the majority of the remainder were right-legged. This pattern was maintained throughout, with the right-side preference reaching significance for the two older age groups. Figure 21.1 depicts the expressive language raw score as a function of age in right-handed subjects (regardless of leg or eye preference). It is thus a partial population of those tested, consisting of 36 of the total number of 61 subjects. The regression function of language scale over age remains practically identical for these two groups: $y = 1.23x - 6.5$ in the 36 right-handed children, as compared to $y = 1.23x - 6.9$ for the total population, with r's of .85 and .88, respectively. Table 21.1 gives regression equations for other subgroups. In no case was there a difference between groups.

Table 21.2
Preference in Relation to Age

	Age (in months)										
	12–18 (N = 18)			18–24 (N = 11)			24–30 (N = 10)			30–36 (N = 22)		
	Right	Left	?[a]	Right	Left	?	Right	Left	?	Right	Left	?
Hand	6	1	11	6	0**	5	6	2	2	18	1*	3
Leg	10	4	4	8	3	0	6	0**	4	15	3*	4
Eye	—	—	—	1 (6)[b]	0 (6)	5 (6)	4 (9)	2 (9)	3 (9)	12 (21)	6 (21)	3 (21)

Note: Right–left differences for each behavior at each age group were tested by the one-tailed binomial test.
[a]Side of preference undetermined.
[b]N = number in parentheses.
*$p < .05$.
**$p < .001$.

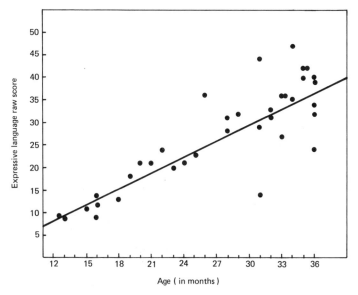

Figure 21.1 The relationship between Reynell's raw scores for expression and age, for those subjects who demonstrated right-arm preference (N = 36).

Our results demonstrate that preference of the right arm and/or leg can be demonstrated at a young age, although not prior to acquisition of the first verbal abilities (since our subjects were all more than 1 year old). However, as shown in Table 21.1, infants who evidently prefer the use of their right side are not necessarily more advanced in their verbal development (whether measured as expressive or comprehensive scores). Regression analyses between age and Reynell's raw scores is shown to be practically identical in children with a right-sided preference and in those without a clear preference (the number of subjects with a clear left-sided preference was small and did not allow meaningful analysis). A similar result is obtained when Reynell's adjusted scores (rather than raw scores) are used. The same conclusion is derived when the results are analysed in the opposite way: Among those who had high scores, children with right-sided preference were not unduly represented.

Several studies have shown that people should not be dichotomously classified into either dextrals or sinistrals, since a large proportion of the population shows a mixture of left- and right-hand preference (Subirana, 1969). In addition, there is no guarantee that a child defined by us as showing right-sided preference will eventually turn out to be right-handed (Gesell & Ames, 1947; Ramsay, Chapter 9, this volume). The results of our study are not necessarily predictive on an individual basis, but the statistical correlations and trends still support our conclusions.

Our results and conclusions relate only to apparently normal children. It is quite possible that in brain-injured children, for example, the relationship will be different. Similarly, our results only apply to the age-range tested. It would be of great interest to test younger or older children and perhaps to monitor individuals longitudinally. However, our observations suggest an independent development of lateral preference and speech.

References

Cohen, A. I. (1966). Hand preference and developmental status of infants. *Journal of Genetic Psychology 108*, 337–345.

Gazzaniga, M. S. (1970). *The bisected brain*. New York: Appelton-Century-Crofts.

Gesell, A., & Ames, L. B. (1947). The development of handedness. *Journal of Genetic Psychology 70*, 155–175.

Kinsbourne, M., & Hiscock, M. (1981). Cerebral lateralization and cognitive development: Conceptual and methodological issues. In G. W. Hynd & J. E. Obrzut (Eds.), *Neuropsychological assessment and the school-age child*. New York: Grune & Stratton.

Korczyn, A. D., Sage, J. I., & Karplus, M. (1978). Lack of limb motor asymmetry in the neonate. *Journal of Neurobiology 9*, 483–488.

Molfese, O. L., Freeman, R. B., & Palermo, S. D. (1975). The ontogeny of brain lateralization for speech and nonspeech stimuli. *Brain and Language 2,* 356–368.

Reynell, J. (1977). *Manual for the Reynell Developmental Language Scales* (Rev. ed.). Windsor, England: National Foundation for Educational Research.

Subirana, A. (1969). Handedness and cerebral dominance. In P. J. Vinken & G. W. Bruyn (Eds.), *Handbook of clinical neurology* (Vol. 4). Amsterdam: North-Holland.

Witelson, S. F., & Pallie, W. (1973). Left hemisphere specialization for language in the newborn: Neuroanatomical evidence of asymmetry. *Brain 96*, 641–646.

Zangwill, O. L. (1975). The ontogeny of cerebral dominance in man. In E. H. Lenneberg & E. Lenneberg (Eds.), *Foundations of language development* (Vol. 1). New York: Academic Press.

22

Changes, Constancies, and Continuities in Lateralization Development

GERALD YOUNG

Changes and Constancies in Development

The infant's manual world in the first year of life appears to be a confusing one in terms of lateralization. By 18, if not 12 months, a right-hand preference for some measures has emerged in a significant majority of infants (Peters, Chapter 19, this volume; Ramsay's (Chapter 9) research, in particular; Treves, Goldshmidt, & Korczyn, Chapter 21; the study of 18-month-olds described in Young, Bowman, Methot, Finlayson, Quintal, & Boissonneault, Chapter 7). Before then, however, variable results are obtained. Young, Segalowitz, Misek, Alp, and Boulet (Chapter 2) documented this pattern in 0–4-month-olds, showing that significant right-side preferences are sometimes found for reaching and grasping-related behaviors (e.g., Liederman, Chapter 16), but there is often only a slight right-hand preference or no preference is evident at all (e.g., Dowd & Tronick, Chapter 15). Similarly, with infants in the middle of the first year, a significant right-hand preference is sometimes found (e.g., Hawn & Harris, Chapter 17), sometimes not (e.g., Peters, Chapter 19), or a mixed pattern of significant and nonsignificant right lateralization is obtained (e.g., Mebert, Chapter 18).

Such inconsistencies may be a subtle clue to researchers that there is no worthwhile manual asymmetry in early life to investigate. However, the results essentially waiver between significant and nonsignificant right-side preferences for the key behaviors. The absence of many left-side preferences, even of a nonsignificant variety, suggests that there is early right lateralization in manual behavior, but, for the most part, it is not marked or stable. The data on head-turning preferences are similarly equivocal; sometimes a marked early right-side preference is found (Harris & Fitzgerald, Chapter 14), sometimes it is less clear (Trehub, Corter, & Shosenberg, Chapter 12), and sometimes it appears in limited circumstances or subgroups (Saling, Chapter 13), but the suggestion of any left-side preference is never encountered. Both changes and constancies then are found in the early development of lateralized function. It would seem that early lateralized behavior, in general, needs developmental time to stabilize (i.e., change) in the primary direction (the right) it manifests from birth onward (i.e., constancy). Moreover, it could be that certain behaviors in early infancy, when tested with appropriate methodology, manifest highly stable and marked right-lateralized patterns analogous to those found in the older child and adult. Also, it could be that the young infant's lateralized hemispheric organization is analogous to that of the older child and adult (Young et al., Chapter 7; on the other hand, see Lewkowicz & Turkewitz, Chapter 20), and that one major differential function, or several such functions, underlies this specialization at all stages of life (e.g., the left hemisphere better controls varieties of inhibition—Young et al., Chapter 7). If this is the case, the constancies between early and later manual and hemispheric specialization may be just as noteworthy as the differences.

However, there may not be a significant relation among all of the various right-side preferences (Liederman, Chapter 4). Moreover, the complexity of the phenomenom must inevitably lead to individual differences in its patterns, course, and antecedants (Harris & Fitzgerald, Chapter 14; Young et al., Chapter 1). Thus, the differences in lateralization over developmental periods and across individuals should always be kept in mind.

Continuities in Development

The longitudinal relations that are being found between measures taken in early infancy and later infancy–childhood (see Goodwin, Coryell in Liederman, Chapter 4; Michel, Chapter 3; Young et al., Chapter 7) suggest important continuity. Though the degree of lateralization and its stability may greatly change with development, the relative position of any one individual compared to the group at different ages may not change as much, even when different measures are involved.

Conclusions to the Volume

Lateralization of peripheral and central function is often seen as a new panacea. Its merits for helping in phenomena as diverse as understanding bicameral consciousness, educating Western children, and reeducating various disabled or abnormal populations are often extolled. At a more conservative level, the development of lateralized function has been suggested as being important to normal language, cognitive, social, emotional, perceptual, and motor development, as well as to the early detection of certain kinds of abnormal development and disabilities. The true relevance of lateralization of function will be ascertained only by careful research that acknowledges that aspects of this function develop throughout the lifespan, beginning at birth, if not before. With this volume, which is first in a fast-growing field, we hope to have guided theory and research in their inexorable movement toward the mainstream of scientific pursuit in developmental psychology and psychobiology.

Index

PERSPECTIVES IN
NEUROLINGUISTICS, NEUROPSYCHOLOGY, AND
PSYCHOLINGUISTICS: A Series of Monographs and Treatises

Harry A. Whitaker, Series Editor
DEPARTMENT OF HEARING AND SPEECH SCIENCES
UNIVERSITY OF MARYLAND
COLLEGE PARK, MARYLAND 20742

HAIGANOOSH WHITAKER and HARRY A. WHITAKER (Eds.).
Studies in Neurolinguistics, Volumes 1, 2, 3, and 4

NORMAN J. LASS (Ed.). Contemporary Issues in Experimental Phonetics

JASON W. BROWN. Mind, Brain, and Consciousness: The Neuropsychology of Cognition

SIDNEY J. SEGALOWITZ and FREDERIC A. GRUBER (Eds.). Language Development and Neurological Theory

SUSAN CURTISS. Genie: A Psycholinguistic Study of a Modern-Day "Wild Child"

JOHN MACNAMARA (Ed.). Language Learning and Thought

I. M. SCHLESINGER and LILA NAMIR (Eds.). Sign Language of the Deaf: Psychological, Linguistic, and Sociological Perspectives

WILLIAM C. RITCHIE (Ed.). Second Language Acquisition Research: Issues and Implications

PATRICIA SIPLE (Ed.). Understanding Language through Sign Language Research

MARTIN L. ALBERT and LORAINE K. OBLER. The Bilingual Brain: Neuropsychological and Neurolinguistic Aspects of Bilingualism

TALMY GIVÓN. On Understanding Grammar

CHARLES J. FILLMORE, DANIEL KEMPLER, and WILLIAM S-Y. WANG (Eds.). Individual Differences in Language Ability and Language Behavior

JEANNINE HERRON (Ed.). Neuropsychology of Left-Handedness

FRANÇOIS BOLLER and MAUREEN DENNIS (Eds.). Auditory Comprehension: Clinical and Experimental Studies with the Token Test

R. W. RIEBER (Ed.). Language Development and Aphasia in Children: New Essays and a Translation of "Kindersprache und Aphasie" by Emil Fröschels

GRACE H. YENI-KOMSHIAN, JAMES F. KAVANAGH, and CHARLES A. FERGUSON (Eds.). Child Phonology, Volume 1: Production and Volume 2: Perception